OFFICE FOR
NATIONAL STATISTICS

Infant Feeding 1995

A survey of infant feeding practices in the United Kingdom

carried out by Social Survey Division of ONS on behalf of

the Department of Health, the Scottish Office Department of Health,

the Welsh Office and the Department of Health and

Social Services in Northern Ireland

Kate Foster

Deborah Lader

Sarah Cheesbrough

London: The Stationery Office

£29.95

Contents

Acknowledgements

We would like to thank everybody who helped to make this survey a success. Any large scale survey relies on team work and we were supported by colleagues in the Social Survey Division of ONS who organised mailings and fieldwork and helped to process the data.

We would also like to thank colleagues in the United Kingdom Health Departments for their advice on the design of the study and on analysing and interpreting the data. Particular thanks are due to Dr P Clarke, Dr S Lader, Ms A Roberts and Mr R Wenlock of the Department of Health.

Finally, we would like to thank the mothers who participated in the study, without whose co-operation the survey would not have been possible.

Notes to tables

1 **Base numbers** are shown in italics and are weighted bases.
   The size of weighted bases is related to the number of mothers who responded at stage one (see Appendix II). At subsequent stages of the survey, weighting factors were adjusted to give the same total weighted sample size as at stage one. Hence, percentages for the second and third stages are based on a smaller number of individuals than is suggested by the weighted base presented.

   In general, very small bases have been avoided by combining adjacent categories. Where the base for a category is less than 30, the actual numbers of cases are shown in brackets [ ].

2 **Missing information**
   The tables exclude cases for which information is missing for the items analysed. This means that the number of cases in a category may vary slightly in different tables.

3 **The conventions** used in tables are as follows:

-	No cases
0	Percentage less than 0.5%
..	Data not available
[]	Number of cases where the base for the category is less than 50

4 **Percentages.** Row or column percentages may add to 99% or 101% because of rounding.

5 **Great Britain and United Kingdom data**
   Unless otherwise specified, tables of 1995 results show United Kingdom data.

   Trend tables usually show data for Great Britain because Northern Ireland has only been included in the Surveys since 1990. Results for Great Britain and the United Kingdom generally differ by 1% or less.

6 **Statistical significance**
   Unless otherwise stated, changes and differences mentioned in the text are statistically significant at the 95% confidence level.

1 Introduction

1.1 Background

The 1995 Infant Feeding Survey is the fifth national survey of infant feeding practices. The survey was carried out by Social Survey Division (SSD) of the Office for National Statistics[1] (ONS) on behalf of the four United Kingdom Health Departments. Fieldwork in Northern Ireland was carried out by the Central Survey Unit of the Northern Ireland Statistics and Research Agency (NISRA).

A series of surveys has been carried out in response to the recommendation of the Committee on Medical Aspects of Food and Nutrition Policy (COMA) that there should be a continuous review of infant feeding. The first survey took place in 1975[2] within England and Wales only. The second and third surveys, in 1980[3] and 1985[4] also included Scotland, and Northern Ireland has been included since 1990.[5]

Government policy has consistently supported breastfeeding as the best way of ensuring a healthy start for the newborn. In the 1970s, a COMA Working Party was set up to review infant feeding because of concerns about the decline in rates of breastfeeding. It recommended that mothers should be encouraged to breastfeed, preferably for four to six months.[6] It also recommended that mothers be discouraged from introducing solid foods before their baby is about four months old. Subsequent reports about infant feeding have continued to endorse these recommendations.[7,8,9]

The expert Working Party also recommended that a national survey be conducted to establish a better basis of information. The first such survey was carried out in England and Wales in 1975 and found that 51% of mothers breastfed at birth. A second survey, in 1980, found that the proportion of mothers who breastfed at birth had increased to 67% (in England and Wales) and was 50% in Scotland. The importance of continuing to monitor this indicator of infant nutrition led to recommendations that national surveys should be repeated every five years. The results of the 1985 Survey showed that breastfeeding rates had not risen and, further, that there was a high rate of early discontinuation of breatfeeding.

Following the 1985 Survey, the Department of Health initiated a series of reviews and programmes to find ways of promoting breastfeeding under the title of the Joint Breastfeeding Initiative. This was particularly concerned to encourage closer working between health professionals and voluntary support groups such as the National Childbirth Trust. The National Network of Breastfeeding Coordinators was established in 1995 with a remit to stimulate and support good practice in breastfeeding promotion. Additional information resources were provided for parents and for health professionals and a National Breastfeeding Awareness Week in May of each year was supported by Government. Similar initiatives have been pursued throughout of the United Kingdom. In Scotland, the Chief Nursing Officer chairs the Scottish Breastfeeding Group which provides a national resource of information and advice on breastfeeding. The Group works with the Health Education Board for Scotland to promote pubic awareness and encourage a multi-disciplinary approach involving all health professionals.

The 1990 Survey failed to show improvement in breastfeeding rates, although it was considered that the programmes of support described above had begun too recently to have had an impact on mothers' behaviour and choices. The 1995 Survey has therefore been of particular interest to the many professional, voluntary and consumer groups concerned to support the new mother. The regular surveys of infant feeding practices also respond to the request from the World Health Organisation to monitor rates of breastfeeding on a national basis.

1.2 The aims of the survey

The main aims of the 1995 Survey match those of earlier Infant Feeding Surveys and were as follows.

- To establish how infants born in 1995 are being fed and to provide national figures on the incidence, prevalence and duration of breastfeeding.

- To examine trends in infant feeding practices over recent years, in particular since 1990.

- To investigate the factors associated with mother's feeding intentions and with the feeding practices adopted in the early weeks.

- To establish the age at which solid foods are introduced and to examine weaning practices up to nine months.

As in 1990, the survey involved approaching a sample of mothers when their babies were aged six to ten weeks, with follow-up questionnaires at four to five months and at about nine months. In 1995, a fourth stage of fieldwork was also carried out for the sample in Great Britain (excluding Northern Ireland) when babies were between 12 and 15 months old. This fourth stage aimed to provide further information on the range of foods given to children at this age and on the age of introduction of liquid cow's milk as a main drink. The results of this stage of the survey are not included in this report and will be published separately.

A separate survey of infant feeding in Asian families in England was recently commissioned by the Department of Health and carried out by ONS in 1994/95.[10] This survey was designed to look at the early feeding practices and growth of babies born to mothers of Indian, Pakistani and Bangladeshi origin.

1.3 Definitions used in the survey

A number of terms defined for the infant feeding surveys since 1975 are used in this report. The definitions are as follows.

Breastfed initially refers to all babies whose mothers put them to the breast at all, even if this was on one occasion only.

Incidence of breastfeeding is the proportion of sampled babies who were breastfed initially.

Prevalence of breastfeeding refers to the proportion of all sampled babies who were wholly or partially breastfed at specified ages.

Duration of breastfeeding is the length of time for which breastfeeding continued at all, regardless of when non-human milk and other drinks or foods were introduced.

Stages of the survey
The approximate age of babies at the different stages of the survey were as follows:
    stage 1: babies aged 6 to 10 weeks
    stage 2: aged 4 to 5 months
    stage 3: aged 8 to 9 months
The average age of sampled babies at each stage of the survey is shown in Table 1.9

1.4 Design and conduct of the 1995 Survey

Sample design and implementation
In order to make comparisons with the previous Infant Feeding Surveys, the sample design of the 1995 Survey was the same as that used for the 1990 Survey. Full details of the design in each country are given in Appendix II.

The sample of mothers included in the survey was selected by drawing a random sample of births occurring between August and October 1995 from birth registers compiled by the General Register Offices in England and Wales, Scotland and Northern Ireland. The sampling procedures used in 1995 differed from those for previous surveys as a result of a review of the guidelines for the release of identifiable information from the registration entry. The conclusion of the review in England and Wales and in Northern Ireland was that data collected for registration purposes, which includes the name and address of the mother, could not be released to a survey organisation although statistical data could be made available in an anonymised form.

As a result of this restriction, the name and address of each sampled mother in these countries could only be passed to the survey agency (SSD or NISRA) after the mother had consented to take part in the survey by returning the first questionnaire. This meant that non-respondents to the first stage of fieldwork could not be approached in person by an interviewer. Similar fieldwork procedures were followed in all countries.

The interviewer follow-up of non-respondents added at least 9% to overall response rates in 1990 and there was concern that this change in survey procedures would result in a reduction in response in 1995, although a further (third) postal reminder was added in an attempt to improve response. There was also concern that lower response levels would achieve a less representative sample because some groups, such as those with fewer educational qualifications or in lower social class groups, are less likely to respond to postal surveys. The effect of the change is discussed in Section 1.5 and Appendix II.

Fieldwork procedures

For the first stage of fieldwork, the approach to mothers was made through the respective Registration Offices in the different countries. The first questionnaire was sent out during October and November 1995 to all mothers included in the initial sample, with the aim of contacting mothers when their babies were between six and ten weeks old. Mothers failing to reply after two weeks were sent a reminder letter and another copy of the questionnaire. If necessary, second and third reminders were sent at two week intervals but, as explained above, there was no interviewer follow-up of non-respondents. Only after the mothers had completed the stage one questionnaire were names and addresses passed to SSD or NISRA.

In January 1996, when the babies were four to five months old, a second stage questionnaire was sent to all mothers who had completed the first questionnaire (apart from a small number of mothers who had specifically asked not to be contacted again). Mothers who had not replied after two weeks were sent a reminder letter and this process was repeated after a further two weeks. Finally, an attempt was made to obtain a response at the second stage by sending an interviewer to contact mothers who had not replied to the various letters.

A similar procedure was followed for the third questionnaire. Mothers who had completed the second-stage questionnaire were contacted again in June 1996, when their babies were about nine months old. This initial letter was followed by two postal reminders and, where necessary, by a visit from an interviewer.

The fourth questionnaire was sent to mothers in Great Britain only (not in Northern Ireland) when their babies were at least 12 months old and the same procedures were followed as at stage three. The results of the fourth stage are not presented here but will be published at a later date.

At each stage of the survey a small number of responding mothers asked not to be contacted again. They were removed from the sample for subsequent stages of the survey.

1.5 Response

Response at stage one

Table 1.1 gives details of response by country at stage one. Overall, 74% of the original sample of women responded to the first stage questionnaire and rates were similar in each country, ranging from 72% in Northern Ireland to 75% in England and Wales.

Mothers whose baby was no longer with them, for example if the baby had died, been adopted or was in hospital, were not expected to complete a questionnaire but were asked to return the form so that they would not be contacted again. Efforts were made to identify any baby deaths among the sampled births before sending out the first questionnaire and only a small number of mothers (UK total of 27) replied that their baby was no longer with them.

Some forms were returned blank with no explanation. These are counted as refusals in the response summary. Post returned/not delivered includes forms sent back either by the post office or by individuals reporting that the mother had gone away or was not known at that address. Where possible, forms were sent to any forwarding address provided.

As seen from Table 1.2, the stage one response rate was between 12% and 18% lower in each country than in 1990. The first stage of the 1995 Survey was conducted entirely by postal questionnaire and up to three reminders were sent at two-week intervals to

Table 1.1	Response rates and non-response at the first stage of the survey (1995)								
	England and Wales		Scotland		Northern Ireland		United Kingdom	
	No.	%	No.	%	No.	%	No.	%
Initial sample	6,972	100	2,908	100	2,434	100	12,314	100
Total response	5,240	75	2,137	73	1,753	72	9,130	74
Total non-response	1,732	25	771	27	681	28	3,184	26
baby not with mother	16	0	5	0	6	0	27	0
refusal	48	1	19	1	41	2	108	1
post returned/ not delivered/ mother living abroad	102	1	71	2	5	0	178	1
no reply	1,566	22	676	23	629	26	2,871	23

Table 1.2   Response rates at the first stage of the survey, 1985 to 1995

	England and Wales			Scotland			Northern Ireland	
	1985	1990	1995	1985	1990	1995	1990	1995
	%	%	%	%	%	%	%	%
Response to postal	82	80	75	83	76	73	75	72
Response to interviewer	9	9	n/a	73	9	n/a	14	n/a
Total response rate	91	89	75	27	85	73	90	72
Base:	*5,805*	*6,467*	*6,972*	*2,349*	*2,597*	*2,908*	*2,041*	*2,434*

mothers who had not replied. In 1990 the arrangements at the first stage were for two postal reminders at two-week intervals, after which mothers were visited by an interviewer. Much of the fall in response can be attributed to the lack of interviewer follow-up in 1995. However, postal response was also slightly lower than in 1990 in spite of the addition of a third reminder letter.

In all countries, response at the first stage was strongly associated with the social class of the mother's husband or partner, as recorded at registration. There was a consistent pattern of lower response among women whose partners were in manual social class groups and for women with no partner. Weights were therefore applied to the data in an attempt to correct for this bias in the achieved sample: details are given in Appendix II.

Response rates at the second and third stages of the survey were higher than at the first stage, ranging from 84% to 94% (Tables 1.3 and 1.4). The improvement in response was mainly due to the use of interviewer follow-up of non-respondents but postal response rates were also higher than at the first stage, presumably because mothers who had already completed a stage of the survey would be motivated to complete another. Interviewer follow-up was particularly successful in Northern Ireland where it added 17% to response rates.

Since mothers were only contacted in later stages of the survey if they had responded at the previous one, the effect of non-response at each stage is cumulative. The effective response rate at each stage should therefore be calculated as a proportion of the initial sample (Table 1.5). Questionnaires were

Table 1.3   Response rates and non-response at the second stage of the survey

	England and Wales		Scotland		Northern Ireland		United Kingdom	
	No.	%	No.	%	No.	%	No.	%
Second stage sample	5,240	100	2,137	100	1,753	100	9,130	100
Total response	**4,490**	**86**	**1,798**	**84**	**1,653**	**94**	**7,941**	**87**
due to postal enquiry	4,155	79	1,688	79	1,347	77	7,190	79
due to interviewer contact	335	6	110	5	306	17	751	8
Total non-response	**750**	**14**	**339**	**16**	**100**	**6**	**1,189**	**13**
refused at first stage	11	0	4	0	6	0	21	0
baby not with mother	9	0	4	0	2	0	15	0
refusal	67	1	36	2	22	1	125	1
post returned/ not delivered/ mother living abroad	72	1	47	2	6	0	125	1
no reply from postal stage and interviewer unable to contact	591	11	248	12	64	4	903	10

Table 1.4   Response rates and non-response at the third stage of the survey

	England and Wales		Scotland		Northern Ireland		United Kingdom	
	No.	%	No.	%	No.	%	No.	%
Third stage sample	4,490	100	1,798	100	1,653	100	7,941	100
Total response	**4,073**	**91**	**1,593**	**89**	**1,532**	**93**	**7,198**	**91**
due to postal enquiry	3,666	82	1,424	79	1,235	75	6,325	80
due to interviewer contact	407	9	169	9	297	18	873	11
Total non-response	**417**	**9**	**205**	**11**	**121**	**7**	**743**	**9**
refused at second stage	17	0	4	0	9	1	30	0
baby not with mother	5	0	3	0	0	0	8	0
refusal	54	1	37	2	28	2	119	1
post returned/ not delivered/ mother living abroad	77	2	44	2	7	0	128	2
no reply from postal stage and interviewer unable to contact	264	6	117	7	77	5	458	6

Table 1.5 Summary of response at stages 1, 2 and 3 of the survey by country

	England and Wales		Scotland		Northern Ireland		United Kingdom	
	No.	%	No.	%	No.	%	No.	%
Initial sample	6,972	100	2,908	100	2,434	100	12,314	100
Response at stage 1	5,240	75	2,137	73	1,753	72	9,130	74
Response at stage 2	4,490	64	1,798	62	1,653	68	7,941	64
Response at stage 3	4,073	58	1,593	55	1,532	63	7,198	58

received at the second stage from 64% of the original sample and this proportion fell to 58% at the third stage, ranging from 55% in Scotland to 63% in Northern Ireland.

Although the higher response rates achieved at stages two and three reduced the likelihood of extreme non-response bias in the achieved sample, there was still evidence of variation in response rates by social class and other characteristics of the mother. Weights were again applied to try to compensate for these differences (see Appendix II).

1.6 Making comparisons with results from the 1990 Survey

One of the main purposes of the 1995 Survey is to provide data on trends in infant feeding, so this section considers the main factors which might affect comparisons over time.

- The results of sample surveys are subject to sampling error due to the chance variations between a particular sample and the whole population from which it has been drawn. When comparing results from two separate survey samples, each will be subject to sampling error and so observed changes over time may not be attributable to sampling variation. Sampling errors are affected both by the size of the sample subgroup on which the estimate is based and by the variability of the particular measure within the sample. They will also be affected by the

complexity of the sample design and larger errors are associated with more clustered designs. Examples of standard errors for key survey estimates are given in Appendix III.

- Both surveys are subject to possible biases due to non-response. The potential for bias is greater in 1995 because of the lower response rate at stage one, but the data were weighted to correct for differential response by social class group at all stages (see Appendix II). The achieved samples in each year, after weighting, can be validated by comparison with registration data for all births in the relevant year (see tables in Appendix I). The comparisons show that the 1995 weighted sample was similar in terms of the characteristics compared, including mother's age and birth order, to all births in Great Britain.

- Any significant changes in the characteristics of the sample of mothers in different years will affect the interpretation of trend data, and this will be particularly influential if these characteristics are themselves associated with key survey measures. Comparison of the main characteristics of mothers in the 1990 and 1995 samples are shown in Tables 1.6 to 1.8 and further details are given in Appendix I. In line with changes in the population as a whole, the 1995 sample showed clear differences from the 1990 sample on each of the three main characteristics of the mother measured by the survey. These changes between 1990 and 1995

Table 1.6 Distribution of the sample by mother's age and country (1990 and 1995)

Mother's age (years)	All births					
	England and Wales		Scotland		Northern Ireland	
	1990	1995	1990	1995	1990	1995
	%	%	%	%	%	%
Under 20	7	6	6	6	7	5
20-24	25	19	25	18	24	16
25-29	37	34	38	34	36	35
30-34 *	|31	28 |40	|30	30 |41	|33	29 |43
35 or over *		12		12		14
Base:	4,942	4,598	1,981	1,863	1,498	1,476

* The 1990 Survey did not separate these two age groups

Table 1.7   Distribution of the sample by age at which mother completed full-time education and country (1990 and 1995)

Age at which mother completed full-time education (years)	All births					
	England and Wales		Scotland		Northern Ireland	
	1990	1995	1990	1995	1990	1995
	%	%	%	%	%	%
16 or under	54	45	54	44	43	32
17 or 18	32	35	29	33	40	43
19 or over	14	20	17	23	18	24
Base:	*4,942*	*4,598*	*1,981*	*1,867*	*1,498*	*1,476*

Table 1.8   Distribution of the sample by social class as defined by current or last occupation of husband or partner and country (1990 and 1995)

Social class of husband or partner	England and Wales		Scotland		Northern Ireland	
	1990	1995	1990	1995	1990	1995
	%	%	%	%	%	%
I	7	7	7	8	4	6
II	20	25	18	21	19	22
IIINM	8	8	8	7	7	11
All non-manual	35	39	33	36	30	38
IIIM	30	24	29	24	30	22
IV	14	11	13	12	9	8
V	2	4	3	4	4	4
All manual	46	38	45	39	43	38
Unclassified	6	6	6	6	8	7
No husband/partner	14	16	15	19	18	17
Base:	*4,942*	*4,598*	*1,981*	*1,863*	*1,497*	*1,476*

continued trends which were also evident between 1985 and 1990.

i. Mothers in the 1995 sample were older than those sampled in 1990. In England and Wales, 40% of women were over the age of 30 compared with 31% in 1990.

ii. Women in the 1995 sample had received more years of education. The proportion of mothers in England and Wales who left school at 16 or under had fallen from 54% in 1990 to 45% in 1995, and the proportion continuing in full-time education beyond the age of 18 had risen from 14% to 20%.

iii. In the 1995 sample, fewer mothers were classified to manual social class groups and a greater percentage to non-manual groups than in 1990. There was also a small increase in the proportion of women with no husband or partner in Great Britain but not in Northern Ireland.

• Many of the questions on the survey relate to feeding practices at the time that the mother completes the questionnaire. Thus, comparison of these variables over time may also be affected by differences in the age distribution of the babies at each stage of the surveys. Differences may result from changes in sampling or registration procedures or simply because of changes in the speed with which mothers respond to the postal request. Table 1.9 compares the age of babies at the various stages in 1990 and 1995.

i. At stage one, babies in the England and Wales sample were, on average, slightly younger than those in the 1990 sample (57 compared with 65 days). This was related to the computerisation of the national birth registration system which meant that records could be sampled more rapidly after the birth than in 1990. Conversely, changes in sampling and fieldwork procedures resulted in a slight increase in the average age of babies in Northern Ireland (from 55 to 61 days). These changes in average age had no effect on the proportion of babies aged between six and ten weeks at stage one (78% for the UK in both years).

ii. The average age of babies at stage two of the survey was similar in 1990 and 1995. At stage

Table 1.9   Age of baby at the 3 stages by country (1990 and 1995)

	England and Wales		Scotland		Northern Ireland		United Kingdom	
	1990	1995	1990	1995	1990	1995	1990	1995
Mean age of babies at:								
Stage 1 (days)	65 days	57 days	70 days	71 days	55 days	61 days	66 days	58 days
Stage 2 (nearest week)	22 wks	22 wks	22 wks	23 wks	26 wks	24 wks	22 wks	22 wks
Stage 3 (nearest week)	41 wks	39 wks	41 wks	41 wks	41 wks	39 wks	41 wks	39 wks
Percentage of babies				*Percentage*				
Aged 6-10 weeks at stage 1	78	78	75	76	77	86	78	78
Base:	*4,942*	*4,598*	*1,965*	*1,867*	*1,497*	*1,476*	*5,529*	*5,181*

three, babies in the 1995 sample were, on average, two weeks younger than those in the 1990 sample.

In summary, the 1995 Infant Feeding Survey sample is representative of all women giving birth in 1995. However, a comparison of the 1995 and 1990 samples shows differences in the age, educational level and social class group of mothers. Where these distributions could be compared with national data it was apparent that the differences reflected changes over the past five years in the characteristics of all mothers. Nevertheless the changes are important when comparing results from the 1990 and 1995 Surveys and may affect the interpretation of trends.

Notes and references

1   The Office for National Statistics (ONS) was formed in April 1996 from a merger of the Office of Population Censuses and Surveys (OPCS) and the Central Statistical Office (CSO).

2   Martin J. *Infant Feeding 1975: attitudes and practice in England and Wales.* HMSO (London: 1978).

3   Martin J and Monk J *Infant Feeding 1980.* OPCS (London: 1982).

4   Martin J and White A *Infant Feeding 1985.* HMSO (London: 1988).

5   White A, Freeth S and O'Brien M. *Infant Feeding 1990.* HMSO (London: 1992)

6   Department of Health and Social Security. *Present day practice in infant feeding.* Report on Health and Social Subjects 9. HMSO (London: 1974)

7   Department of Health and Social Security. *Present day practice in infant feeding: 1980.* Report on Health and Social Subjects 20. HMSO (London: 1980)

8   Department of Health and Social Security. *Present day practice in infant feeding: third report.* Report on Health and Social Subjects 32. HMSO (London: 1988)

9   Department of Health. *Weaning and the weaning diet. Report of the working group on the Weaning Diet of the Committee on Medical Aspects of Food Policy* Report on Health and Social Subjects 45. HMSO (London: 1994)

10 Thomas M and Avery V. *Infant feeding in Asian Families.* The Stationery Office (London: 1997)

2 Incidence and duration of breastfeeding

Summary

Initial incidence of breastfeeding

- Initial breastfeeding rates in 1995 were 68% in England and Wales, 55% in Scotland and 45% in Northern Ireland.

- The incidence of breastfeeding increased significantly between 1990 and 1995 in all countries. Breastfeeding rates were higher for first than for later babies but the increase in incidence was similar for both groups.

- The associations between breastfeeding and the mothers' characteristics were similar to previous years. The same groups which had high initial breastfeeding rates were also more likely to continue breastfeeding over the first four weeks. This includes mothers who had breastfed a previous child and those who had continued in full-time education after the age of 18.

- The increase in breastfeeding incidence in Great Britain since 1990 could be accounted for by changes in the age and educational profiles of mothers. The increase in incidence in Northern Ireland, however, remained significant even after taking account of changes in the characteristics of the sample of mothers.

Prevalence of breastfeeding

- The higher rates of breastfeeding in 1995 continued over the first six weeks.

Duration of breastfeeding

- In all countries the increase since 1990 in breastfeeding continued over the first six weeks of life.

- In Northern Ireland, as in 1990, there was a sharper decline in the rates of breastfeeding in the first few weeks than in England and Wales or Scotland. For example, 56% continued to breastfeed by six weeks, compared with 66% in Scotland and 65% in England and Wales.

- The associations between duration of breastfeeding and the mothers' characteristics were similar to previous years. Mothers who had breastfed a previous child were most likely to continue to breastfeed after the first few weeks, as were mothers educated beyond the age of 18 and women in non-manual social class groups.

2.1 Incidence of breastfeeding

Incidence of breastfeeding is defined as the proportion of babies who were breastfed initially. This includes all babies who were put to the breast at all, even if this was on one occasion only.

Figure 2.1 illustrates the trends in the incidence of breastfeeding by country for all available years since 1975. All countries showed a statistically significant increase in the incidence of breastfeeding between 1990 and 1995. In England and Wales and in Scotland the recent increases follow a period since 1980 in which rates have shown little change. The greatest increase since 1990 occurred in Northern Ireland where incidence increased from 36% in 1990 to 45% in 1995, although the incidence of breastfeeding remained lower in Northern Ireland than elsewhere in the United Kingdom.

Table 2.1, Figure 2.1

Although these changes represent a significant increase in breastfeeding in each country, it is important to place the results in the context of changes in the composition of the sample since 1990, as detailed in Section 1.6 (and Appendix I). It is well known that the incidence of breastfeeding is associated with the socio-demographic characteristics of mothers, so changes in the composition of the sample with respect to these characteristics would be expected to lead to changes in national incidence even if other factors remained constant. The effects of these compositional changes in the sample are discussed in Section 2.2.

Birth order

Previous surveys have shown that the incidence of breastfeeding is higher among mothers of first rather than later babies. This continued to be the case in 1995 and was seen in all countries (Table 2.2). In England and Wales, for example, 74% of mothers of first babies and 62% of mothers of later babies breastfed their babies at birth. The increase in the incidence of breastfeeding between 1990 and 1995 was seen consistently for both first and later babies (Figure 2.2).

Table 2.2, Figure 2.2

There is clear evidence from previous surveys that the likelihood of a mother breastfeeding a second or subsequent baby is closely related to her experience of feeding previous children. Changes in the incidence of breastfeeding first babies may subsequently be reflected in the breastfeeding rates

Table 2.1	Incidence of breastfeeding by country (1975, 1980, 1985, 1990 and 1995)																
	England and Wales					Scotland				Northern Ireland		Great Britain				United Kingdom	
	1975	1980	1985	1990	1995	1980	1985	1990	1995	1990	1995	1980	1985	1990	1995	1990	1995
Percentage who breastfed initially	51	67	65	64	68	50	48	50	55	36	45	65	64	63	67	62	66
Base	*1,544*	*3,755*	*4,671*	*4,942*	*4,598*	*1,718*	*1,895*	*1,981*	*1,863*	*1,497*	*1,476*	*4,224*	*5,223*	*5,413*	*5,018*	*5,533*	*5,181*

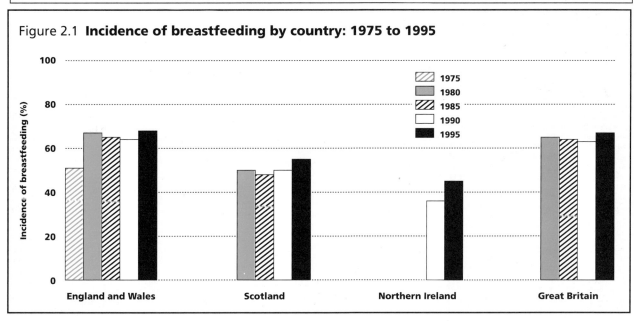

Figure 2.1 **Incidence of breastfeeding by country: 1975 to 1995**

Table 2.2	Incidence of breastfeeding by birth order and country (1990 and 1995)							
Birth order	England and Wales		Scotland		Northern Ireland		United Kingdom	
	1990	1995	1990	1995	1990	1995	1990	1995
	Percentage who breastfed initially							
First birth	70	74	56	61	42	52	68	72
Second or later births	59	62	45	50	32	40	57	60
Bases								
First birth	*2,204*	*2,076*	*949*	*867*	*567*	*578*	*2,475*	*2,335*
Second or later births	*2,738*	*2,522*	*1,032*	*996*	*930*	*898*	*3,058*	*2,845*

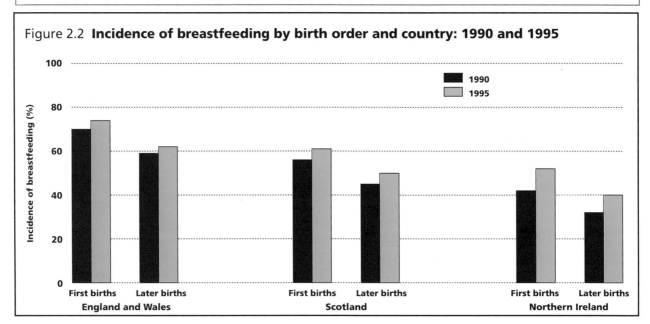

Figure 2.2 **Incidence of breastfeeding by birth order and country: 1990 and 1995**

for mothers of later babies. Thus recent increases in the breastfeeding rates for first babies may indicate further increases in future years for mothers of later babies.

The relationship between current feeding choices and previous experience was again seen from the 1995 Survey and was similar in all countries. In the United Kingdom as a whole, just under one fifth (18%) of mothers who had not breastfed earlier children at all had tried breastfeeding their new baby. This compared with 93% of mothers who had breastfed a previous child for six weeks or more and 59% of those who had previously breastfed for a shorter period of up to six weeks. The lower breastfeeding rate for the latter group is not unexpected because mothers may have previously given up breastfeeding at a relatively early stage because they experienced difficulties or did not enjoy breastfeeding.

Table 2.3

Social class (as defined by the current occupation of the husband or partner)

For compatibility with earlier surveys, the analyses in this report use information taken from the survey questionnaires about the husband's or partner's occupation to assign social class. Information from the questionnaire was used in preference to the classification based on information collected at registration because the questionnaires usually gave more detail about whether the woman had a partner and his occupation. Women who were not married or

Table 2.3	Incidence of breastfeeding among mothers of more than one child according to length of time for which previous children were breastfed			
Length of time previous children breastfed	England and Wales	Scotland	Northern Ireland	United Kingdom
	Percentage who breastfed initially			
Never breastfed	18	15	12	18
Breastfed for less than 6 weeks	60	46	43	59
Breastfed for 6 weeks or more	93	93	88	93
All later births*	**62**	**51**	**40**	**60**
Bases				
Never breastfed	*782*	*414*	*462*	*926*
Breastfed for less than 6 weeks	*525*	*184*	*156*	*584*
Breastfed for 6 weeks or more	*1,154*	*374*	*262*	*1,267*
All later births*	***2,522***	***996***	***898***	***2,845***

* Includes some cases where mother's method of feeding previous children was not known

Table 2.4	Incidence of breastfeeding by social class based on current or last occupation of husband/partner by country			
Social class of husband/partner	England and Wales	Scotland	Northern Ireland	United Kingdom
	Percentage who breastfed initially			
I	91	82	79	90
II	82	71	59	81
IIINM	72	65	55	71
All non-manual	**82**	**72**	**61**	**80**
IIIM	65	52	41	63
IV	58	48	38	57
V	50	56	36	50
All manual	**61**	**51**	**40**	**60**
Unclassified	62	56	33	61
No partner	49	30	24	46
All babies	**68**	**55**	**45**	**66**
Bases				
I	*303*	*149*	*83*	*346*
II	*1,150*	*398*	*318*	*1,275*
IIINM	*354*	*138*	*156*	*402*
All non-manual	***1,807***	***685***	***557***	***2,023***
IIIM	*1,113*	*439*	*383*	*1,254*
IV	*483*	*220*	*121*	*546*
V	*164*	*65*	*56*	*185*
All manual	***1,760***	***724***	***560***	***1,985***
Unclassified	*294*	*105*	*107*	*330*
No partner	*737*	*347*	*251*	*843*
All babies	***4,598***	***1,863***	***1,476***	***5,181***

living with a partner are shown as a separate category in the tables as are women who could not be assigned to a social class group either because inadequate information was given about the partner's occupation or because he had never worked.

The social class gradient in breastfeeding, with the highest rates among mothers in the non-manual social class groups, continued in 1995. In all countries, mothers who had no partner showed the lowest incidence of breastfeeding, with rates ranging from 24% in Northern Ireland to 49% in England and Wales. Breastfeeding rates for mothers in Social Class I were 91% in England and Wales and around 80% in Scotland and Northern Ireland.

Table 2.4

Trend data for Great Britain are shown in Table 2.5. Although there appeared to be an increase in breastfeeding rates between 1990 and 1995 in most social class groups, the changes were not generally significant. The only statistically significant increase was for mothers in all manual social class groups taken together, from 57% to 61%. Manual social class groups also showed the greatest increase over the whole period since 1985.

Table 2.5, Figure 2.3

Age at which mother completed full-time education

As in previous years, mothers who left full-time education at 16 years were least likely to breastfeed, while those who had continued in education beyond 18 years were most likely to do so. The association between breastfeeding and the mother's educational level was evident in all countries. For example, rates in Scotland ranged from 39% for mothers who had left school at 16 to 80% for mothers who remained in education beyond the age of 18.

Table 2.6

Trend data for Great Britain show very little change since 1990 in breastfeeding rates according to

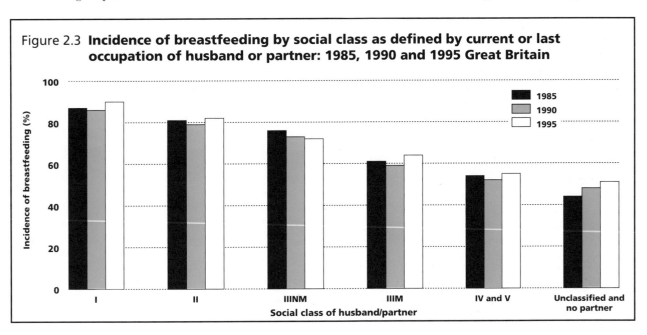

Figure 2.3 **Incidence of breastfeeding by social class as defined by current or last occupation of husband or partner: 1985, 1990 and 1995 Great Britain**

Table 2.5   Incidence of breastfeeding by social class based on current or last occupation of husband/partner for first and later births (1985, 1990 and 1995 Great Britain)

Social class of husband/partner	First birth			Later births			All babies		
	1985	1990	1995	1985	1990	1995	1985	1990	1995
	Percentage who breastfed initially								
I	93	89	91	83	84	89	87	86	90
II	87	86	88	76	74	77	81	79	82
IIINM	85	76	79	68	70	66	76	73	72
All non-manual	**88**	**85**	**87**	**75**	**74**	**77**	**81**	**79**	**81**
IIIM	69	68	73	55	53	57	61	59	64
IV	68	63	67	51	47	51	58	53	57
V	50	50	64	38	36	40	43	41	50
All manual	**67**	**66**	**71**	**52**	**50**	**54**	**58**	**57**	**61**
Unclassified	59	66	72	53	57	55	55	61	62
No partner	41	47	51	37	38	42	39	43	47
All babies	**69**	**69**	**73**	**59**	**58**	**61**	**64**	**63**	**66**
Bases									
I	*136*	*191*	*157*	*171*	*207*	*179*	*307*	*398*	*337*
II	*444*	*447*	*555*	*584*	*605*	*685*	*1,028*	*1,052*	*1,240*
IIINM	*213*	*200*	*177*	*223*	*227*	*208*	*436*	*427*	*385*
All non-manual	*793*	*838*	*889*	*978*	*1,039*	*1,072*	*1,771*	*1,877*	*1,962*
IIIM	*703*	*684*	*501*	*962*	*927*	*710*	*1,666*	*1,611*	*1,212*
IV	*284*	*306*	*214*	*453*	*430*	*318*	*738*	*736*	*532*
V	*103*	*39*	*79*	*144*	*78*	*100*	*247*	*117*	*179*
All manual	*1,090*	*1,029*	*794*	*1,559*	*1,435*	*1,128*	*2,651*	*2,464*	*1,923*
Unclassified	*81*	*126*	*136*	*125*	*187*	*182*	*207*	*313*	*318*
No partner	*383*	*437*	*453*	*212*	*322*	*362*	*595*	*760*	*815*
All babies	*2,347*	*2,430*	*2,271*	*2,875*	*2,983*	*2,745*	*5,223*	*5,413*	*5,017*

Table 2.6   Incidence of breastfeeding by age at which mother completed full-time education and country

Age at which mother completed full-time education	England and Wales	Scotland	Northern Ireland	United Kingdom
16 or under	53	39	26	51
17 or 18	74	59	46	72
Over 18	90	80	68	88
All babies*	68	55	45	66
Bases				
16 or under	*2,042*	*805*	*471*	*2,275*
17 or 18	*1,600*	*618*	*634*	*1,810*
Over 18	*913*	*432*	*356*	*1,049*
*All babies**	*4,598*	*1,863*	*1,476*	*5,181*

* Includes some cases where mother's age at finishing full-time education was not known

sample structure will, in itself, tend to result in higher overall breastfeeding rates providing the association between breastfeeding and education stays the same. The effects of changes in sample composition are discussed more fully in the next section.

Table 2.7, Figure 2.4

Mother's age

Analysis of the relationship between breastfeeding and mother's age usually focuses on first rather than later babies as this is easier to interpret. A mother's age at the birth of second or subsequent children depends on her age at the first birth, the number of children she has had and the spacing between them.

Table 2.8 shows that the strong association between breastfeeding of first babies and mother's age continued in 1995 and was evident in all countries. In Northern Ireland, for example, the incidence of breastfeeding ranged from 24% for mothers under the age of 20 to 65% for mothers aged 30 or over. The association between feeding method and age was also evident for later births. This is presumably because, as already seen from Table 2.3, the feeding choices made for later babies are strongly affected by the method chosen for previous babies.

Table 2.8

educational level. The only statistically significant change was that first-time mothers who completed their education at 19 or over were less likely to breastfeed in 1995 (89% compared with 93% in 1990).

The lack of change since 1990 in the rates for individual groups suggests that some of the observed increase in national rates between 1990 and 1995 may be due to changes in the characteristics of mothers over time. As shown in Table 1.7, the proportion of mothers who finished full-time education at 19 or over was much greater in 1995 than in 1990 in all countries. As this group has the highest incidence of breastfeeding, the change in

Table 2.7 **Incidence of breastfeeding by age at which mother completed full-time education and birth order (1985, 1990 and 1995 Great Britain)**

Age at which mother completed full-time education	First birth			Later births			All babies		
	1985	1990	1995	1985	1990	1995	1985	1990	1995
	Percentage who breastfed initially								
16 or under	58	57	59	49	46	47	53	50	52
17 or 18	80	75	78	70	68	67	75	71	72
Over 18	94	93	89	86	88	88	89	91	89
All babies*	**69**	**69**	**73**	**59**	**58**	**61**	**64**	**63**	**66**
Bases									
16 or under	*1,310*	*1,184*	*907*	*1,800*	*1,697*	*1,316*	*3,110*	*2,881*	*2,223*
17 or 18	*698*	*839*	*836*	*648*	*871*	*904*	*1,346*	*1,710*	*1,739*
Over 18	*328*	*387*	*508*	*397*	*388*	*502*	*725*	*775*	*1,010*
*All babies**	*2,347*	*2,430*	*2,271*	*2,875*	*2,983*	*2,745*	*5,223*	*5,413*	*5,017*

*Includes some cases where mother's age at finishing full-time education was not known.

Figure 2.4 **Incidence of breastfeeding by mother's education: 1985, 1990 and 1995 Great Britain**

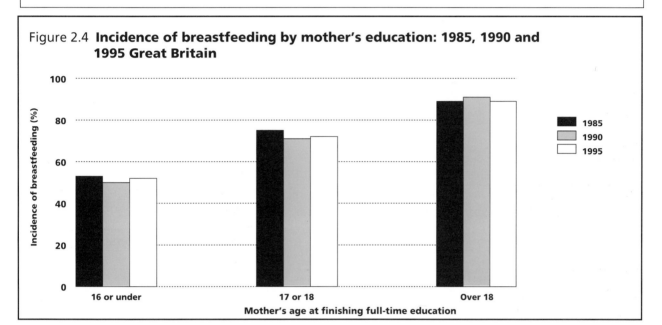

Table 2.8 **Incidence of breastfeeding by mother's age, birth order and country**

Mother's age	First births				Later births				All births			
	England and Wales	Scotland	Northern Ireland	United Kingdom	England and Wales	Scotland	Northern Ireland	United Kingdom	England and Wales	Scotland	Northern Ireland	United Kingdom
	Percentage who breastfed initially											
Under 20	46	25	24	43					46	24	24	43
20-24*	65	52	40	63	44	28	26	43	57	43	34	55
25-29	81	67	60	79	57	45	36	55	68	55	46	66
30 or over	86	76	65	85	71	60	46	69	76	65	50	74
All babies	**74**	**61**	**52**	**72**	**62**	**50**	**40**	**60**	**68**	**55**	**45**	**66**
Bases												
Under 20	*249*	*111*	*69*	*282*					*284*	*121*	*73*	*319*
*20-24 **	*538*	*209*	*154*	*602*	*380*	*143*	*89*	*422*	*883*	*342*	*240*	*986*
25-29	*699*	*294*	*229*	*790*	*868*	*332*	*292*	*975*	*1,566*	*629*	*521*	*1,765*
30 or over	*586*	*253*	*126*	*656*	*1,270*	*518*	*515*	*1,443*	*1,855*	*771*	*640*	*2,100*
All babies	*2,076*	*867*	*578*	*2,335*	*2,522*	*996*	*898*	*2,845*	*4,598*	*1,867*	*1,476*	*5,181*

* Aged 24 or under for mothers of later babies
   Includes some cases where mother's age was not known

Trend data for Great Britain show that there has been little change since 1985 in breastfeeding rates for different age groups. After a small decline between 1985 and 1990 in rates for mothers aged up to 29, the incidence of breastfeeding in 1995 has returned to similar levels to 1985. There has been no change since 1985 in rates of breastfeeding among mothers aged 30 or over.

Table 2.9, Figure 2.5

Region

Previous surveys have shown that, within Great Britain, the incidence of breastfeeding varies with region. A similar pattern was seen in 1995, with the highest rates in London and the South East and the lowest rates in Scotland and the North. Thus the incidence of breastfeeding ranged from 76% in London and the South East to 56% in Northern England and 55% in Scotland.

Between 1990 and 1995, breastfeeding rates in the South West and Wales increased significantly, from 65% to 70%. There was a similar increase in the Midlands and East Anglia from 59% to 64%. Breastfeeding rates for mothers in the North and in London and the South East showed no change over this period.

Table 2.10

The 1994 Survey of Infant Feeding in Asian Families[2] found that Bangladeshi mothers were the most likely to ever breastfeed (90%), followed by Indian (82%) and Pakistani (76%) mothers.

2.2 Explanation of trends in incidence of breastfeeding

As detailed in Section 1.6, there were some important changes between 1990 and 1995 in the composition of the survey sample which reflect changes over that period in the characteristics of all mothers. The 1995 sample contained greater proportions of mothers who were aged 30 or over, had continued in full-time education beyond the age of 18 or were classified to non-manual social class groups. The changes continued trends evident since 1985.[1]

As already discussed, these three characteristics of mothers — their age, educational level and social class — are all strongly associated with the incidence of

Table 2.9	Incidence of breastfeeding by mother's age (first births only, 1985, 1990 and 1995 Great Britain)					
Mother's age	1985	1990	1995	*1985*	*1990*	*1995*
		Percentage who breastfed initially			*Base*	
Under 20	42	39	44	*380*	*315*	*274*
20-24	65	61	64	*898*	*756*	*585*
25-29	81	77	80	*729*	*874*	*765*
30 or over	86	86	85	*337*	*479*	*643*
All first babies*	69	69	73	*2,347*	*2,430*	*2,271*

*Includes some cases where mother's age was not known

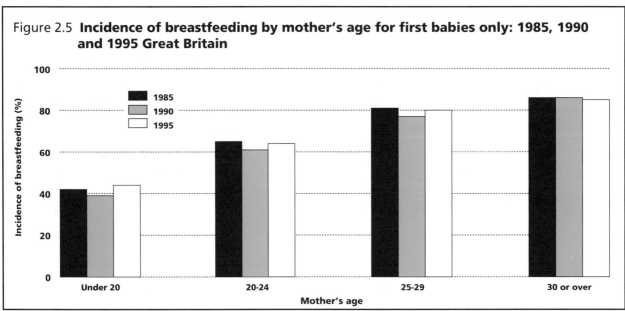

Figure 2.5 **Incidence of breastfeeding by mother's age for first babies only: 1985, 1990 and 1995 Great Britain**

Table 2.10 **Incidence of breastfeeding by region and birth order (1985, 1990 and 1995 Great Britain)**

Region	First birth			Later births			All babies		
	1985	1990	1995	1985	1990	1995	1985	1990	1995
	Percentage who breastfed initially								
London and South East	81	78	82	69	70	70	74	74	76
South West and Wales	74	75	78	63	58	63	68	65	70
Midlands and East Anglia	66	67	70	59	53	59	62	59	64
North	63	61	62	50	50	51	56	55	56
Scotland	53	56	61	45	45	50	48	50	55
All babies	**69**	**69**	**73**	**59**	**58**	**61**	**64**	**63**	**66**
Bases									
London and South East	*747*	*795*	*806*	*928*	*990*	*1,011*	*1,675*	*1,785*	*1,818*
South West and Wales	*298*	*275*	*316*	*359*	*391*	*367*	*657*	*666*	*684*
Midlands and East Anglia	*3,419*	*447*	*405*	*541*	*594*	*502*	*960*	*1,041*	*907*
North	*628*	*689*	*549*	*750*	*763*	*641*	*1,378*	*1,452*	*1,190*
Scotland	*875*	*949*	*867*	*1,020*	*1,032*	*996*	*1,895*	*1,981*	*1,867*
All babies	***2,347***	***2,430***	***2,271***	***2,875***	***2,983***	***2,745***	***5,223***	***5,413***	***5,017***

breastfeeding. Moreover, the groups which have increased in size are those with higher breastfeeding rates. Explanation of observed national trends in breastfeeding is therefore complicated by the fact that, even if the rates for different groups had remained constant, overall rates would have increased simply as a result of changes in the composition of the sample.

The technique of standardisation can be used to separate the contribution of compositional change from what might be termed "real" change over the period since 1985 (1990 for Northern Ireland). The calculated standardised rates show the breastfeeding rates which would have been expected in 1990 and in 1995 if the samples of mothers in those two surveys had had the same characteristics as the 1985 sample. It should be noted that the technique assumes that the breastfeeding rates observed for a particular group in any survey would have applied even if that group had been a smaller or larger proportion of the sample. In this case it has already been seen that the breastfeeding rates within groups showed little change between 1990 and 1995.

Standardisation was carried out separately for the samples in each country for each of the three main characteristics. This indicated that changes in the composition of the sample with respect to mother's age and educational level had a greater effect than changes in social class distribution. A further analysis to standardise for the combined effects of age and educational level shows the rates standardised both for the combined effects of age and educational level and for age alone.

Table 2.11

As already seen in Table 2.1, survey estimates of the incidence of breastfeeding in England and Wales

were 65% in 1985, 64% in 1990 and 68% in 1995. The standardised rates, assuming that the age distribution of the sample had remained the same as in 1985, were 63% and 65% respectively. Standardising for both mother's age and the age she completed full-time education reduces the rates still further, to 62% in both years. Thus the observed change in breastfeeding rates between 1990 and 1995 can be entirely attributed to changes in the sample composition.

Standardising for the age and educational level of mothers in Scotland again removed much of the observed increase in breastfeeding since 1990, and reduced 1995 rates to the same level as in 1985. Calculated rates were 46% in 1990 and 48% in 1995 compared with 48% in 1985.

Changes in sample composition also had some effect on estimates of incidence in Northern Ireland but the standardised rates still indicated a substantial

Table 2.11 **Estimated incidence of breastfeeding standardised for composition of the sample, by country**

	1985	1990	1995
	Percentage who breastfed initially		
England and Wales			
Unstandardised percentage	65	64	68
Standardised for age group of mother	65	63	65
Standardised for mother's age and age finished full-time education	65	62	62
Scotland			
Unstandardised percentage	48	50	55
Standardised for age group of mother	48	48	51
Standardised for mother's age and age finished full-time education	48	46	48
Northern Ireland			
Unstandardised percentage	..	36	45
Standardised for age group of mother	..	36	43
Standardised for mother's age and age finished full-time education	..	36	41

23

increase in breastfeeding between 1990 and 1995 (from 36% to 41%).

Clearly standardisation is only a technique to aid explanation of observed changes and it is the survey estimates themselves which give the true picture of the proportion of mothers in the population who are breastfeeding at a particular time. Nonetheless, standardisation can be helpful in indicating how national estimates might change if the recent compositional changes were reversed, for example if the proportion of women having children in their thirties were to fall.

2.3 Prevalence of breastfeeding

Prevalence of breastfeeding refers to the proportion of babies still breastfed at specific ages, even if the babies were also receiving infant formula or solid food.

Table 2.12 illustrates the changes in the prevalence of breastfeeding by country since 1990. As already seen, initial breastfeeding rates in all countries were higher in 1995 than in 1990 and the higher rates of breastfeeding continued over the first few weeks. As for initial breastfeeding rates, the improvements in breastfeeding rates at six weeks were more marked in Northern Ireland than in England and Wales and Scotland. Rates increased from 39% to 44% in England and Wales, from 30% to 36% in Scotland and from 27% to 32% in Northern Ireland. In all countries, breastfeeding rates fell by about 10% in the first week after birth and by a further 10% to 14% in the next five weeks. However, as initial rates were lower in Northern Ireland, the rate of decrease is proportionately greater.

By four months, just over a quarter of all mothers in the United Kingdom were breastfeeding: ranging from 12% in Northern Ireland to 28% in England and Wales. These rates are slightly higher than in 1990.

In 1995, babies were, on average, younger at the time the stage three questionnaire was completed than in 1990. Thus, for 1995, the tables show the prevalence rates at nine months for only those babies who were aged nine months or more at stage three. The prevalence rates for all babies at eight months are also included in Table 2.12 and it can be seen that there was very little difference in the prevalence of breastfeeding at eight and at nine months.

Table 2.12

Tables 2.13 to 2.16 show the trends in prevalence in Great Britain since 1985 by birth order, educational level, social class and region. As the prevalence of breastfeeding at six weeks depends largely on the proportion of mothers who start breastfeeding, it is not surprising to find that the patterns of variation are similar to those already discussed for the initial incidence of breastfeeding. Differences in the length of time for which mothers breastfeed can be separated from the effect of different initial incidence by basing the analysis only on mothers who start to breastfeed.

Tables 2.13 to 2.16

2.4 Duration of breastfeeding

The duration of breastfeeding refers to the length of time that mothers who breastfed initially continue to do so even if they were also giving their baby other foods. The results presented in this section relate only to mothers who ever breastfed and show the proportion who were still breastfeeding at one week, two weeks, six weeks, four months, six months and nine months after the birth.

Table 2.12 **Prevalence of breastfeeding at ages up to nine months by country (1990 and 1995 United Kingdom)**

Age of baby	England and Wales		Scotland		Northern Ireland		United Kingdom	
	1990	1995	1990	1995	1990	1995	1990	1995
	Percentage breastfeeding at each age							
Birth	64	68	50	55	36	45	62	66
1 week	54	58	41	46	29	35	53	56
2 weeks	51	54	39	44	27	32	50	53
6 weeks	39	44	30	36	17	25	39	42
4 months	25	28	20	24	8	12	25	27
6 months	21	22	16	19	5	8	21	21
8 months	15	16	12	14	3	6	..	15
9 months *	12	14	9	13	3	5	11	14
Base	*4,942*	*4,598*	*1,981*	*1,863*	*1,497*	*1,476*	*5,533*	*5,181*

* Based on a reduced number of cases in 1995

Table 2.13 Prevalence of breastfeeding at ages up to nine months for first and later births (1985, 1990 and 1995 Great Britain)

Age of baby	First birth			Later births			All babies		
	1985	1990	1995	1985	1990	1995	1985	1990	1995
	Percentage breastfeeding at each age								
Birth	69	69	73	60	58	61	64	63	66
1 week	57	57	60	53	50	54	55	53	57
2 weeks	53	52	56	50	48	51	51	50	53
6 weeks	39	39	44	38	38	42	38	39	43
4 months	25	23	26	27	26	30	26	25	28
6 months	19	18	19	22	22	24	21	21	21
9 months *	10	10	12	12	13	16	11	11	14
Base	*2,347*	*2,430*	*2,271*	*2,875*	*2,983*	*2,745*	*5,223*	*5,413*	*5,017*

* Based on a reduced number of cases in 1995

Table 2.14 Prevalence of breastfeeding at ages up to nine months by age at which mother finished full-time education (1985,1990 and 1995 Great Britain)

| Age of baby | Age at which mother finished full-time education | | | | | | | | | All babies* | | |
| | 16 or under | | | 17 or 18 | | | Over 18 | | | | | |
	1985	1990	1995	1985	1990	1995	1985	1990	1995	1985	1990	1995
	Percentage breastfeeding at each age											
Birth	53	50	52	75	71	72	89	91	89	64	63	66
1 week	43	40	41	66	61	62	85	84	83	55	53	57
2 weeks	39	37	37	63	57	57	82	81	81	51	50	53
6 weeks	26	26	27	48	45	45	73	71	74	38	39	43
4 months	15	14	16	30	30	27	59	53	56	26	25	28
6 months	12	12	12	24	24	19	50	44	45	21	21	21
9 months†	6	7	8	13	14	10	28	25	31	11	11	14
Base	*3,110*	*2,881*	*2,223*	*1,346*	*1,710*	*1,739*	*725*	*775*	*1,010*	*5,223*	*5,413*	*5,017*

* Includes some cases where mother's education was not known
† Based on a reduced number of cases in 1995

Table 2.15 Prevalence of breastfeeding at ages up to nine months by social class based on current or last occupation of husband/partner (1985, 1990 and 1995 Great Britain)

| Age of baby | Social class | | | | | | | | | | | |
| | I | | | II | | | IIINM | | | IIIM | | |
	1985	1990	1995	1985	1990	1995	1985	1990	1995	1985	1990	1995
	Percentage breastfeeding at each age											
Birth	87	86	90	81	79	82	76	73	72	61	59	64
1 week	83	81	84	73	70	72	67	62	64	51	48	52
2 weeks	79	77	83	69	67	68	62	59	60	48	45	48
6 weeks	71	68	73	58	56	59	46	47	48	34	33	36
4 months	54	48	56	43	39	41	30	28	30	21	20	21
6 months	45	40	42	37	34	31	24	22	23	16	16	16
9 months *	23	22	31	21	18	19	11	13	18	8	10	10
Base	*307*	*398*	*337*	*1,028*	*1,052*	*1,240*	*436*	*427*	*385*	*1,666*	*1,611*	*1,212*

| Age of baby | Social class | | | | | | | | | | | |
| | IV | | | V | | | No Partner | | | Unclassified | | |
	1985	1990	1995	1985	1990	1995	1985	1990	1995	1985	1990	1995
	Percentage breastfeeding at each age											
Birth	58	53	57	43	41	50	55	43	47	39	61	62
1 week	47	42	46	36	32	40	46	33	37	30	54	54
2 weeks	43	39	43	33	29	36	43	30	34	27	51	51
6 weeks	29	27	33	20	20	23	30	40	25	16	19	38
4 months	16	16	21	9	10	13	20	25	13	8	10	25
6 months	12	15	17	7	9	11	19	22	9	6	7	19
9 months*	5	8	11	2	4	5	13	11	6	4	4	14
Base	*738*	*736*	*532*	*247*	*117*	*179*	*595*	*760*	*815*	*207*	*313*	*318*

* Based on a reduced number of cases in 1995

Table 2.16 Prevalence of breastfeeding at ages up to nine months by region (1985, 1990 and 1995 England and Wales)

Age of baby	London and South East			South West and Wales			Midlands and East Anglia			North		
	1985	1990	1995	1985	1990	1995	1985	1990	1995	1985	1990	1995
	Percentage breastfeeding at each age											
Birth	74	74	76	68	65	70	62	59	64	56	55	56
1 week	67	65	67	60	57	59	53	48	53	46	44	46
2 weeks	63	61	63	56	55	56	49	45	50	42	41	43
6 weeks	47	49	51	47	45	46	35	33	39	30	29	35
4 months	32	31	33	34	32	31	23	20	25	18	18	21
6 months	26	25	25	27	28	23	11	17	19	14	15	16
9 months *	13	14	16	15	15	17	8	10	12	9	9	11
Base	*1,675*	*1,785*	*1,818*	*657*	*666*	*684*	*960*	*1,041*	*907*	*1,378*	*1,452*	*1,190*

* Based on a reduced number of cases in 1995

Table 2.17 compares the duration of breastfeeding in 1990 and 1995 by country. In England and Wales there was a statistically significant increase in the proportion of women who were still breastfeeding when their baby was six weeks old; 65% of mothers who breastfed initially were still doing so at six weeks, compared with 62% in 1990. Similarly, in Scotland the proportion of women still breastfeeding at six weeks increased from 60% in 1990 to 66% in 1995, and in Northern Ireland the proportion increased from 49% to 56% over the same time period.

As in 1990, Northern Ireland showed a steeper decline than the other countries in the proportion of women who continued to breastfeed at six weeks, with a particularly sharp fall after one week. In 1995, 21% of breastfeeding mothers in Northern Ireland had given up after one week compared with 16% of mothers in Scotland, and 56% continued to breastfeed at six weeks compared with 66% of mothers in Scotland.

By four months, over half the women who had breastfed at birth had given up: 42% continued in England and Wales, 45% in Scotland and 27% in Northern Ireland. The proportion of women still breastfeeding at four months increased between 1990 and 1995 in England and Wales and in Scotland. The apparent increase in Northern Ireland (from 23% to 27%) was not statistically significant.

When the babies were 9 months old, 21% of mothers were still breastfeeding in England and Wales, 24% in Scotland and 11% in Northern Ireland, an increase on 1990 in England and Wales and in Scotland.

Table 2.17, Figures 2.6 and 2.7

Birth order

As found in previous surveys, mothers of second or later babies breastfed for longer than mothers of first babies. Data for Great Britain in Table 2.18 show that 84% of later babies were still breastfed at two weeks, compared with 77% of first babies. By six months, 39% of mothers of second or later babies were still breastfeeding, compared with 26% of mothers of first babies.

Overall, mothers in Great Britain in 1995 were more likely than those in 1990 to continue breastfeeding to six weeks — 65% and 61% respectively — and to nine months. When birth order was taken into account there was no statistically significant difference between the two surveys among women having their

Table 2.17 Duration of breastfeeding by country (1990 and 1995)

	England and Wales		Scotland		Northern Ireland		United Kingdom	
	1990	1995	1990	1995	1990	1995	1990	1995
	Percentage breastfeeding at each age							
Birth	100	100	100	100	100	100	100	100
1 week	85	86	83	84	81	79	85	85
2 weeks	80	81	77	79	75	73	80	80
6 weeks	62	65	60	66	49	56	61	65
4 months	39	42	39	45	23	27	39	42
6 months	33	32	33	35	15	19	33	32
9 months *	18	21	19	24	8	11	18	21
Base:	*3,149*	*3,106*	*994*	*1,029*	*531*	*659*	*3,438*	*3,410*

* Based on a reduced number of cases in 1995

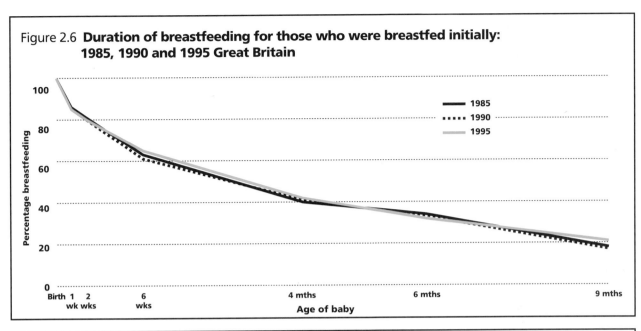

Figure 2.6 **Duration of breastfeeding for those who were breastfed initially: 1985, 1990 and 1995 Great Britain**

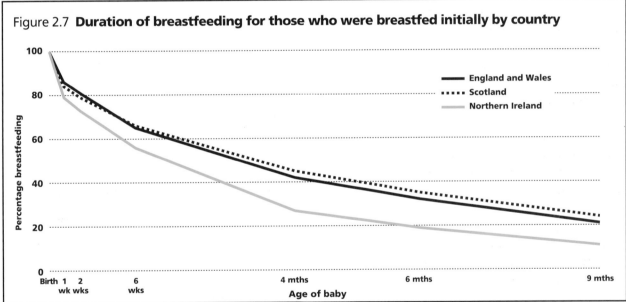

Figure 2.7 **Duration of breastfeeding for those who were breastfed initially by country**

first baby. Among women having their second or later baby, women in 1995 were more likely to be still breastfeeding at six weeks, compared with 1990, but the increase did not continue as the baby got older, and there were no significant differences at four and nine months.

Table 2.18

As with incidence, there is clear evidence from previous surveys that the likelihood of a mother continuing to breastfeed successfully a second or subsequent baby is closely related to her experience of feeding previous children. Table 2.19 shows that, for the small number of women who chose to breastfeed after bottle feeding their previous child or children, there was a very sharp decline in breastfeeding over the first few weeks. By six weeks only 34% of these mothers continued to

breastfeed compared with 74% of mothers who had breastfed a previous child. By the time their baby was six months old, 42% of mothers with previous experience were still breastfeeding compared with 15% of those who had not breastfed before.

Table 2.19, Figure 2.8

Social class (as defined by the current occupation of the husband or partner)

There continues to be a strong relationship between the duration of breastfeeding and social class, with a regular pattern of shorter duration of breastfeeding in each consecutively lower social class group. In 1995, 82% of mothers in Social Class I who breastfed initially were still doing so at six weeks compared with 46% of mothers in Social Class V. Similarly, 63% of mothers in Social Class I were still breastfeeding at

Table 2.18 **Duration of breastfeeding for those who were breastfed initially for first and later births (1985, 1990 and 1995 Great Britain)**

	First births			Later births			All babies		
	1985	1990	1995	1985	1990	1995	1985	1990	1995
				Percentage still breastfeeding					
Birth	100	100	100	100	100	100	100	100	100
1 week	83	82	83	90	87	88	86	85	85
2 weeks	76	76	77	85	83	84	81	80	80
6 weeks	56	57	60	65	66	70	63	61	65
4 months	36	34	35	46	45	49	40	41	42
6 months	28	27	26	38	42	39	34	33	32
9 months *	14	14	16	21	30	27	18	17	21
Base	*1,642*	*1,620*	*1,657*	*1,677*	*1,725*	*1,680*	*3,319*	*3,395*	*3,337*

* Based on a reduced number of cases in 1995

Table 2.19 **Duration of breastfeeding for those who were breastfed initially by mother's previous experience of breastfeeding (1985, 1990 and 1995 Great Britain)**

	No experience of breastfeeding			Experience of breastfeeding			All second and later babies		
	1985	1990	1995	1985	1990	1995	1985	1990	1995
				Percentage still breastfeeding					
Birth	100	100	100	100	100	100	100	100	100
1 week	74	62	67	92	91	90	90	88	88
2 weeks	63	56	58	87	87	87	85	84	84
6 weeks	43	31	34	68	70	74	65	66	70
4 months	20	15	17	48	49	52	46	45	49
6 months	14	11	15	40	42	42	38	39	39
9 months *	6	8	11	22	25	28	21	23	27
Base	*157*	*159*	*158*	*1,498*	*1,492*	*1,506*	*1,677*	*1,725*	*1,680*

* Based on a reduced number of cases in 1995

Figure 2.8 **Duration of breastfeeding for those who were breastfed initially by previous experience of breastfeeding: 1995 Great Britain**

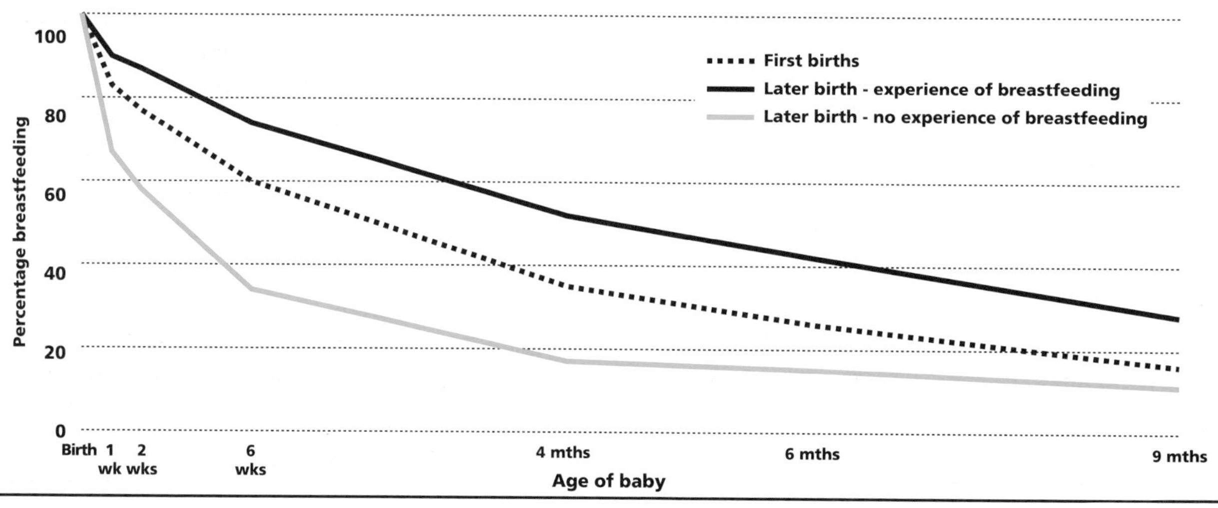

four months compared with 26% of those in Social Class V. Almost one half (48%) of those mothers in Social Class I who had breastfed initially continued for at least 6 months, compared with 22% of their counterparts in Social Class V. As in previous years, mothers with no partner showed a steep rate of decline in breastfeeding over the first few weeks.

The figures for duration of breastfeeding have shown little change over the last five years although there is a tendency for mothers with no partner to have continued breastfeeding for longer in 1995 than in 1990.

Table 2.20

Age at which mother completed full-time education

Table 2.21 shows that in 1995, as in previous years, duration of breastfeeding in Great Britain was longest among mothers who continued in full-time education

Table 2.20 **Duration of breastfeeding for those who were breastfed initially by social class based on current or last occupation of husband/partner (1985, 1990 and 1995 Great Britain)**

| | Social class | | | | | | | | | | | |
| | I | | | II | | | IINM | | | IIIM | | |
	1985	1990	1995	1985	1990	1995	1985	1990	1995	1985	1990	1995
					Percentage still breastfeeding							
Birth	100	100	100	100	100	100	100	100	100	100	100	100
1 week	95	94	94	91	89	88	88	86	90	84	82	82
2 weeks	91	90	92	86	85	84	82	82	83	79	76	76
6 weeks	81	78	82	72	71	73	61	65	66	56	57	58
4 months	62	56	63	54	50	50	40	38	42	36	34	33
6 months	52	46	48	45	43	38	33	30	33	27	28	26
9 months*	27	27	35	26	23	23	15	18	24	14	16	17
Base	*268*	*343*	*303*	*830*	*833*	*1,011*	*332*	*332*	*276*	*1,009*	*951*	*771*

| | Social class | | | | | | | | | | | |
| | IV | | | V | | | No Partner | | | Unclassified | | |
	1985	1990	1995	1985	1990	1995	1985	1990	1995	1985	1990	1995
					Percentage still breastfeeding							
Birth	100	100	100	100	100	100	100	100	100	100	100	100
1 week	82	80	80	85	80	79	77	77	80	85	90	88
2 weeks	74	73	76	76	73	72	69	71	72	79	85	83
6 weeks	51	51	59	46	51	46	43	45	55	56	67	62
4 months	29	31	36	22	26	26	22	23	28	39	41	41
6 months	22	28	29	17	23	22	18	17	21	36	36	31
9 months*	9	15	19	6	11	10	11	9	12	25	19	23
Base	*425*	*393*	*304*	*107*	*47*	*90*	*235*	*326*	*386*	*114*	*190*	*197*

* Based on a reduced number of cases in 1995

after the age of 18 and shortest among those who left school at 16 or below. At six weeks, 83% of mothers who finished education at 19 or above were still breastfeeding compared with 53% of those who had left school at 16. This pattern can also be seen at four and six months.

There were no significant changes in duration of breastfeeding by educational level between 1990 and 1995.

Table 2.21, Figure 2.9

Region

Within England and Wales there continued to be a slight regional variation in the duration of breastfeeding. Table 2.22 shows that, in 1995, the duration tended to decrease from south to north in England and Wales; at six weeks, 68% of mothers in London and the South East continued to breastfeed compared with 61% of mothers in the Midlands and East Anglia and in the North. Similarly, 66% of mothers in London and the South East and in the South West and Wales had given up breastfeeding by six months, compared with 70% in the Midlands and East Anglia and 71% in the North.

There have been some changes in this pattern since 1990, with a higher proportion of mothers in the Midlands and East Anglia and the North still breastfeeding at six weeks. In the Midlands and East

Table 2.21 **Duration of breastfeeding for those who were breastfed initially by age at which mother finished full-time education (1985, 1990 and 1995 Great Britain)**

| | Age at which mother finished full-time education | | | | | | | | | All babies | | |
| | 16 or under | | | 17 or 18 | | | Over 18 | | | | | |
	1985	1990	1995	1985	1990	1995	1985	1990	1995	1985	1990	1995
					Percentage still breastfeeding							
Birth	100	100	100	100	100	100	100	100	100	100	100	100
1 week	82	80	79	89	86	85	95	93	94	86	85	85
2 weeks	75	74	73	83	81	79	91	90	92	81	80	80
6 weeks	50	52	53	64	63	63	81	79	83	61	62	65
4 months	30	28	30	40	42	37	66	59	63	41	39	42
6 months	24	24	24	32	34	27	56	49	51	33	33	32
9 months *	12	13	17	17	19	15	31	28	35	17	18	21
Base	*1,633*	*1,446*	*1,152*	*1,013*	*1,217*	*1,261*	*647*	*702*	*897*	*3,319*	*3,395*	*3,337*

* Based on a reduced number of cases in 1995

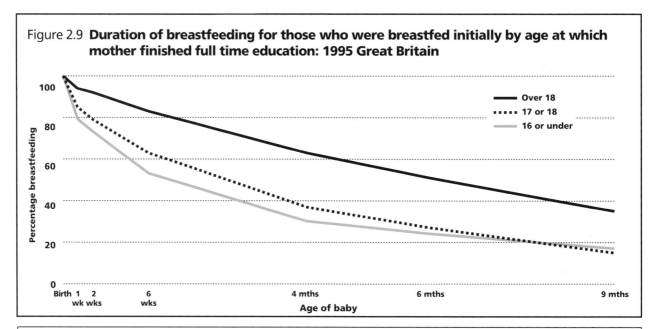

Figure 2.9 **Duration of breastfeeding for those who were breastfed initially by age at which mother finished full time education: 1995 Great Britain**

Table 2.22 **Duration of breastfeeding for those who were breastfed initially by region (1985, 1990 and 1995 England and Wales)**

	London and South East			South West and Wales			Midlands and East Anglia			North		
	1985	1990	1995	1985	1990	1995	1985	1990	1995	1985	1990	1995
	Percentage still breastfeeding											
Birth	100	100	100	100	100	100	100	100	100	100	100	100
1 week	89	88	88	88	89	84	86	83	83	82	80	82
2 weeks	84	83	84	82	85	79	80	77	79	76	75	77
6 weeks	64	67	68	69	70	67	57	56	61	54	54	61
4 months	43	43	44	49	49	44	38	35	39	32	33	37
6 months	36	35	34	40	43	34	30	30	30	26	27	29
9 months *	18	18	22	22	24	24	13	17	19	16	17	19
Base	*1,241*	*1,320*	*1,375*	*449*	*432*	*481*	*595*	*610*	*579*	*766*	*797*	*671*

* Based on a reduced number of cases in 1995

Anglia the proportion continuing to breastfeed at six weeks increased from 56% to 61% and, as shown in Table 2.10, there was also an increase in the initial incidence of breastfeeding. In contrast, mothers in the South West and Wales, who were also significantly more likely to breastfeed initially than in 1990, continued for a shorter period; only 67% were still breastfeeding at six weeks in 1995 compared with 70% in 1990.

Table 2.22, Figure 2.10

Mother's employment status

As in 1990, mothers were classified according to their working status during the first eight to nine months of their baby's life. Mothers were classified into one of five groups as follows:

(i)   those who were working when the baby was about six weeks old and continued working throughout the rest of the nine months ('working all the time' in table 2.23);

(ii) those who returned to work when the baby was

between six weeks and four months old ('went back to work by four months');

(iii) those who returned to work when the baby was between four months and nine months old ('went back to work by nine months');

(iv) those who did not work at all during the first nine months ('not working any of the time');

(v)   those whose pattern of work followed some other arrangement ('others').

Table 2.23 shows that the duration of breastfeeding was similar for all the groups of mothers, although returning to work when the baby was about four months old reduced slightly the length of time for which mothers continued to breastfeed. Thus, 32% of women who went back to work when their baby was aged between six weeks and four months were still breastfeeding when their baby was four months old, compared with 46% of those returning at between

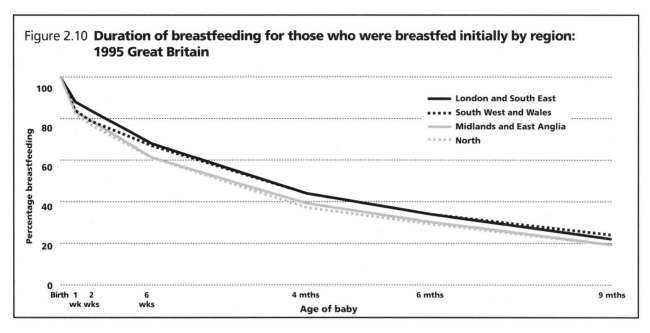

Figure 2.10 **Duration of breastfeeding for those who were breastfed initially by region: 1995 Great Britain**

five and nine months and those not working any of the time and 45% of those working all the time.

There were no significant differences in the duration of breastfeeding among mothers in the different work status groups between 1990 and 1995.

Table 2.23, Figure 2.11

The tables and figures presented above show the proportion of mothers breastfeeding at different ages and these mothers may also be giving manufactured baby milk or cow's milk. It is not possible to use the information collected in the survey to look at the age of introduction of manufactured milks among breastfeeding mothers, but it is possible to look at whether mothers were exclusively breastfeeding or combining breast and non-human milk at the time they filled in each questionnaire.

Figure 2.12 (and Table 2.24) shows the decline in both exclusive breastfeeding and breastfeeding in

conjunction with use of non-human milk over the three stages among women who breastfed their baby at birth. For example, at stage one, 34% of these mothers were exclusively breastfeeding, falling to 21% at stage two and 10% at stage three. Similarly, the proportion of women who had initially breastfed who were combining breast and non-human milk at later stages decreased over the three stages from 27% at stage one to 16% at stage two and 10% at stage three. The use of non-human milk in conjunction with breastfeeding is discussed further in Chapter 6.

Table 2.24, Figure 2.12

2.5 Conclusion

The tables presented above show that there is a relationship between the incidence, prevalence and duration of breastfeeding and birth order and socio-demographic characteristics of the mother. However these relationships are themselves affected by

Table 2.23 **Duration of breastfeeding for those who were breastfed initially by mother's working status during the first nine months (1985, 1990 and 1995 Great Britain)**

	Working all the time			Went back to work by four months			Went back to work by nine months			Not working any of the time			Others		
	1985	1990	1995	1985	1990	1995	1985	1990	1995	1985	1990	1995	1985	1990	1995
						Percentage still breastfeeding									
Birth	100	100	100	100	100	100	100	100	100	100	100	100	100	100	100
1 week	87	84	84	88	85	85	91	86	85	86	85	87	90	93	82
2 weeks	82	81	79	82	78	80	87	83	80	80	80	82	85	89	78
6 weeks	60	63	66	59	61	63	67	69	68	61	61	66	68	60	67
4 months	41	37	45	34	31	32	46	48	46	41	42	46	54	36	41
6 months	33	30	36	22	22	20	34	37	35	34	36	37	44	30	29
9 months *	17	17	26	12	10	10	14	21	19	18	20	27	18	24	20
Base	*121*	*179*	*149*	*266*	*561*	*782*	*406*	*580*	*620*	*2,438*	*1,898*	*1,615*	*90*	*73*	*62*

* Based on a reduced number of cases in 1995

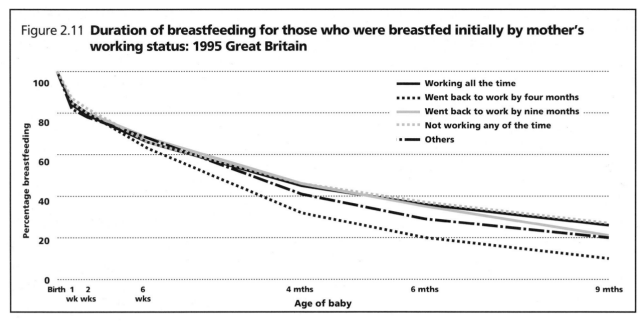

Figure 2.11 **Duration of breastfeeding for those who were breastfed initially by mother's working status: 1995 Great Britain**

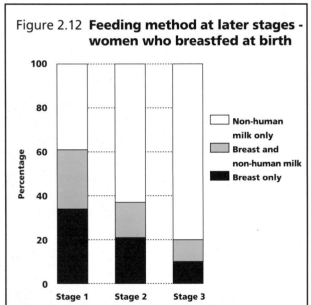

Figure 2.12 **Feeding method at later stages - women who breastfed at birth**

interrelationships between the different explanatory variables. Analysis is carried out in Chapter 5 to identify which characteristics were most strongly associated with initiation of breastfeeding and duration of breastfeeding up to two weeks. That chapter discusses the relationship between socio-demographic characteristics, events during pregnancy and around the time of the birth and the influence of friends and relatives, and the incidence and duration of breastfeeding.

Notes and references

1   White A, Freeth S and O'Brien M. *Infant Feeding 1990*, HMSO (London: 1992).

2   Thomas M and Avery V. *Infant Feeding in Asian Families*, The Stationery Office (London: 1997).

Table 2.24 **Feeding method at survey stages**
Women who breastfed at birth

Feeding method	Stage 1	Stage 2	Stage 3
	%	%	%
Breast only	34	21	10
Combination of breast and non-human milk	27	16	10
Non-human milk only	39	63	81
Base	*3,418*	*3,418*	*3,418*

3 Antenatal care, smoking and drinking

Summary

- Almost all mothers (99%) had antenatal checkups during pregnancy and about 70% of mothers of first babies had been to antenatal classes.

- Three quarters (75%) of mothers knew that increasing their intake of folic acid in early pregnancy could be good for them.

- A majority of mothers took supplementary iron or vitamins during pregnancy. The proportion was higher in Northern Ireland (85%) than elsewhere (61% in England and Wales).

- One third (35%) of women smoked before they became pregnant. One third of these (33%) gave up during pregnancy and about one half (47%) smoked fewer cigarettes.

- More women smokers had given up smoking during pregnancy than in 1990 (33% compared with 27% for mothers in GB).

- 86% of mothers drank alcohol before they became pregnant and two thirds (66%) drank during pregnancy, although most (70% of drinkers) drank less than one unit per week on average.

- Most smokers (86%) had received information on the effects of smoking during pregnancy and 71% of women who drank had received advice about drinking.

3.1 Antenatal checkups, classes and home visits

Almost all mothers (99%) had antenatal checkups during pregnancy. The proportions were similar in all countries and for first and later births. Between a half and three fifths of mothers had been seen at home by a midwife or health visitor in connection with their pregnancy and before the birth of their baby. Women in Northern Ireland were less likely than those in other countries to have been visited at home (49% compared with 62% in England and Wales). In all countries, visits were equally likely for first and later births.

Mothers were asked if they had gone to any classes to prepare for having their baby and by whom the classes had been organised. Women in Scotland were most likely to have attended classes (46%) and those in Northern Ireland were least likely (35%). As would be expected, women expecting their first child were more likely to have been to classes than were women who already had children: in England and Wales the rates were 70% and 17% respectively.

Table 3.1

Attendance at antenatal classes was strongly associated with social class. Among mothers of first babies, 87% of mothers whose partner was in Social Class I had been to classes compared with 62% of those classified to Social Class V. Less than one half

(44%) of women with no partner had been to classes. A similar pattern was also seen for later births.

Table 3.2, Figure 3.1

There was some variation between countries in who had organised the antenatal classes. In Northern Ireland, women were most likely to have been to classes run by a hospital (71%) whereas in England and Wales they were more likely to be organised by a clinic, surgery or health centre (63%). Only a small proportion of women had been to classes run by a voluntary organisation and this was more common in England and Wales (7% of women who attended classes) than elsewhere (3% in Scotland and 1% in Northern Ireland).

Table 3.3

3.2 Folic acid and dietary supplements

In 1995, mothers were asked for the first time whether, when they became pregnant, they knew that increasing their intake of folic acid could be good for them. The Department of Health advises women to take a daily supplement of 400 micrograms of folic acid prior to conception and during the first twelve weeks of pregnancy and, in addition, to ensure that their diet is rich in foods containing folic acid.

It is well known that there are difficulties in asking retrospective questions about factual knowledge at

Table 3.1 Proportion of mothers who reported antenatal checkups, classes and home visits by birth order and by country

Type	England and Wales			Scotland			Northern Ireland		
	First births	Later births	All	First births	Later births	All	First births	Later births	All
				Percentage					
Had antenatal checkups	99	99	99	100*	99	99	100*	100*	100*
Went to antenatal classes	70	17	41	74	21	46	68	13	35
Had home visit	62	63	62	61	61	61	51	47	49
Base	*2,076*	*2,522*	*4,598*	*867*	*996*	*1,863*	*578*	*898*	*1,476*

* More than 99.5%

Table 3.2 Proportion of mothers who went to antenatal classes by social class of husband or partner and birth order

Social class of husband/partner	First births	Later births	All	*First births*	*Later births*	*All*
	Percentage who went to antenatal classes			*Bases*		
I	87	24	53	*160*	*184*	*344*
II	87	23	52	*567*	*701*	*1,268*
IIINM	84	21	50	*183*	*217*	*400*
IIIM	72	16	39	*514*	*730*	*1,244*
IV	69	12	35	*218*	*320*	*538*
V	62	10	32	*81*	*104*	*185*
Unclassified	55	10	30	*139*	*187*	*326*
No partner	44	11	29	*467*	*373*	*840*
All mothers	**70**	**17**	**41**	***2,328***	***2,817***	***5,145***

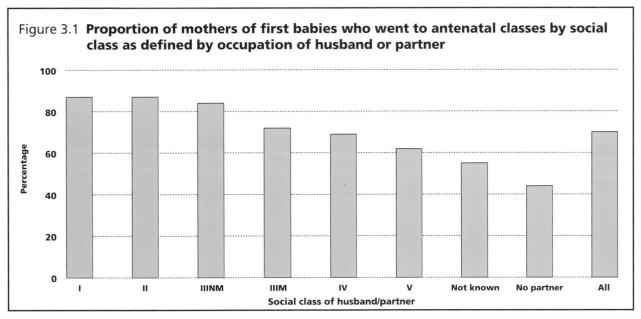

Figure 3.1 **Proportion of mothers of first babies who went to antenatal classes by social class as defined by occupation of husband or partner**

an earlier time. In the case of knowledge about the benefits of folic acid, it is possible that some women could have first become aware of the recommendations when they had contact with health professionals in the early weeks of their pregnancy. Their responses to the question might therefore be affected by their current knowledge or a desire to give what they thought was a more acceptable response. Even without these influences, responses would depend on how closely they had read the wording of the question which referred to "when they became pregnant", and on their memory of when they first gained this information.[1] The operation of all of these factors would tend towards an overstatement of knowledge of folic acid

recommendations. Nonetheless, the survey results are of interest in identifying how knowledge of folic acid varies between different groups of mothers.

In all countries three quarters (75%) of mothers said they knew that increasing their intake of folic acid was good for them in early pregnancy. Mothers who had continued in full-time education beyond the age of 16 were more likely to say that they knew about the benefits of folic acid. In England and Wales, for example, the proportions ranged from 86% for those who continued in education beyond the age of 18 to 68% for mothers who left school at 16 or under. Also, as illustrated by Figure 3.2, mothers in higher social class groups, as defined by the occupation of their husband or partner, were more likely than others to know about the recommendations (90% of women in Social Class I compared with 60% of women with no husband or partner).

Table 3.4, Figure 3.2

Most women who knew about the benefits of folic acid also said they had taken some action to increase their intake of folic acid. Overall, one quarter (26%) of mothers had changed their diet and one half had taken supplements to increase their intake of folic

Table 3.3 Who organised antenatal classes by country
Women who went to antenatal classes

Social class of husband/partner	England and Wales	Scotland	Northern Ireland	United Kingdom
		Percentage		
Hospital	39	57	71	41
Clinic/Surgery/ Health Centre	63	48	31	61
Voluntary organisation	7	3	1	7
Other	2	2	2	2
Base	*1,863*	*850*	*510*	*2,353*

Percentages do not add up to 100 as some mothers gave more than one answer.

Table 3.4 Knowledge of folic acid recommendations by age mother finished full-time education and by country

Age mother finished full-time education	England and Wales	Scotland	Northern Ireland	United Kingdom	England and Wales	Scotland	Northern Ireland	United Kingdom
	Percentage who knew about recommendations					*Bases*		
16 or under	68	64	66	68	*2,031*	*800*	*468*	*2,263*
17 or 18	80	80	75	80	*1,593*	*616*	*631*	*1,802*
Over 18	86	89	86	86	*909*	*432*	*354*	*1,045*
All	75	75	75	75	*4,576*	*1,856*	*1,468*	*5,111*

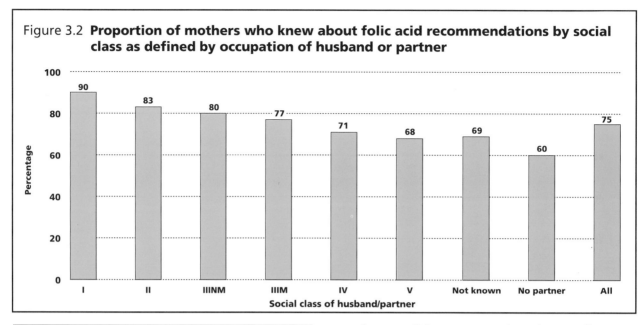

Figure 3.2 **Proportion of mothers who knew about folic acid recommendations by social class as defined by occupation of husband or partner**

Table 3.5	Action taken to increase intake of folic acid by country			
Action taken	England and Wales	Scotland	Northern Ireland	United Kingdom
		Percentage		
Changed diet	26	27	22	26
Took supplements	50	46	54	50
No action taken	39	41	38	39
Base	*4,598*	*1,863*	*1,476*	*5,181*

Percentages do not add up to 100 as some mothers gave more than one answer.

acid; some mothers had done both. These levels should be treated with some caution in the light of the difficulties of retrospective recall outlined above. In particular, there is no indication of when women took this action, whether before conception, in the first few weeks of pregnancy or at a later stage. Mothers in Northern Ireland were more likely than those elsewhere to have taken supplements (54%) and less likely to have changed their diet (22%).

Table 3.5

Looking more generally at dietary supplements, mothers were asked if they had taken any vitamin or iron supplements at all during pregnancy. Overall, 62% of mothers had done so and taking supplements was more common in Northern Ireland (85% of mothers) than elsewhere. The likelihood of taking

supplements did not vary consistently according to educational level (Table 3.6) or other socio-demographic characteristics of mothers. Most women (95%) who took supplements had taken iron. About one quarter had taken extra vitamins.

Tables 3.6 and 3.7

3.3 Smoking during pregnancy

At the first stage of the survey, when the babies were aged between six and ten weeks, women were asked whether they smoked and the number of cigarettes smoked at three different stages — before they became pregnant, during pregnancy and at the time they completed the stage one questionnaire. These data are of interest with reference to the government's Health of the Nation strategy.[2,3]

Table 3.7	Type of supplements taken by country			
Women taking supplements				
Type of supplement taken	England and Wales	Scotland	Northern Ireland	United Kingdom
		Percentage		
Iron	95	95	97	95
Vitamins	25	23	19	25
Other supplements	3	5	3	4
Base	*2,779*	*1,063*	*1,251*	*3,157*

Percentages do not add up to 100 as some mothers gave more than one answer.

Table 3.6	Whether took extra iron or vitamins during pregnancy by age mother finished full-time education and by country							
Age mother finished full-time education	England and Wales	Scotland	Northern Ireland	United Kingdom	England and Wales	Scotland	Northern Ireland	United Kingdom
	Percentage who took supplements				Bases			
16 or under	60	57	85	60	2,020	794	468	2,250
17 or 18	59	58	86	60	1,587	611	630	1,794
Over 18	67	59	85	67	908	431	353	1,044
All	**61**	**58**	**85**	**62**	**4,555**	**1,844**	**1,466**	**5,088**

Taking the United Kingdom as a whole, 35% of mothers smoked before they became pregnant, this fell to 24% during pregnancy, and 26% of mothers were smoking at the time of the stage one interview. At each stage the incidence of smoking was higher in Scotland and Northern Ireland than in England and Wales.

Table 3.8

The Health of the Nation specifies a target of at least one third of women smokers to stop smoking at the start of their pregnancy by the year 2000, and Table 3.9 shows that this target has been achieved in advance of the target year: overall, one third (33%) of women smokers in the United Kingdom (and GB) reported that they gave up during pregnancy. Mothers in England and Wales were more likely than those in Scotland and Northern Ireland to have given up smoking during pregnancy (33% compared with 27%). Although the majority of smokers continued to smoke while pregnant, many appeared to have cut down on the number of cigarettes smoked.[4] In all countries, almost one half of women who smoked before pregnancy reported that, on average, they smoked fewer cigarettes per day during pregnancy than before they became pregnant.

Table 3.9

Looking at trends for Great Britain, mothers in 1995 were less likely than in 1990 to have smoked before pregnancy (35% compared with 38%) and were more likely to have given up smoking (33% compared with 27%). Hence mothers in the 1995 Survey were less likely to have smoked during pregnancy (23% compared with 28% in 1990).

Table 3.10

It is well known that there is a strong association between smoking and social class and this pattern was also seen in this survey. Women in non-manual social class groups (Social Classes I, II and III non-manual) were less likely than other mothers to have smoked either before or during pregnancy and were more likely to have given up smoking during pregnancy. At least 44% of mothers in non-manual groups who had smoked before pregnancy gave up smoking, compared with about 30% of mothers in Social Classes IV and V and 24% of mothers with no partner.

Table 3.11, Figure 3.3

In all countries the majority (85% to 89%) of women who smoked were given advice or information on the

Table 3.8	Smoking prevalence before pregnancy, during pregnancy and at stages 1 and 2 by country			
	England and Wales	Scotland	Northern Ireland	United Kingdom
	Percentage			
Smoked before pregnancy	35	38	37	35
Smoked during pregnancy	23	28	27	24
Smoked at stage one interview	25	29	30	26
Smoked at stage two interview	24	29	29	25
Base	*4,541*	*1,838*	*1,457*	*5,116*

Table 3.9	Changes to smoking habits during pregnancy by country			
Mothers who smoked before pregnancy				
	England and Wales	Scotland	Northern Ireland	United Kingdom
	Percentage			
Gave up smoking during pregnancy	33	27	27	33
Reduced smoking during pregnancy *	47	48	49	47
No change or increase in amount smoked	20	25	24	21
All who continued smoking during pregnancy	67	73	73	67
Base	*1,567*	*698*	*538*	*1,784*

* Average number smoked per day during pregnancy was at least five less than the average number smoked before pregnancy

Table 3.10	Smoking prevalence before and during pregnancy and whether women gave up smoking during pregnancy (1985,1990 and 1995 GB)		
Smoking prevalence	1985	1990	1995
	Percentage		
Smoked before pregnancy	39	38	35
Smoked during pregnancy	30	28	23
Base	*5,223*	*5,413*	*4,956*
Gave up smoking during pregnancy	24	27	33
Base = women who smoked before pregnancy	*2,031*	*2,035*	*1,724*

effect of smoking during pregnancy. Most women had received information from more than one source. The most common sources in all countries were midwives (79% for the United Kingdom) and doctors (60%). Almost one half (46%) of women had received information via leaflets or books and about one third (32%) had been given advice by friends or relatives. There were only minor differences between countries in the sources of advice.

Table 3.12

As in previous surveys, there was no evidence that being given information on smoking during pregnancy had encouraged women to give up smoking. In fact, as shown in Table 3.13, smokers who said that they had received advice or

Table 3.11 Smoking prevalence before and during pregnancy and whether women gave up smoking during pregnancy by social class of husband or partner

Social class of husband or partner	Smoked before pregnancy	Smoked during pregnancy	Base: all mothers	Gave up smoking during pregnancy	Base: smoked before pregnancy
	Percentage			Percentage	
I	14	7	344	50	49
II	22	12	1,259	44	276
IIINM	27	14	397	47	107
IIIM	35	23	1,244	33	428
IV	40	28	541	31	217
V	52	37	182	29	93
Unclassified	32	23	323	29	103
No partner	62	47	827	24	511
All mothers	**35**	**24**	**5,118**	**33**	**1,784**

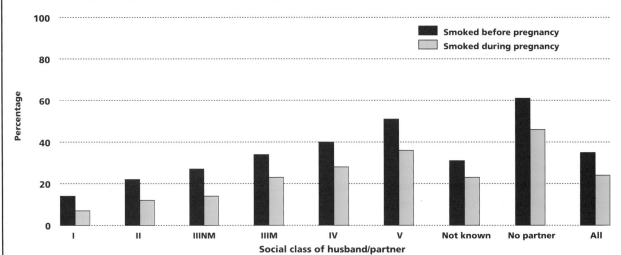

Figure 3.3 Prevalence of smoking before and during pregnancy by social class as defined by occupation of husband or partner

information were less likely to have given up smoking than were the small group who did not receive information (29% compared with 55%). This may be because some of the women who did not receive advice had given up smoking before they came into contact with medical personnel and so were not given further information. Women who had received advice were more likely than others to have reduced their level of smoking, so similar proportions of women in the two categories reported no change in their smoking habits during pregnancy.

Table 3.13

Table 3.12 Sources of information about smoking during pregnancy by country
Mothers who smoked before pregnancy

	England and Wales	Scotland	Northern Ireland	United Kingdom
	Percentage			
Percentage of smokers who received advice on smoking	85	89	88	86
Base	1,560	696	534	1,776
Source of information				
Midwife	80	68	71	79
Doctor	60	67	62	60
Printed material	46	48	49	46
Friend or relative	32	35	32	32
Health visitor	20	36	23	21
Nurse	11	14	20	12
Voluntary organisation	1	0	0	1
Others	1	1	1	1
Base: smokers who received information on smoking	1,332	618	472	1,523

Percentages do not add up to 100 as some mothers gave more than one answer

Table 3.13 Changes to smoking habits during pregnancy by whether woman was given advice on smoking
Mothers who smoked before pregnancy

Change to smoking habits during pregnancy	Given advice on smoking	Not given advice on smoking	All mothers who smoked before pregnancy
	Percentage		
Gave up smoking during pregnancy	29	55	33
Reduced number of cigarettes smoked during pregnancy *	50	27	47
No change or increase in amount smoked	21	18	21
All who continued smoking during pregnancy	71	45	67
Base	1,523	253	1,784

* Average number smoked per day during pregnancy was at least five less than the average number smoked before pregnancy

Table 3.14 **Changes to smoking habits during pregnancy and in the first months after the birth by country**
Mothers who smoked before pregnancy

	England and Wales	Scotland	Northern Ireland	United Kingdom
	Percentage			
Gave up during pregnancy, smoking at stage one	10	8	11	10
Gave up during pregnancy, not smoking at stage one	23	19	16	23
Total who gave up during pregnancy	**33**	**27**	**27**	**33**
Smoked during pregnancy, smoking at stage one	62	69	69	63
Smoked during pregnancy, not smoking at stage one	4	4	4	4
Total who continued smoking during pregnancy	**67**	**73**	**73**	**67**
Base	*1,560*	*688*	*534*	*1,773*

Table 3.14 looks at changes in women's smoking habits both during and after pregnancy, up to the time of the stage one interview when their baby was about six to ten weeks old. As already seen (Table 3.9), the majority of women who smoked before pregnancy continued to smoke at some level while they were pregnant (67% in the United Kingdom). Most of these mothers continued smoking after the birth of their baby (63% of those who smoked before pregnancy) although a small proportion (4% of all smokers) appeared to have given up after the birth of their baby. Most mothers who gave up smoking while they were pregnant were still not smoking at stage one of the survey. In the United Kingdom as a whole, 23% of smokers had given up during pregnancy and were still not smoking at this stage and a further 10% had given up but subsequently started smoking again.

Table 3.14

Table 3.15 summarises the change in smoking behaviour after the birth of their baby for mothers who had given up smoking during pregnancy. Seventy per cent of smokers who gave up during pregnancy were still abstinent by the first stage interview, about two months after their baby was born. The proportion was lower in Northern Ireland (59%) than elsewhere (70%). There was little change in smoking behaviour up to the second stage interview, when babies were about four months old. By this stage, 67% of smokers were still abstinent and mothers in Northern Ireland were still more likely to have resumed smoking (55% were still abstinent compared with 67% elsewhere).

Table 3.15

Table 3.15 **Smoking status at stages 1 and 2 of women who gave up smoking during pregnancy**
Smokers who gave up during pregnancy

	England and Wales	Scotland	Northern Ireland	United Kingdom
	Percentage			
Non-smoking at stage one interview	70	70	59	70
Non-smoking at stage two interview	68	67	55	67
Base *	*521*	*184*	*146*	*581*

* Bases are the reweighted numbers for stage two

3.4 Drinking during pregnancy

As in 1990, mothers were asked whether they had drunk alcohol during the past two years and whether they had done so while they were pregnant. Information about drinking during pregnancy included an assessment of the number of units consumed per week based on the frequency of drinking different types of alcohol and the amount usually consumed each time they had a drink.

For the United Kingdom as a whole, 86% of mothers had sometimes drunk alcohol before pregnancy and 66% drank alcohol while they were pregnant; 24% of drinkers gave up during pregnancy. These results were similar to those in the 1990 Survey in spite of differences in the age composition of the sample. As shown in Table 3.16, there were clear age differences in drinking behaviour during pregnancy. Older mothers, aged 30 or over, were less likely than those under the age of 25 to have given up drinking (around 20% compared with 30%) and so were more likely to have drunk alcohol during pregnancy (68% or more compared with 59% or less). Women who had continued in full-time education beyond the age of 16 and those whose partner was in a non-manual occupation were also more likely than others to have drunk alcohol during pregnancy.

Table 3.16, Figure 3.4

39

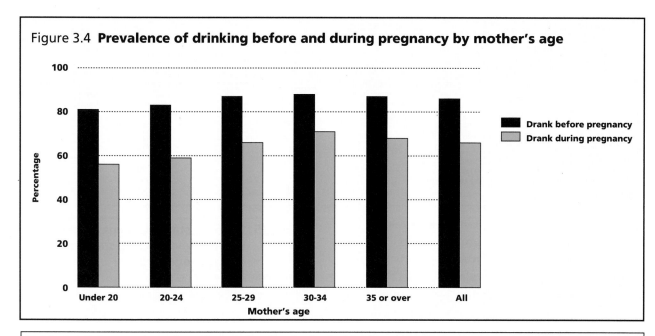

Figure 3.4 **Prevalence of drinking before and during pregnancy by mother's age**

Table 3.16 **Proportion of mothers who drank alcohol before and during pregnancy and proportion who gave up during pregnancy by mother's age: 1995 UK, 1995, 1990 totals for GB**

Mother's age	Drank before pregnancy	Drank during pregnancy	Base: all mothers	Gave up drinking during pregnancy	Base: drank before pregnancy
	Percentage			*Percentage*	
Under 20	81	56	*317*	31	*257*
20-24	83	59	*980*	29	*812*
25-29	87	66	*1,764*	24	*1,527*
30-34	88	71	*1,473*	20	*1,303*
35 or over	87	68	*622*	22	*540*
All mothers: 1995 UK	86	66	*5,165*	24	*4,446*
All mothers: 1995 GB	86	66	*5,002*	24	*4,321*
All mothers: 1990 GB	86	67	*5,143*	22	*4,652*

As in 1990, women who drank during pregnancy had, on average, a very low consumption of alcohol: 70% of drinkers consumed less than 1 unit of alcohol per week on average, and only 3% drank more than 7 units per week or an average of one unit per day. Only 1% of women drank more than 14 units per week, which was the then recommended safe level for women who are not pregnant. There was some variation by age in the amount drunk. Older mothers tended to have slightly higher consumption: 39% of mothers aged 35 or over drank more than one unit per week compared with 27-29% of mothers aged under 30.

Table 3.17

Table 3.18 looks in more detail at changes in drinking habits during pregnancy by country. As well as giving information about the amount of alcoholic drinks consumed during pregnancy, women were asked whether they drank more, less or about the same amount of alcohol than previously. In addition to the 24% who had given up drinking completely, 69% of women claimed to have reduced their intake. The majority (90%) of women who drank less said they changed their habits because alcohol might harm their baby. In addition, 16% of women said that alcohol made them feel sick and 14% that they disliked the taste.

Table 3.17 **Estimated weekly alcohol consumption of mothers who drank during pregnancy by age of mother**

Mothers who drank during pregnancy

Units of alcohol consumed per week	Mother's age					All drinkers
	Under 20	20-24	25-29	30-34	35 or over	
	%	%	%	%	%	%
Less than 1 unit	71	70	73	69	61	70
1-7 units	25	27	25	29	35	28
8-14 units	3	2	2	2	4	2
15 units or more	1	2	0	0	0	1
Base	*176*	*572*	*1,152*	*1,037*	*422*	*3,365*

Women in Northern Ireland were less likely than those in the rest of the United Kingdom to drink alcohol: 77% drank before and 52% drank during pregnancy compared with 86% and 66% respectively for mothers in England and Wales. Women in England and Wales were the least likely group to have given up drinking during pregnancy (23% of drinkers compared with more than 30% elsewhere) but were more likely to say that they had reduced the amount that they drank during pregnancy.

Table 3.18

Table 3.18 Changes to drinking habits during pregnancy by country

	England and Wales	Scotland	Northern Ireland	United Kingdom
	Percentage			
Drank before pregnancy	86	89	77	86
Drank during pregnancy	66	62	52	66
Base: all mothers	*4,583*	*1,861*	*1,473*	*5,165*
Change in drinking habits during pregnancy				
Gave up drinking	23	31	33	24
Drank less	70	64	62	69
No change/ drank more	8	5	5	7
Base: usual drinkers	*3,949*	*1,654*	*1,128*	*4,446*

Women were less likely to have received advice on the effect of alcohol during pregnancy (71%) than on the effect of smoking (86%) and the proportions receiving advice were similar in all countries. The sources of advice on drinking were similar to those on smoking. Women were most likely to have heard about the effects of drinking from a midwife (73%) or from books or leaflets (50%). They were less likely to have received advice on drinking as compared with smoking from a friend or relative (17% compared with 32% for smoking) or a doctor (41% compared with 60% for smoking).

Table 3.19

As also seen for smoking, receiving advice about the effects of drinking was not related to whether women gave up drinking during pregnancy. However, women who received advice were more likely to have reduced the amount they drank during pregnancy (70% compared with 65% of those not given advice).

Table 3.20

Table 3.19 Sources of information about drinking during pregnancy by country

	England and Wales	Scotland	Northern Ireland	United Kingdom
	Percentage			
Percentage of drinkers who received advice on drinking	71	71	74	71
Base	*3,929*	*1,648*	*1,121*	*4,423*
Source of information				
Midwife	74	64	66	73
Printed material	50	51	54	50
Doctor	40	47	45	41
Friend or relative	17	18	18	17
Health visitor	13	26	15	14
Nurse	6	9	13	7
Voluntary organisation	1	1	0	1
Others	1	1	0	1
Base: drinkers who received information on drinking	*2,785*	*1,166*	*829*	*3,139*

Percentages do not add up to 100 as some mothers gave more than one answer

Table 3.20 Changes to drinking habits during pregnancy by whether woman was given advice on drinking
Mothers who drank before pregnancy

Change to drinking habits during pregnancy	Given advice on drinking	Not given advice on drinking	All mothers who drank before pregnancy
	%	%	%
Gave up drinking during pregnancy	23	25	24
Drank less during pregnancy	70	65	69
No change/ drank more	6	10	7
Base	*3,139*	*1,285*	*4,423*

Notes and references

1 The actual question was 'Thinking back to when you became pregnant, did you know that increasing your intake of folic acid can be good for you in the early stages of pregnancy?'

2 Department of Health. *The Health of the Nation: a strategy for health in England.* HMSO (London: 1992).

3 Department of Health. *The Health of the Nation: Specification of national indicators.* 1992.

4 Women were counted as having cut down if the average number of cigarettes smoked during pregnancy was at least five less than the average number smoked before they became pregnant.

4 Choice of feeding method

Summary

- The proportion of mothers who planned to breastfeed their baby ranged from 65% in England and Wales to 54% in Scotland and 44% in Northern Ireland.

- Mothers of first babies were more likely to plan to breastfeed than were those who already had children (70% compared with 58% for the United Kingdom).

- Mothers who had breastfed a previous child for 6 weeks or more were much more likely to plan to breastfeed their latest baby than were mothers who had previously bottle fed exclusively (91% compared with 18%).

- The most common reason for choosing to breastfeed was that it was best for the baby; the most common reason for not breast feeding was that by using bottles others could help with feeding.

- Whether mothers of first babies intended to breastfeed was associated with a range of characteristics including the age at which the mother finished full-time education, whether she had been breastfed, how her friends fed their babies and whether she had been to antenatal classes. For mothers of later babies, previous experience of breastfeeding was clearly the most important factor.

4.1 Planned method of feeding

The majority of mothers said that they had planned before the birth how to feed their baby. Only 6% of all mothers, and 8% of mothers of first babies, had not decided on a feeding method.

The percentage planning to breastfeed ranged from 65% in England and Wales to 54% in Scotland and 44% in Northern Ireland; the variation corresponds to differences between countries in the prevalence of breastfeeding. In all countries, mothers expecting their first baby were more likely to plan to breastfeed than were those expecting their second or a later child. For example, in England and Wales, 72% of mothers of first babies planned to breastfeed compared with 60% of mothers of later babies.

Between 1990 and 1995 there was an increase in the proportion of mothers who intended to breastfeed, from 59% to 64% for mothers in Great Britain. The increase was evident for mothers of both first and later babies. As discussed in earlier chapters (see sections 1.6 and 2.4) some of this change will be attributable to compositional change in the Great Britain sample between 1990 and 1995.

Tables 4.1 and 4.2

The effect of previous experience on the choices made by mothers of later babies is illustrated by Figure 4.1. As in previous years, mothers who had previously breastfed were more likely than others to choose to breastfeed their latest baby, and the probability increased with the length of time for which they had previously breastfed. Compared with the 1990 Survey, mothers with breastfeeding experience were more likely to plan to breastfeed again: 54% compared with 45% in 1990 for mothers who had breastfed for less than six weeks, and 91% compared with 88% for mothers who had breastfed for longer than this. The proportion of mothers who had previously only bottle fed and who planned to breastfeed their latest baby decreased between 1990 and 1995 (from 22% to 18%).

Table 4.3, Figure 4.1

As found in previous surveys, almost all mothers (96%) carried out their intentions with regard to feeding, although this needs to be interpreted with caution given that behavioural intentions may be forgotten or rationalised when they are collected retrospectively. As before, mothers were included as having breastfed if they had ever put their baby to the breast. In general, mothers who planned to breast or bottle feed were equally likely to have carried out their intentions although the proportions did differ in Northern Ireland: 99% of mothers who planned to bottle feed had done so compared with 94% of mothers who planned to breastfeed.

Table 4.4

Because of the strong association between intended and actual feeding method for the women in this survey, analysis of the factors affecting choices before birth also throws light on factors associated with the method of feeding used at birth. These may be of

Table 4.1 Mother's intended method of feeding by birth order and country

Intended method of feeding	England and Wales			Scotland			Northern Ireland			United Kingdom		
	First births	Later births	All	First births	Later births	All	First births	Later births	All	First births	Later births	All
	%	%	%	%	%	%	%	%	%	%	%	%
Breast *	72	60	65	60	50	54	50	40	44	70	58	64
Not breast	21	35	29	31	45	38	39	55	48	22	37	30
Had not decided	8	5	6	10	6	8	12	5	8	8	5	6
Base	2,076	2,522	4,598	867	996	1,863	578	898	1,476	2,335	2,845	5,181

* Includes mothers who intended to combine breast and bottle feeding

Table 4.2 Mother's intended method of feeding by birth order (1980, 1985, 1990 and 1995, Great Britain)

Intended method of feeding	First births				Later births				All babies			
	1980	1985	1990	1995	1980	1985	1990	1995	1980	1985	1990	1995
	%	%	%	%	%	%	%	%	%	%	%	%
Breast	70	67	65	71	55	55	54	59	61	61	59	64
Not breast	22	25	26	22	39	40	41	36	32	33	34	29
Had not decided	8	7	9	8	6	5	5	5	7	7	7	6
Base	1,831	2,347	2,430	2,271	2,377	2,875	2,983	2,745	4,224	5,223	5,413	5,017

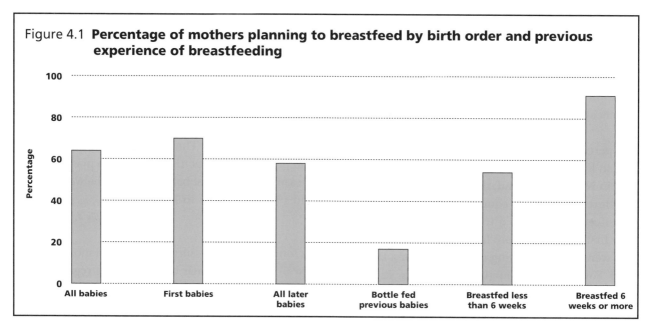

Figure 4.1 **Percentage of mothers planning to breastfeed by birth order and previous experience of breastfeeding**

Table 4.3 **Mother's intended method of feeding by previous experience of breastfeeding (1980, 1985, 1990 and 1995 Great Britain)**

Intended method of feeding	No experience of breastfeeding				Breastfed for less than 6 weeks				Breastfed for 6 weeks or more			
	1980	1985	1990	1995	1980	1985	1990	1995	1980	1985	1990	1995
	%	%	%	%	%	%	%	%	%	%	%	%
Breast	22	20	22	18	53	45	45	54	91	87	88	91
Not breast	71	74	72	77	40	46	48	37	6	10	10	7
Had not decided	7	6	5	6	7	9	7	9	3	3	3	2
Base	*879*	*924*	*1,148*	*875*	*679*	*704*	*541*	*567*	*835*	*1,248*	*1,244*	*1,238*

Table 4.4 **Proportion of mothers who fed their baby in the way they had planned by method and country**
All who had decided on method

Planned method	England and Wales	Scotland	Northern Ireland	United Kingdom
			Percentage	
Breast	97	95	94	97
Not breast	95	96	99	95
All	**96**	**96**	**97**	**96**
Bases				
Breast	*3,002*	*1,008*	*650*	*3,301*
Not breast	*1,319*	*715*	*712*	*1,558*
All	*4,320*	*1,723*	*1,361*	*4,859*

interest to practitioners involved in promoting breastfeeding, and they are considered further in Sections 4.3 to 4.5.

4.2 Reasons for choice of feeding method

The relative importance of the various reasons women gave for their choice of feeding method were similar to those given in the 1990 Survey.

The most common reason for choosing to breastfeed was that mothers thought it was best for the baby;

this was cited by more mothers of first babies (89%) than mothers of later babies (77%). The next most common reason, given by 37% of mothers, was convenience, and one fifth of mothers who planned to breastfeed mentioned either that it was cheaper (21%) or that it created a closer bond between mother and baby (20%). These three reasons were equally common for first and later babies. One third (33%) of mothers of second or later babies mentioned their own experience of feeding earlier babies, usually that they had previously breastfed but also, in a minority of cases, that they had previously bottle fed but wanted to breastfeed their latest baby.

Very few women (3% or less) specifically mentioned the influence of other people - medical personnel, relatives or friends. This may be because, at this question, mothers concentrate on the perceived benefits of breastfeeding rather than on how they came to learn about these benefits. The possible influence of other people is covered in Section 4.3.

Table 4.5

The reasons given were similar to those given by women in the 1994 Survey of Infant Feeding in Asian

Table 4.5 Mother's reasons for planning to breastfeed by birth order (1990 Great Britain and 1995 United Kingdom)
Mothers who planned to breastfeed

Mother's reasons	First births		Later births		All babies	
	1990	1995	1990	1995	1990	1995
	Percentage giving reason					
Breastfeeding is best for baby	88	89	75	77	82	83
Breastfeeding is more convenient	35	36	38	37	36	37
Breastfeeding is cheaper	18	23	15	19	17	21
Closer bond between mother and baby	24	21	21	19	23	20
Mother's own experience	0	0	29	33	15	17
Breastfeeding is natural	16	14	11	10	14	12
Breastfeeding is good for mother *	8	13	8	10	8	12
Influenced by medical personnel	3	3	1	2	2	3
Influenced by friends or relatives	2	2	1	1	1	2
No particular reason	0	0	1	0	1	0
Other reasons	0	2	1	3	0	2
Base	*1,574*	*1,640*	*1,612*	*1,661*	*3,186*	*3,301*

* 1995 counts include comments about mother losing weight
Percentages do not add to 100 as some mothers gave more than one reason

Table 4.6 Mother's reasons for planning to bottle feed by birth order (1990 Great Britain and 1995 United Kingdom)
Mothers who planned to bottle feed

Mother's reasons	First births		Later births		All babies	
	1990	1995	1990	1995	1990	1995
	Percentage giving reason					
Other people can feed baby	47	46	34	32	39	36
Did not like the idea of breastfeeding	28	34	17	23	21	27
Mother's own previous experience	1	1	39	44	26	30
Would be embarrassed to breastfeed	10	11	5	4	7	7
Can see how much the baby has	8	7	5	5	6	6
Expecting to return to work soon	8	12	3	3	5	6
Bottle feeding is less tiring	n/a	2	n/a	6	n/a	4
Medical reasons for not breastfeeding	2	3	4	4	3	4
Persuaded by other people	3	5	0	2	1	3
No particular reasons	4	2	3	1	3	1
Other reasons	6	6	5	5	6	6
Base	*629*	*513*	*1,223*	*1,044*	*1,852*	*1,557*

Percentages do not add to 100 as some mothers gave more than one reason

Families,[2] which found that over 80% of Bangladeshi, Pakistani and Indian mothers who planned to breastfeed said it was because it was 'best for baby'.

The most common reasons for choosing not to breastfeed and to use infant formula instead were that other people could help with feeding the baby (36%) and that some women did not like the idea of breastfeeding (27%). Both of these reasons were more likely to be mentioned by mothers of first rather than later babies. More than two fifths (44%) of mothers who already had children mentioned their own experience as a reason for choosing to bottle feed; this could either be experience of feeding previous children with infant formula or having had problems with breastfeeding. Some of the "other" responses were also related to the presence of other children. For example, a small number of women planned not to breastfeed when they knew that they were expecting twins, and others chose not to breastfeed because they were concerned

about the effect that breastfeeding might have on an older child.

Table 4.6

The reasons given above for planning to bottlefeed were slightly different to those given by women in the 1994 Survey of Infant Feeding in Asian Families.[2] This found that Bangladeshi, Pakistani and Indian mothers who planned to bottle feed were most likely to say it was because of their previous experience.

4.3 Factors associated with planned feeding method

Social and cultural factors are an important influence on a woman's choice of feeding method. As would be expected from the earlier analysis of incidence of breastfeeding by the mother's characteristics, the intended feeding method was also associated with the mother's age, social class and the age she finished full-time education. The relationships were broadly similar

45

across all countries and are illustrated using United Kingdom data in Figures 4.2 to 4.4.

Younger mothers were less likely than older women to plan to breastfeed. There were also strong associations between intended feeding method and the age the mother finished full-time education and her partner's social class. Women who had continued their full-time education beyond the age of 18 and those whose partner was in a professional or intermediate non-manual occupation (Social Classes I or II) were more likely than other women to plan to breastfeed. These two associations are also age-related.

Figures 4.2 to 4.4

The way women were themselves fed as babies and how their friends fed their babies were both strongly associated with their planned method of feeding. This suggests either that contact with other people who have breastfed may be influential or at least that other people may help to create an environment which supports and encourages breastfeeding.

Women who knew that they had been breastfed, even if in combination with bottle feeding, were more likely to plan to breastfeed their baby than were women who were entirely bottle fed or who did not know how they had been fed. Results were broadly similar across all countries. In England and Wales, 81% of women who had themselves been breastfed now planned to breastfeed their baby compared with 54% of mothers who were entirely bottle fed.

Table 4.7

Figure 4.2 Percentage of mothers planning to breastfeed by mother's age

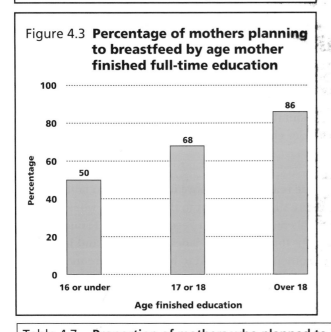

Figure 4.3 Percentage of mothers planning to breastfeed by age mother finished full-time education

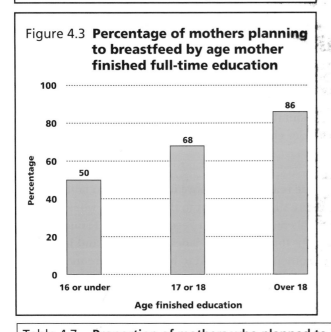

Figure 4.4 Percentage of mothers planning to breastfeed by social class of husband or partner

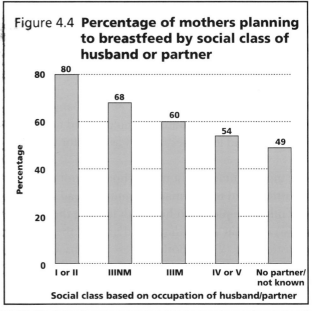

Table 4.7 Proportion of mothers who planned to breastfeed their baby by how mother was fed and by country

How mother was fed	England and Wales	Scotland	Northern Ireland	United Kingdom	England and Wales	Scotland	Northern Ireland	United Kingdom
	Percentage who planned to breastfeed				*Bases*			
Breastfed entirely	81	76	63	80	1,006	296	134	1,087
Breast and infant formula	78	70	65	77	942	269	139	1,018
Not breastfed	54	47	40	53	2,179	1,154	1,077	2,558
Not known	58	39	33	56	471	143	126	517
All	**65**	**54**	**44**	**64**	**4,598**	**1,863**	**1,476**	**5,181**

Table 4.8 Proportion of mothers who planned to breastfeed their baby by how most of her friends fed their babies and by country

How mother's friends fed their babies	England and Wales	Scotland	Northern Ireland	United Kingdom	England and Wales	Scotland	Northern Ireland	United Kingdom
	Percentage who planned to breastfeed				Bases			
Most breastfed	88	84	78	87	1,048	334	136	1,139
Half breast/ half not breast	67	61	52	66	1,091	394	263	1,208
Most did not breastfeed	53	41	37	51	1,946	950	974	2,268
Don't know	63	54	46	62	512	185	103	565
All	65	54	44	64	4,598	1,863	1,476	5,181

Table 4.8 illustrates that women were also likely to be influenced in their choices by how their friends fed their babies. In Scotland, the proportion of women intending to breastfeed ranged from 84% among women who said that most of the mothers they knew breastfed their babies to 41% among those who said that most of their friends and acquaintances bottle fed. These patterns may, of course, reflect the fact that a woman's friends would be likely to have similar characteristics to herself and so may be related to the associations with age, educational level and social class already mentioned. This is explored further in Section 4.5.

Table 4.8

4.4 Contact with health professionals

Almost all mothers (99%) had had some antenatal checkups during pregnancy. Most reported that they had discussed feeding their baby at these checkups although proportions were consistently higher for women expecting their first baby than for those who already had children. Women in Scotland were most likely to have discussed feeding (68% of all mothers) and those in England and Wales were least likely (57%). About three tenths of mothers (UK 29%) had not discussed feeding but had been asked about their plans, so 12% of women had neither discussed feeding nor been asked about their plans.

Between 1990 and 1995 there was an increase in the proportion of women who had discussed feeding during antenatal checks. This increase was evident both for first births (from 53% to 64%) and for later births (from 40% to 53%). There were corresponding decreases in the proportions of women who had not discussed feeding but had been asked about their plans.

Tables 4.9 and 4.10

As discussed in the previous chapter, mothers were asked if they had gone to classes to prepare for having their baby and whether the classes had included any talks or discussions about feeding. Women expecting their first child were more likely than mothers of later babies to have been to antenatal classes and, as most classes included talks or discussions about feeding, they were also more likely to have attended talks on feeding. About three fifths (60%) of mothers of first babies and one tenth (11%) of mothers of later babies had been to classes which included talks on feeding.

Table 4.11

Previous surveys have shown a positive association between attendance at antenatal classes and feeding intentions. For 1995, Table 4.12 compares the proportions of mothers who intended to breastfeed according to whether they had discussed feeding at antenatal checkups or classes.

Table 4.9 Whether mother was asked about plans or discussed feeding at antenatal checkups by country

	England and Wales			Scotland			Northern Ireland			United Kingdom		
	First births	Later births	All	First births	Later births	All	First births	Later births	All	First births	Later births	All
	%	%	%	%	%	%	%	%	%	%	%	%
Had discussion about feeding	63	52	57	75	61	68	70	59	64	64	53	58
No discussion but asked about plans	24	34	29	18	30	25	22	30	26	23	33	29
No discussion and not asked about plans	12	13	13	6	8	7	8	11	10	12	13	12
All who had antenatal checkups	99	99	99	100	99	99	100	100	100	99	99	99
Base	2,073	2,517	4,590	866	996	1,862	576	897	1,473	2,332	2,840	5,172

Table 4.10 Whether mothers were asked about plans or discussed feeding at antenatal checkups (1990 and 1995 Great Britain)
Mothers who had antenatal checks

	First births		Later births		All babies	
	1990	1995	1990	1995	1990	1995
	%	%	%	%	%	%
Had discussion about feeding	53	64	40	53	45	58
No discussion but asked about plans	36	24	47	34	42	29
No discussion and not asked about plans	12	12	12	13	12	12
Base	*2,412*	*2,247*	*2,961*	*2,709*	*5,372*	*4,956*

Table 4.11 Whether mother went to classes to prepare for having the baby and whether classes included talks or discussions about feeding by country

	England and Wales			Scotland			Northern Ireland			United Kingdom		
	First births	Later births	All	First births	Later births	All	First births	Later births	All	First births	Later births	All
						Percentage who:						
Went to classes	70	17	41	74	21	46	68	13	35	70	17	41
Went to classes with talks on feeding	59	11	33	65	13	37	58	9	28	60	11	33
Base	*2,070*	*2,495*	*4,565*	*866*	*990*	*1,856*	*575*	*893*	*1,469*	*2,328*	*2,817*	*5,145*

Table 4.12 Proportion of mothers intending to breastfeed by whether discussed feeding at antenatal checkups or whether went to classes with talks about feeding, by birth order

	First births	Later births	All	*First births*	*Later births*	*All*
	Percentage planning to breastfeed				*Bases*	
Antenatal checkups						
Discussed feeding at antenatal checks	71	58	65	*1,492*	*1,508*	*3,001*
Did not discuss feeding or did not have checkup	69	58	63	*843*	*1,337*	*2,180*
Antenatal classes						
Went to classes with talks or discussion about feeding	80	78	80	*1,382*	*314*	*1,696*
Went to classes, no talks on feeding	72	78	75	*253*	*162*	*415*
Did not go to classes	50	54	53	*700*	*2,370*	*3,070*
All	**70**	**58**	**64**	***2,335***	***2,846***	***5,181***

Discussion of feeding at antenatal checks was not associated with feeding intentions. The proportion of women who had discussed feeding at antenatal checks and who intended to breastfeed was, at 65%, similar to the proportion for those who had not discussed feeding (63%).

Attendance at classes was, however, associated with feeding intentions. Mothers who had not attended classes were less likely than others to plan to breastfeed (53%). However, among women who had attended classes, there was little difference in intentions between those who attended talks about feeding (80%) and those who did not (75%). Thus it appears that mothers who went to antenatal classes were anyway more motivated to breastfeed, and attending specific talks on feeding had little further effect.

Table 4.12

4.5 Influences on the intention to breastfeed

We have so far identified a number of characteristics that were associated with the likelihood of a mother planning to breastfeed her child. However, the interpretation of some of these results is difficult because of the inter-relationship between many of the characteristics themselves. Thus, for example, it may be that the relationship between intended feeding method and the mother's educational level mainly reflects the association between feeding method and social class and so is not significant after allowing for the effects of social class.

The analysis to identify which characteristics were most strongly associated with intentions to breastfeed used logistic regression. The method identifies those characteristics which are associated with the dependent measure, in this case whether the mother planned to breastfeed her baby or not, after controlling for the effects of other variables in the model. The results shown here list all the variables included in the logistic regression analysis. Those not selected into the final model are marked as being not significant (NS).

Logistic regression also produces an estimate of the odds of the dependent variable being positive (the mother planned to breastfeed) for mothers in each category of the independent variables included in the model. The odds are defined as the ratio of the probability of an event occurring (p) compared with the probability of it not occurring. Thus odds = p/(1-p). The results shown here give the odds ratios for each category as compared with a defined reference category, which has an odds ratio of 1.0. The usual conventions are used to show which odds ratios are significantly different from 1.0.

The dependent variable in this analysis was whether the mother planned to breastfeed or not; the negative category includes women who had not decided how to feed their baby as well as those who planned to bottle feed. There were separate analyses for each country in order to identify differences in patterns of association. As there are also clear differences in the factors which influence mothers of first and later babies, separate models were run for these two groups in each country.

The main interest in carrying out this analysis was to test whether the influences of other people - medical personnel, mother and friends - were distinct and separate effects and whether they were present after allowing for associations with socio-demographic characteristics. In order to make this more explicit, the three socio-demographic variables - age of mother, age finished education and social class of partner - were entered into the models first. Further variables were therefore only selected if they were significant after allowing for the effects of these characteristics. The odds ratios shown in the tables are for the final models, after inclusion of all significant variables.

Table 4.13 shows results of the analyses for mothers of first babies. The patterns were broadly similar across countries in spite of differences in the overall proportions of women who planned to breastfeed. In all cases, three of the four variables relating to the influence of other people were included in the model. These therefore had significant and separate effects after allowing for the effects of the socio-demographic characteristics in the models. Mothers who had been breastfed were consistently more likely than others to plan to breastfeed, as were women whose friends had mainly breastfed and those who had attended antenatal classes, whether or not the classes had included talks on breastfeeding. However, discussion of feeding at antenatal checkups was not significantly associated with feeding intentions.

Table 4.13 Characteristics associated with mothers planning to breastfeed their first baby, by country

Characteristic		England and Wales	Scotland	Northern Ireland
Percentage planning to breastfeed		*72%*	*60%*	*50%*
			Odds ratios	
Mother's age	Under 20	1.00	1.00	NS
	20-24	1.64 **	2.34 **	
	25-29	1.90 ***	2.76 ***	
	30 or over	2.12 ***	2.57 **	
Age mother completed full-time education	16 or under	1.00	1.00	1.00
	17 or 18	1.47 ***	1.60 **	2.28 ***
	Over 18	2.00 ***	3.02 ***	2.82 ***
Social class of partner	I or II	2.04 ***	NS	2.75 ***
	III Non-Manual	1.45		2.27 *
	III Manual	1.17		1.57 *
	IV or V	1.12		1.57 *
	No partner/ Not classified	1.00		1.00
Discussed feeding at antenatal checkups	No	NS	NS	NS
	Yes			
Went to classes with talks or discussion of feeding	Did not go to classes	1.00	1.00	1.00
	Classes with no talks on feeding	2.07 ***	2.22 **	2.34 **
	Classes with talks on feeding	2.27 ***	3.23 ***	3.31 ***
How mother was fed	Not breastfed or method not known	1.00	1.00	1.00
	Breastfed	2.83 ***	3.26 ***	2.61 ***
How friends fed their babies	Most did not breastfeed	1.00	1.00	1.00
	Half breast/ half not breast	1.41 **	1.90 **	1.06
	Most breastfed	2.77 ***	3.10 ***	3.71 ***
	Don't know	1.16	1.48	1.87

Significance of odds ratio: * $p<0.05$ ** $p<0.01$ *** $p<0.001$

As expected, age, educational level and social class also showed strong associations with planned feeding method and at least two of the variables were included in the final model for each country.

Table 4.13

The models for mothers of later babies show the very strong effect of previous experience of breastfeeding. Mothers who had breastfed a previous child had odds ratios which were significantly greater than 1.0, and the odds ratios were particularly high (between 27 and 51) for mothers who had breastfed a previous child for six weeks or more. The strength of this effect displaced many of the variables which were included in the models for first babies. Thus, how the mother was fed and her socio-demographic characteristics were usually not significant after allowing for her own previous experience of breastfeeding. The socio-demographic variables were, however, highly significant in a separate model, which excluded the mother's previous experience of breastfeeding.

Although, for mothers of later babies, previous experience was the characteristic most strongly associated with intention to breastfeed, other variables also had significant effects. In all countries, mothers who had attended talks on feeding at antenatal classes and those whose friends had mainly breastfed were more likely to plan to breastfeed. Thus, the influence of other mothers remains strong even for mothers of later babies. As already discussed, the association with attendance at antenatal classes may indicate that the small proportion of mothers who attend classes for a later baby are predisposed to breastfeeding rather than that the classes themselves have a strong influence on intentions.

Table 4.14

Notes and references

1   Logistic regression uses a dichotomous dependent variable, such as whether the mother planned to breastfeed her baby or not, and the characteristics of the mother are entered as categorical independent variables. In this case a forward stepwise method of logistic regression analysis was used, in which the variable that is most strongly associated with the dependent measure is first selected into the model and then, after allowing for this effect, all remaining variables are tested for significance.

2   Thomas M and Avery V. *Infant Feeding in Asian Families.* The Stationery Office (London: 1997).

Table 4.14 Characteristics associated with mothers planning to breastfeed later babies, by country		England and Wales	Scotland	Northern Ireland
Characteristic				
Percentage planning to breastfeed		60%	49%	40%
			Odds ratios	
Mother's age	Under 24	NS †	1.00	NS
	25-29		1.03	
	30-34		0.98	
	35 or over		2.11 *	
Age mother completed full-time education	16 or under	1.00	NS †	NS †
	17 or 18	1.25 *		
	Over 18	2.01 ***		
Social class of partner	I or II	NS †	NS †	NS †
	III Non-Manual			
	III Manual			
	IV or V			
	No partner/ Not classified			
Mother's previous experience of breastfeeding	No experience/ not known	1.00	1.00	1.00
	Breastfed for less than 6 weeks	4.30 ***	3.96 ***	4.96 ***
	Breastfed for 6 weeks or more	27.12 ***	41.59 ***	51.17 ***
Discussed feeding at antenatal checkups	No	NS	NS	NS
	Yes			
Went to classes with talks or discussion of feeding	Did not go to classes	1.00	1.00	1.00
	Classes with no talks on feeding	2.55 ***	1.20	3.07 **
	Classes with talks on feeding	2.47 ***	2.31 **	3.48 ***
How mother was fed	Not breastfed or method not known	1.00	NS	NS
	Breastfed	1.83 **		
How friends fed their babies	Most did not breastfeed	1.00	1.00	1.00
	Half breast/ half not breast	1.07	0.88	1.64 *
	Most breastfed	2.34 ***	2.80 ***	4.31 ***
	Don't know	1.24	1.19	1.24

† significant in a model excluding previous experience
Significance of odds ratio: * p<0.05   ** p<0.01   *** p<0.001

5 The birth and post-natal care

Summary

- Delays in first holding the baby significantly affected the likelihood of breastfeeding. Only half (51%) of mothers who were separated from their baby for more than 12 hours after the birth initiated breastfeeding compared with 66% overall.

- Whether mothers of first babies began breastfeeding was associated with a range of socio-demographic characteristics, the influence of family and friends and whether the mother attended antenatal classes. Events around the time of the birth had little effect. For mothers of later babies, previous experience of breastfeeding outweighed all the other influences.

- Mothers who experienced a delay before they first fed their baby were more likely to have given up breastfeeding in the first two weeks than were mothers who first breastfed their baby within one hour of birth.

- If the baby was given formula milk in hospital, it is a strong indicator that the mother will not continue breastfeeding after leaving hospital. Thirty four per cent of mothers whose babies had been given a bottle in hospital had stopped breastfeeding within two weeks compared with 11% of mothers whose babies had not been given a bottle.

- Thirty five per cent of breastfeeding mothers experienced problems feeding their baby in hospital. Although the group is small, mothers who did not receive help for these problems were more likely to have given up breastfeeding within the first two weeks (48%) than those who received help (29%).

- As with incidence, there were a range of factors that influenced whether a mother continued to breastfeed beyond the first two weeks. The most important factors were age, educational level, how her friends fed their babies, and whether a nurse had fed the baby in hospital.

5.1 Introduction

Events around the time of the birth and certain practices in hospital may all affect whether a mother carries out her initial intention to breastfeed and the likelihood of her continuing to do so. This chapter examines which factors are important in determining whether the mother initially breastfeeds and the success of breastfeeding in the early weeks. It also considers the reasons given by mothers who switched to bottle feeding and the problems experienced by breastfeeding mothers in the early weeks.

5.2 The birth and initial incidence of breastfeeding

Although the vast majority of mothers who plan to breastfeed do carry out their intentions, it is questioned whether events during labour and delivery influence the initiation of breastfeeding.

The type of delivery

If a mother underwent a caesarean delivery, there was no significant effect on the likelihood of her initiating breastfeeding. However, there was a difference in the incidence of breastfeeding according to the type of analgesic that the mothers received for the birth. Whilst 69% of mothers who received an epidural injection went on to breastfeed, only 55% of mothers who received a general anaesthetic did so.

Although the use of general anaesthetic may have a small effect on the initiation of breastfeeding, it is important to consider other characteristics of mothers receiving each type of analgesic. Table 5.2 shows, for example, that mothers who had an epidural injection were more likely than those who had a general anaesthetic to be classified to non-manual social groups. Therefore the variation in the incidence of breastfeeding with the type of analgesic may be related to other socio-demographic factors. This is explored further by multivariate analysis in Section 5.3.

Tables 5.1 and 5.2

Birthweight, special care and time before holding the baby

As in previous years, mothers were asked if their baby had been put under a lamp for jaundice or been put into special care at all. This might be because of low birth weight, prematurity or other complications. Only a small group of babies had received special care so it was not appropriate to split the group according to the length of time for which they received this care. Overall it appeared that babies who received special care were less likely to be breastfed but the association was not strong. Mothers of lower birthweight babies, those under 3000 grammes, were also less likely than mothers of larger babies to have tried at least once to breastfeed. It should be noted that there will be some overlap between babies who receive special care and those with low birthweight.

Tables 5.3 and 5.4

Although birthweight and being in special care have some effect on the incidence of breastfeeding, the

---

Table 5.1 Incidence of breastfeeding by type of analgesic

	Type of analgesia						All births
	Epidural	Injections eg pethidine	Gas	General anaesthetic	Other treatment	Nothing	
Percentage who breastfed initially	69	64	66	55	86	64	66
*Base ***	*1,469*	*2,125*	*3,697*	*279*	*546*	*401*	*5,181*

* Mothers may have received more than one analgesic

Table 5.2 Distribution of mothers who had an epidural or general anaesthetic by social class of husband/partner

	Type of analgesia	
	Epidural	General anaesthetic
	%	%
Non-manual	43	29
Manual	35	44
Unclassified/No partner	21	27
Base	*1,469*	*279*

Table 5.3 Incidence of breastfeeding by whether baby received special care

	Special care			All births
	Baby put in special care	Put under a lamp	No special care	
Percentage who breastfed initially	61	68	66	66
Base	*505*	*215*	*4,419*	*5,181*

Table 5.4 Incidence of breastfeeding by weight of baby					
	Weight of baby (grammes)				All births
	Less than 2500	2500-2999	3000-3499	3500 or more	
Percentage who breastfed initially	63	61	66	68	66
Base	*336*	*846*	*1,912*	*2,051*	*5,181*

Table 5.5 Incidence of breastfeeding by length of time before the mother held the baby					
	Time until first held baby				All births
	Immediately	Less than 1 hour	1, up to 12 hours	12 hours or more	
Percentage who breastfed initially	66	69	61	51	66
Base	*4,040*	*641*	*319*	*152*	*5,181*

length of time before the mother held her baby is more strongly associated with the likelihood of her breastfeeding. Two thirds (66%) of mothers who held their baby immediately said that they had tried breastfeeding compared with one half (51%) of mothers who were separated from their baby for more than 12 hours after the birth, either because the baby was in special care or because the mother was not well.

Table 5.5

5.3 Multivariate analysis of factors associated with initial incidence of breastfeeding

Chapter 2 examined the relationship between the socio-demographic characteristics of a mother and her likelihood of breastfeeding. As certain events at the time of the birth may affect whether the mother actually starts breastfeeding it is useful to include these variables in an analysis of the factors which are most important in influencing the likelihood of breastfeeding.

The analysis used logistic regression to identify which characteristics were most strongly associated with initiation of breastfeeding. Details of this method are given in Section 4.5. The dependent variable for this analysis was whether the mother ever breastfed. The independent variables used in the analysis were the socio-demographic characteristics of the mother, events during pregnancy and around the time of the birth, and the influence of friends and relatives.

Each country was analysed separately in order to identify differences in patterns of association between countries. As with the intention to breastfeed, there are differences in the factors which influence mothers of first and later babies and so

separate models were run for these two groups in each country.

Table 5.6 shows the results of the analyses for mothers of first babies. As expected from the discussion in the previous section, events around the time of the birth were not very influential in affecting the likelihood of breastfeeding. Mothers in England and Wales were less likely to breastfeed if there was a delay of 12 hours or more before they held their baby and, in Scotland only, mothers were more likely to have breastfed initially if their baby was in special care.

Other results were similar to those for intention to breastfeed (Section 4.5). Mothers who were breastfed themselves as well as those whose friends had mainly breastfed were more likely to breastfeed their baby. The educational level, age and social class of the mother, and whether or not she attended antenatal classes were also significantly associated with initial breastfeeding. In addition, in England and Wales only, the mother's smoking behaviour during pregnancy was also significant with non-smokers more likely to have initiated breastfeeding.

The model for mothers of later babies shows the strong effect of the mother's previous experience of breastfeeding with odds ratios of between 38 and 54 for mothers who previously breastfed for at least six weeks. This effect displaced other socio-demographic variables such as the age of the mother, her social class and, in Scotland and Northern Ireland, the mother's educational level.

As with the analyses for first babies, events around the time of the birth were not associated with initial breastfeeding. The exceptions were, in England and Wales, the time before the mother first held the baby and, in Scotland, whether the baby was in special care.

53

Table 5.6   Characteristics associated with mothers who initially breastfed first babies, by country

Characteristic		England and Wales	Scotland	Northern Ireland
Percentage who breastfed initially		*74%*	*61%*	*52%*
			Odds ratios	
Mother's age	Under 20	1.00	1.00	NS
	20-24	1.56**	2.15**	
	25-29	2.00***	2.82***	
	30 or over	2.20***	2.76***	
Age mother completed full-time education	16 or under	1.00	1.00	1.00
	17 or 18	1.73***	1.58**	2.25***
	Over 18	2.32***	2.37***	2.94***
Social Class of partner	I or II	2.06***	NS	2.82***
	III non-manual	1.17		2.65**
	III manual	1.35		1.38
	IV or V	1.03		1.17
	No partner/not classified	1.00		1.00
How mother was fed	Bottle fed or method not known	1.00	1.00	1.00
	Breastfed	3.24***	3.37***	2.93***
How friends fed their babies	Most bottle fed	1.00	1.00	1.00
	Half breastfed, half bottle fed	1.43*	2.20***	1.18
	Most breastfed	3.31***	4.32***	6.21***
	Don't know	1.52*	1.37	1.77
Went to classes with talks or discussion of feeding	Did not go to classes	1.00	1.00	1.00
	Classes with no talks on feeding	2.43***	1.91*	2.52**
	Classes with talks on feeding	2.27***	2.97***	4.24***
Whether mother smoked during pregnancy	Smoked	1.00	NS	NS
	Did not smoke	1.44**		
Whether baby in special care	Not in special care	NS	1.00	NS
	In special care		1.60*	
When mother first held the baby	Immediately	2.19**	NS	NS
	Within 1 hour	1.75		
	More than 1 and less than 12 hours	2.19*		
	Over 12 hours	1.00		

Variables not significant in any country
Type of delivery
Weight of baby
Whether health professional discussed breastfeeding at antenatal checkup
Whether mother drank during pregnancy

Significance of odds ratios
* $p < 0.05$
** $p < 0.01$
*** $P < 0.001$

Other factors that continued to be associated with initiation of breastfeeding were whether the mother's friends breastfed and, for mothers in England and Wales, whether the mother smoked during pregnancy and how she was fed as a baby. Although there was an association between breastfeeding and attending talks on feeding at antenatal classes, as discussed in relation to feeding intentions, it is likely that the small number of mothers of later babies who attend such talks have a predisposition to breastfeed.

Tables 5.6 and 5.7

5.4 The experience in hospital and the duration of breastfeeding

Chapter 2 showed that, among breastfeeding mothers, there has been little change since 1985 in the length of time for which they continued to breastfeed. About one fifth of mothers who started breastfeeding had stopped within two weeks, and 15% had stopped within one week. The mother's experience in hospital will be influential in whether she continues to breastfeed because the steepest fall in prevalence occurs in the first week, and particularly in the first two days after birth.

The length of stay in hospital

As in previous surveys, virtually all babies (98%) were delivered in hospital. Between 1990 and 1995 there continued to be a decline in the length of time that breastfeeding mothers stayed in hospital. In 1995, nearly half (48%) of all mothers left hospital within 48 hours compared with two fifths (38%) in 1990. Mothers of first babies were more likely to stay in hospital for longer, although the proportion of these women who left hospital within 48 hours rose from 14% in 1990 to 32% in 1995.

Table 5.8

Although women are spending less time in hospital, there has been no change in the proportion of mothers who have stopped breastfeeding by the time they are discharged (12% in 1990 and 1995). This lack

Table 5.7 Characteristics associated with mothers who initially breastfed later babies, by country

Characteristic		England and Wales	Scotland	Northern Ireland
Percentage who breastfed initially		*62%*	*50%*	*40%*
			Odds ratios	
Age mother completed full-time education	16 or under	1.00	NS	NS
	17 or 18	1.34*		
	Over 18	2.04***		
How mother was fed	Bottle fed or method not known	1.00	NS	NS
	Breastfed	1.75***		
How friends fed their babies	Most bottle fed	1.00	1.00	1.00
	Half breastfed, half bottle fed	1.08	1.58*	1.64~*
	Most breastfed	2.21***	5.44***	4.81***
	Don't know	1.61**	1.49	1.35
Mother's previous experience of breastfeeding	No experience/not known	1.00	1.00	1.00
	Breastfed for less than 6 weeks	5.82***	4.44***	5.19***
	Breastfed for 6 weeks or more	38.30***	54.36***	48.90***
Went to classes with talks or discussion of feeding	Did not go to classes	1.00	1.00	1.00
	Classes with no talks on feeding	1.5	1.46	3.64**
	Classes with talks on feeding	2.08***	2.53***	3.19***
Whether mother smoked during pregnancy	Smoked	1.00	NS	NS
	Did not smoke	1.53***		
Whether baby in special care	Not in special care	NS	1.00	NS
	In special care		1.67*	
When mother first held the baby	Immediately	1.67	NS	NS
	Within 1 hour	2.38*		
	More than 1 and less than 12 hours	1.15		
	Over 12 hours	1.00		

Variables not significant in any country	Significance of odds ratios
Mother's age	
Social class of husband or partner	* p < 0.05
Type of delivery	** p < 0.01
Weight of baby	*** P < 0.001
Whether health professional discussed breastfeeding at antenatal checkup	
Whether mother drank during pregnancy	

Table 5.8 Length of time breastfeeding mothers stayed in hospital by birth order (1985, 1990 and 1995 Great Britain)

Breastfeeding mothers who had a hospital birth

Length of stay	First birth			Later births			All babies		
	1985	1990	1995	1985	1990	1995	1985	1990	1995
	%	%	%	%	%	%	%	%	%
2 days or less	7	14	32	53	62	64	30	38	48
3-5 days	44	60	51	29	26	26	36	43	39
6 or 7 days	32	19	12	10	8	6	21	14	9
8-10 days	14	5	4	6	3	2	10	4	3
More than 10 days	3	2	2	2	1	1	2	1	2
Base	*1,627*	*1,670*	*1,657*	*1,654*	*1,724*	*1,680*	*3,281*	*3,392*	*3,337*

of change, despite the reduction in the time spent in hospital, reflects the fact that the majority of mothers who give up breastfeeding in the first week do so on the first or second day. Mothers of first babies were more likely to have given up breastfeeding by the time they left hospital (15%) than mothers of second or later babies (9%). As seen in Chapter 2, a similar pattern was seen for duration of breastfeeding in the first weeks after birth: almost one quarter (23%) of mothers of first babies had given up breastfeeding before two weeks compared with 16% of mothers of second or later babies (Table 2.18).

Table 5.9

Reasons for giving up breastfeeding

Mothers who gave up breastfeeding were asked their reasons for doing so. Those who gave up in the first two weeks were most likely to cite an insufficiency of milk: 32% of mothers who gave up within one week and 44% of mothers who gave up in the second week. Other common reasons at this stage included painful breasts or that the baby would not suck or rejected the breast. The latter was more common in the first than the second week (29% compared with 20%) whereas mothers were more likely to mention painful breasts as a reason for giving up in the second week (36% compared with 28%).

Table 5.9 Proportion of mothers who stopped breastfeeding before leaving hospital by birth order (1985, 1990 and 1995 Great Britain)

Breastfeeding mothers who had a hospital birth

	First birth			Later births			All babies		
	1985	1990	1995	1985	1990	1995	1985	1990	1995
	%	%	%	%	%	%	%	%	%
Breastfeeding:	81	88	85	89	88	92	85	88	88
Breastfeeding completely	70	72	74	77	77	80	73	74	77
Breastfeeding and bottle feeding	11	16	12	12	11	12	12	14	12
Stopped breastfeeding in hospital	19	12	15	11	12	9	15	12	12
Base	*1,627*	*1,670*	*1,657*	*1,654*	*1,724*	*1,680*	*3,281*	*3,392*	*3,337*

Table 5.10 Reasons given by mothers for stopping breastfeeding at Stage 1 (1990 and 1995 Great Britain)

Reasons for stopping breastfeeding	Baby's age when breastfeeding ceased:			
	Less than 1 week		1 week but less than 2 weeks	
	1990	1995	1990	1995
	Percentage giving reason			
Insufficient milk	35	32	51	44
Painful breasts or nipples	30	28	30	36
Baby would not suck/ rejected breast	25	29	20	20
Breastfeeding took too long/was tiring	6	11	8	16
Mother was ill	7	11	10	16
Did not like breastfeeding	10	10	10	5
Domestic reasons	3	6	3	10
Baby was ill	7	7	7	4
Difficult to judge how much baby had drunk*	..	4	..	2
Baby could not be fed by others	1	3	1	1
Mother had inverted nipples	4	2	3	1
Embarrassment	1	1	3	2
Returning to work	1	1	1	1
Had breastfed as long as intended	1	1	1	-
Inconvenient/no place to feed	-	-	0	-
Other reasons	3	10	3	12
Base	*482*	*480*	*165*	*164*

* Code introduced in 1995
Percentages do not add up to 100 as some mothers gave more than one reason.

The importance of various other reasons also differed according to whether mothers had given up in the first or second week after the birth. Mothers who gave up in the first few days were more likely to say that they did not like breastfeeding; those who continued breastfeeding for between one and two weeks were more likely to say that breastfeeding took too long or was tiring, or to mention domestic reasons.

Table 5.10

Delays in starting breastfeeding

The previous section showed that, after controlling for the characteristics of the mother, the only factor at the time of the birth that was significantly associated with the incidence of breastfeeding was the separation of

Table 5.11 Length of time until baby was put to the breast (1985, 1990 and 1995 Great Britain)

Breastfeeding mothers who had a hospital birth

Time until baby was put to the breast	1985	1990	1995
	%	%	%
Immediately	27	26	25
Within an hour	32	37	43
More than 1 hour, up to 4 hours later	17	18	17
More than 4 hours, up to 12 hours later	14	10	8
More than 12 hours later	10	10	8
Base	*3,319*	*3,395*	*3,337*

the mother and baby in the first few hours. Similarly, delays in the initiation of breastfeeding have previously been shown to be associated with giving up breastfeeding in the early weeks.

Between 1990 and 1995 there was an increase in the proportion of mothers who began breastfeeding within one hour of giving birth. The proportion rose from 63% in 1990 to 68% in 1995. The duration of breastfeeding continues to show a relationship with the length of time before the baby is put to the breast. Increasing delays in first feeding the baby are associated with an increasing likelihood of stopping breastfeeding in the first two weeks. In 1995, only 14% of mothers who breastfed immediately had given up by the end of the second week, compared with 26% of those who, for one reason or another, had not put their baby to the breast for more than an hour after birth.

Tables 5.11 and 5.12

The prevalence of breastfeeding at two weeks did not show a statistically significant relationship with whether the baby was in special care or had low birthweight. The delay before the baby was held or put to the breast therefore appeared to be more closely related both to the initial incidence of breastfeeding and to prevalence at two weeks.

Table 5.12 Proportion of mothers who had stopped breastfeeding within two weeks by the length of time until the baby was first put to the breast (1985, 1990 and 1995 Great Britain)
Breastfeeding mothers who had a hospital birth

Time until baby was put to the breast	1985	1990	1995	1985	1990	1995
	Percentage who had given up breastfeeding within 2 weeks			Bases		
Immediately	14	12	14	869	843	804
Within an hour	15	18	16	1,011	1,196	1,381
More than 1 hour, up to 4 hours later	21	25	26	553	593	564
More than 4 hours, up to 12 hours later	24	24	26	446	328	249
More than 12 hours later	31	32	30	327	314	252
Total*	19	19	19	3,319	3,395	3,337

* Includes some cases where the time until baby was put to breast was not known

Table 5.13 Contact between breastfeeding mothers and babies while in hospital (1985, 1990 and 1995 Great Britain)
Breastfeeding mothers who had a hospital birth

	1985	1990	1995
	%	%	%
Mother and baby together continuously	47	63	74
Baby away sometimes:			
mother always fed baby	18	15	9
nurses sometimes fed baby	26	16	8
Baby in incubator or special care			
most of the time (more than 1 day)	9	7	9
Base	3,281	3,392	3,243

Table 5.14 Frequency with which bottles of formula milk were given to breastfed babies in hospital (1985,1990 and 1995 Great Britain)
Breastfeeding mothers who had a hospital birth

Frequency of giving bottles of milk in hospital	1985	1990	1995
	%	%	%
No bottles given	48	54	61
Bottles given once or twice only	23	23	20
Bottles given during the night	9	6	4
Bottles given at every feed	9 50*	9 45*	7 36*
Bottles given, other arrangements	7	5	5
Bottles given, mother not sure how often	1	2	0
Mother uncertain whether bottles given	2	1	3
Base	3,281	3,392	3,243

* Percentages do not add up to total as some mothers failed to say how often their baby had received a bottle.

Contact between mother and baby in hospital

Keeping the baby by the mother's side at all times makes it easier for the mother to breastfeed on demand. The practice of placing some new-born babies in a nursery has continued to decline so that, by 1995, 74% of mothers had their baby with them continuously in hospital compared to 63% in 1990 and 47% in 1985. A further 9% of mothers always fed their baby even though they were sometimes separated and a similar proportion of babies were in special care most of the time. The proportion of babies who were sometimes fed by a nurse or midwife decreased by one half between 1990 and 1995, from 16% to 8%.

Table 5.13

Giving bottles to breastfed babies

Previous surveys have shown a strong association between giving bottles of formula milk to breastfed babies in hospital and the likelihood of the mother stopping breastfeeding in the early weeks. Between 1990 and 1995 there has been a fall in the proportion of breastfed babies who were given bottles in hospital, from 45% to 36%.

Table 5.14, Figure 5.1

Breastfeeding mothers whose babies were given bottles were still more likely to stop breastfeeding in the first two weeks than were other mothers. One third (34%) of mothers whose babies had been given a bottle had stopped breastfeeding at this stage compared with 11% of mothers whose babies had not been given a bottle. Over half of women (58%) whose babies had been given a bottle at most feeds had given up by two weeks. However, this measurement might reflect the proportion of women who are already having difficulties breastfeeding rather than the use of formula milk having an effect on their behaviour.

Table 5.15

5.5 Problems feeding the baby and the role of health professionals

In 1995, 86% of mothers of first babies were given help, usually by a midwife or nurse, the first time that they breastfed their baby. Mothers of second or later babies were understandably much less likely to receive advice at this stage. Although being shown how to breastfeed does not significantly affect the chances of the mother continuing to breastfeed, 95% of mothers said that they found the advice helpful.

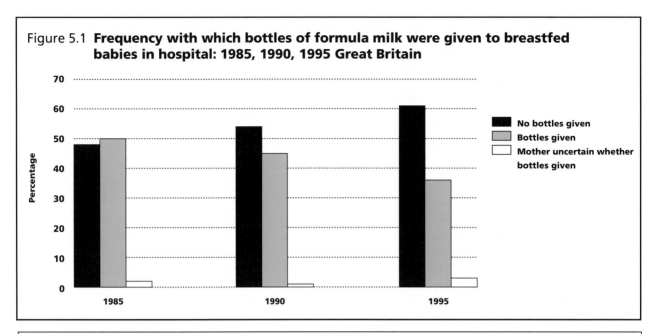

Figure 5.1 **Frequency with which bottles of formula milk were given to breastfed babies in hospital: 1985, 1990, 1995 Great Britain**

Legend:
- No bottles given
- Bottles given
- Mother uncertain whether bottles given

Table 5.15 **Proportion of mothers who had stopped breastfeeding within two weeks by frequency with which bottles of milk had been given in hospital (1985, 1990 and 1995 Great Britain)**
Breastfeeding mothers who had a hospital birth

Frequency of giving bottles of milk in hospital	1985	1990	1995	1985	1990	1995
	Percentage who had given up breastfeeding within two weeks			Base		
No bottles given	8	9	11	1,544	1,759	1,983
Bottles given occasionally or at night	20	23	27	997	939	746
Bottles given at most feeds	57	56	58	301	295	229
All babies who received a bottle while being breastfed	28	32	34	1,606	1,438	1,142
All breastfed babies *	**20**	**20**	**20**	**3,281**	**3,392**	**3,243**

* Does not include home births

More than half of mothers of first babies who did not receive help (8% of all mothers of first babies) would have liked to have done so and a similar proportion (7%) of mothers of second or later babies would have liked to receive advice.

Table 5.16

Problems feeding the baby in hospital

While in hospital, 35% of breastfeeding mothers experienced problems feeding their baby: there was no change in this proportion between 1990 and 1995. Not surprisingly, mothers of first babies were more likely to report problems (46%) than mothers of second or later babies (24%). As in previous surveys, the most common problems were that the baby would not suck or latch on to the breast (48% of mothers who experienced problems) or that the mother had sore or cracked nipples (24% of mothers). One tenth or more of the mothers who reported problems mentioned that the baby appeared to be hungry or they had insufficient milk (16%), that the baby was ill, for example in special

Table 5.16 **Proportion of mothers of first babies who received help or advice the first time they breastfed**
Mothers of first babies who ever breastfed

	First births	Later births	All births
	%	%	%
Received advice	86	44	65
Did not receive advice	14	56	35
of which .... would have liked advice	8	7	8
.... did not want advice	6	49	27
Base	*1,690*	*1,720*	*3,410*

care, (13%) or that the baby was feeding slowly or not gaining weight (10%).

Tables 5.17 and 5.18

The majority of women (82%) received help or advice for these problems, almost all mothers talked to either a midwife or a nurse. Although it is a small group, mothers of first babies who said that they did not get help in hospital were significantly more likely to have stopped breastfeeding by two weeks (48%) than those who had received help (29%).

Table 5.19

Table 5.17 Feeding problems experienced by breastfeeding mothers while in hospital (1985, 1990 and 1995 Great Britain)

Breastfeeding mothers who had a hospital birth

Whether experienced feeding problems while in hospital	First birth			Later births			All babies		
	1985	1990	1995	1985	1990	1995	1985	1990	1995
	%	%	%	%	%	%	%	%	%
Had problems	39	47	46	21	25	24	30	36	35
Did not have problems	61	53	54	79	75	76	70	64	65
Base	1,612	1,657	1,638	1,643	1,681	1,583	3,254	3,338	3,243

Table 5.18 Feeding problems experienced by breastfeeding mothers while in hospital or after leaving hospital, by birth order

Breastfeeding mothers who had feeding problems in hospital

Type of feeding problem	Problems in hospital			Problems after leaving hospital		
	First birth	Later birth	All births	First birth	Later birth	All births
	Percentage having problem					
Baby would not suck/rejected breast	52	39	48	21	16	19
Mother had sore or cracked nipples	25	22	24	38	40	39
Baby was hungry/ insufficient milk	16	16	16	48	41	45
Baby was ill	12	15	13	2	4	3
Baby falling asleep/slow feeding/not gaining weight	8	12	10	13	12	12
Mother found breastfeeding uncomfortable	6	6	6	4	5	4
Baby didn't like milk	5	2	4	4	5	4
Baby vomiting	2	3	3	4	6	5
Baby constipated	-	-	-	1	1	1
Baby had wind	1	2	1	6	7	7
Other problems affecting mother	8	5	7	8	11	10
Other problems with baby	4	5	4	3	3	3
Base	761	392	1,153	556	446	1,002

Percentages do not add up to 100 as some mothers experienced more than one problem.

Table 5.19 Proportion of mothers who had stopped breastfeeding at 2 weeks by whether they received help with problems in hospital

Breastfeeding mothers who had feeding problems in hospital

	First births		Later births		All babies	
	Received help	Did not receive help	Received help	Did not receive help	Received help	Did not receive help
Percentage who had stopped breastfeeding within two weeks	29	48	24	[8]	28	38
Base	684	57	344	35	1,028	92

Problems feeding the baby after leaving hospital

Among mothers who were still breastfeeding when they left hospital, 35% reported having problems breastfeeding in the early weeks. Again, mothers of first babies were more likely to experience problems (40%) than mothers of second or later births (30%). By this stage, the problems most frequently mentioned by mothers were that the baby appeared hungry or the mother had insufficient milk (45%) and painful breasts (39%). In addition, one fifth of mothers (19%) still reported problems with the baby rejecting the breast or not latching on. About one tenth (12%) of mothers who had feeding problems continued to say that the baby was prone to falling asleep or was slow feeding.

Tables 5.20 and 5.18

The vast majority of women received advice for these problems. The number of women who did not receive help is too small to compare their duration of breastfeeding with mothers who did. Overall, midwives and health visitors were the most common source of advice for all mothers: 64% of mothers who had received advice were helped by a nurse or midwife and 59% by a health visitor. About one fifth of the mothers had received help from their GP or doctor (21%), from a friend or relative (23%) and 16% had been helped by reading books, leaflets or magazines. Mothers having their second or later baby were more likely to consult their GP whilst new mothers were more likely to turn to relatives and friends or to consult relevant books or leaflets.

Table 5.21

At the first stage of the survey, mothers were asked whether, during their pregnancy, they had been given either of the books covering pregnancy and the early years of life which are produced by the Health

Table 5.20 Feeding problems experienced by breastfeeding mothers after leaving hospital (1985, 1990 and 1995 Great Britain)

Mothers who were breastfeeding when they left hospital

Whether experienced feeding problems after leaving hospital	First births			Later births			All babies		
	1985	1990	1995	1985	1990	1995	1985	1990	1995
	%	%	%	%	%	%	%	%	%
Had problems	36	39	40	32	30	30	34	34	35
Did not have problems	64	61	60	68	70	70	66	66	65
Base	*1,298*	*1,377*	*1,407*	*1,448*	*1,480*	*1,464*	*2,746*	*2,857*	*2,878*

Table 5.21 Sources of advice for mothers experiencing feeding problems after leaving hospital

Mothers who received help for problems breastfeeding after leaving hospital

Source of advice	First births	Later births	All babies
Doctor/GP	17	26	21
Health Visitor	59	59	59
Midwife/Nurse	64	62	64
Friend or relative	30	15	23
Books, leaflets or magazines	19	12	16
Voluntary agency counsellor	2	1	2
Other	4	5	5
Base	*514*	*396*	*910*

Percentages do not add up to 100 as some mothers received advice from more than one source.

Education Authority or the Health Education Board for Scotland. These are *The Pregnancy Book* and *Birth to Five*. More than four fifths (84%) of mothers in the United Kingdom said that they had received at least one of the two books. Mothers of first babies were more likely to have received one of the books (94% compared with 75% of mothers of later babies) and mothers in Northern Ireland were less likely than those in other countries to have done so (76% compared with 92% in Scotland). Mothers in all countries were more likely to have received *The Pregnancy Book* than *Birth to Five* and this difference was particularly great among mothers in Northern Ireland (64% compared with 37%).

Table 5.22

Mothers were also specifically asked whether they had received help or advice from a voluntary organisation which helps new mothers, such as the National Childbirth Trust, La Leche League or the Association of Breastfeeding Mothers. This question was placed with other general questions about development checks and visits from health visitors, and so was not linked to the questions about feeding problems and advice received. One tenth of breastfeeding mothers said that they had received help or advice from a voluntary agency. This compares with only 2% of mothers who had feeding problems after leaving hospital who said that they had received advice from a voluntary agency counsellor. Mothers of first babies were more likely than others to have received help from a voluntary organisation, and mothers in Northern Ireland were least likely to have done so.

Table 5.23

Table 5.22 Whether mothers had been given a copy of books on pregnancy and the early years by birth order and by country

Title of book	Birth order		Country			United Kingdom
	First births	Later births	England and Wales	Scotland	Northern Ireland	
			Percentage of mothers who were given			
The Pregnancy Book	76	61	67	75	64	68
Birth to Five	77	39	55	69	37	56
One or other book	94	75	84	92	76	84
Neither book	6	25	16	8	24	16
Base	*2,335*	*2,845*	*4,598*	*1,863*	*1,476*	*5,181*

Table 5.23 Whether mothers had received help or advice from a voluntary organisation by birth order and by country

If had received help	Birth order		Country			United Kingdom
	First births	Later births	England and Wales	Scotland	Northern Ireland	
	%	%	%	%	%	%
Received help or advice	13	8	10	9	6	10
Had not received help or advice	87	92	90	91	94	90
Base	*1,405*	*1,466*	*2,623*	*843*	*523*	*2,871*

Women who received such advice were more likely to continue breastfeeding: 92% were still breastfeeding at two weeks compared with 79% of other mothers. However, they were also more likely to be in non-manual social class groups (69% compared to 39% in the survey sample), and it is therefore difficult to identify the separate effect of receiving such advice from a predisposition to breastfeed or other factors related to duration of breastfeeding.

5.6 The influence of relatives and friends on the duration of breastfeeding

Chapter 3 showed that relatives and friends exert a strong influence on the mother's decision whether or not to breastfeed. Once a mother has begun to breastfeed, the support of relatives and friends continues to influence the duration of breastfeeding. Thus, women who were themselves entirely bottle fed are more likely to give up in the first two weeks (26%) than mothers who were breastfed themselves (12%). These differences were not, however, evident among mothers who continued breastfeeding beyond the first fortnight: 9% of mothers who had themselves been bottle fed and 8% of mothers who had been breastfed gave up at between two and four weeks.

Table 5.24

Similarly, mothers whose friends mostly bottle fed were more likely to have given up in the first two

weeks (28%) than those whose friends mostly breastfed (8%). Again, this influence was much reduced after the first fortnight.

Table 5.25

Overall, the combined influence of family and friends can be one of the strongest determinants not only of whether a mother breastfeeds at all, but also of her chances of continuing to do so beyond the first two weeks. In total, 34% of mothers who were bottle fed themselves and whose friends mostly bottle fed had given up breastfeeding in the first two weeks, compared with 20% of all mothers.

5.7 Multivariate analysis of factors associated with the duration of breastfeeding up to two weeks

As with incidence of breastfeeding, it can be difficult to interpret which factors may be influencing a mother's likelihood of continuing to breastfeed independent of basic socio-demographic characteristics.

Again, a logistic regression was performed to explore which factors were most strongly associated with whether the mother had given up breastfeeding in the first two weeks. The model was tested separately for mothers of first and later babies and, at this stage, mainly the same variables affect the duration of breastfeeding. Therefore the model presented

Table 5.24 Duration of breastfeeding to four weeks by how mother was fed
Mothers who ever breastfed

Baby's age when breastfeeding ceased	How mother was fed				All babies
	Breastfed entirely	Breast and bottle fed	Bottle fed entirely	Don't know	
	Percentage who gave up breastfeeding				
Less than 2 weeks	12	16	26	25	20
2 weeks, less than 4 weeks	8	9	9	10	9
	Percentage still breastfeeding				
Breastfed at 4 weeks	81	75	65	65	72
Base	*890*	*807*	*1,377*	*297*	*3,410*

Table 5.25 Duration of breastfeeding to four weeks by how mother's friends fed their babies
Mothers who ever breastfed

Baby's age when breastfeeding ceased	How mother's friends fed their babies				All babies
	Breastfed entirely	Half breastfed, half bottle fed	Bottle fed entirely	Don't know	
	Percentage who gave up breastfeeding				
Less than 2 weeks	8	28	21	26	20
2 weeks, less than 4 weeks	6	11	9	10	9
	Percentage still breastfeeding				
Breastfed at 4 weeks	86	61	70	64	72
Base	*1,007*	*1,161*	*830*	*86*	*3,410*

* Includes some cases where mother had no friends with babies

includes all mothers who breastfed initially and shows the odds ratios associated with giving up breastfeeding within two weeks.

After taking account of other factors in the model, mothers of first babies in England and Wales and in Scotland were more likely than mothers of second or later babies to give up within two weeks. Birth order was not a significant factor in Northern Ireland. Younger mothers and those who had lower educational levels were also more likely to have given up. After allowing for factors such as age and education, social class was not significant in any country.

Other influences in England and Wales and Scotland included how the mother was fed and how the mother's friends fed their babies, as described in the previous section. In Scotland and Northern Ireland, whether the mother smoked during pregnancy affected the duration of breastfeeding, although it was not associated with initial incidence in these countries. In both countries, mothers who smoked during pregnancy were more likely than non-smokers to have given up breastfeeding within two weeks.

A variety of events around the time of the birth had an independent effect on the duration of breastfeeding. In all countries, if the hospital staff sometimes fed the baby the mother was more likely to give up breastfeeding. However, although this is statistically significant, it is possible that nurses feeding the baby is an indication of other problems with either the mother or the baby.

The significance of other factors such as whether there was a delay in starting to breastfeed, the baby's weight and the type of delivery varied between countries. In England and Wales and in Scotland, the likelihood of giving up breastfeeding was affected by when the mother first breastfed. Where there was a delay of more than one hour after the birth, mothers were less likely to be still breastfeeding at two weeks. In Scotland only, mothers who had a caesarean birth were less likely to continue breastfeeding.

In Scotland and Northern Ireland, mothers of low birthweight babies (under 2500g) were more likely than mothers of larger babies to continue breastfeeding beyond two weeks. It therefore appears that, although mothers of low birthweight babies were no more likely than others to breastfeed initially (Tables 5.6 and 5.7), when other factors were taken into account those mothers that did breastfeed were more likely to continue beyond two weeks.

Table 5.26

Table 5.26 Characteristics associated with mothers giving up breastfeeding within 2 weeks
Mothers who breastfed initially

Characteristic		England and Wales	Scotland	Northern Ireland
Percentage who gave up within two weeks		*19%*	*21%*	*27%*
			Odds ratios	
Birth order	First baby	1.34**	1.70**	NS
	Second or later baby	1.00	1.00	
Mother's age	Under 20	2.26***	2.35*	5.27***
	20-24	1.46**	2.00**	1.77*
	25-29	1.16	1.34	2.42***
	30 or over	1.00	1.00	1.00
Age mother completed full-time education	16 or under	2.78***	3.46***	2.88***
	17 or 18	2.15***	2.50***	1.98**
	Over 18	1.00	1.00	1.00
How mother was fed	Bottle fed or method not known	1.87***	1.44*	NS
	Breastfed	1.00	1.00	
How friends fed their babies	Most bottle fed	3.05***	2.66***	NS
	Half breastfed, half bottle fed or don't know	2.68***	2.31***	
	Most breastfed	1.00	1.00	
Whether mother smoked during pregnancy	Smoked	NS	1.74**	1.92**
	Did not smoke		1.00	1.00
Whether the mother always fed the baby	Nurses sometimes fed baby	1.78***	1.89**	3.59***
	Mother always fed baby	1.00	1.00	1.00
When the mother first breastfed	One or more hours after the birth	1.51***	1.49*	NS
	Within one hour of birth	1.00	1.00	
Type of delivery	Ceasarian	NS	2.00***	NS
	Normal, forceps or vacuum extraction		1.00	
Weight of baby	2500 grammes or more	NS	2.33*	13.15***
	Less than 2500 grammes		1.00	1.00

Variables not significant in any country	Significance of odds ratios
Social class of husband or partner	* p < 0.05
Whether the mother had a general anaesthetic	** p < 0.01
Whether the mother felt well after the birth	*** P < 0.001

6 The use of non-human milk

Summary

- By the first stage interview, at six to ten weeks old, four fifths (79%) of mothers were giving their baby bottles of infant formula: 62% were exclusively giving infant formula and 18% were giving additional manufactured feeds while breastfeeding.

- Mothers in Great Britain who were breastfeeding at stages one and two were more likely than in 1990 to have introduced infant formula as an additional feed (43% at stage two compared with 27% in 1990).

- The main change between 1990 and 1995 in the type of non-human milk given was the decrease in the use of cow's milk at stage three, from 42% in 1990 to 16% in 1995 (results for GB).

- Mothers who were also breastfeeding their baby were more likely to use a whey dominant formula in the early months than were mothers who did not breastfeed (70% compared with 36% at stage two).

- At stage one, 6% of mothers giving manufactured baby milk sometimes made additions to bottles of milk. This increased to 11% at stage three.

- Between 1990 and 1995, the use of cow's milk for any purpose, including to mix food, decreased at all ages. In 1995, 17% of mothers in Great Britain had introduced cow's milk at 6 months compared with 30% of mothers in 1990.

- About one quarter (27%) of mothers of first babies attended antenatal classes and were taught how to make up a bottle.

6.1 The use of infant formula milk

Infant formulas are artificial feeds which are manufactured to take the place of human milk in providing a sole source of nutrition for babies up to the age of four to six months. In the early stages of a mixed diet, breast milk or infant formula milks continue to provide the majority of energy and nutrients for the infant.

In 1995, 34% of mothers in the United Kingdom (32% GB) gave infant formula from birth. At the time of the first stage of the survey, when the babies were around six to ten weeks old, three fifths (62%) of mothers in the United Kingdom were using formula milks exclusively. As well as those mothers who gave non-human milk from birth, 42% of women who had breastfed initially had changed exclusively to giving non-human milk by the first stage interview and a further 27% were giving infant formula as well as breast milk. Thus, in total, four fifths (79%) of all mothers were using infant formula when their baby was around two months old.

Table 6.1

Mothers who breastfeed may give their babies additional feeds of manufactured baby milk. At each stage of the survey, breastfeeding mothers were asked whether they were also giving milk from a bottle or a cup and what was the main type of non-human milk used although no information was collected on the frequency of giving it.

In 1995, almost half (46%) of mothers in Great Britain who were breastfeeding at the time of completing the first questionnaire were also giving infant formula. This is significantly higher than the 39% of mothers using additional manufactured baby milk in 1990 and continues the increase seen since 1985 (34% of mothers).

By the second stage of the survey, when their babies were around four months old, 43% of mothers who were breastfeeding were also giving non-human milk compared with 27% in 1990. This was a more marked increase in the incidence of combining human and non-human milk than was evident at 6 to 10 weeks. Thus, as discussed in Chapter 2, although there has been a small increase in the overall incidence and duration of breastfeeding, there has been a more marked increase in the use of additional infant formula milk to supplement breastfeeding during the first weeks.

Table 6.2

There was some variation by country in the use of additional feeds of infant formula. Table 6.3 shows that, at the first two stages of the survey, breastfeeding mothers in Scotland were least likely to give infant formula in addition to breast milk. This is unlikely to be explained by differences in the age of babies in different countries as babies in Scotland were, on average, the oldest group at the stage one interview (Table 1.9).

Table 6.3

6.2 The different types of infant formula

The majority of infant formulas are based on cow's milk and can be classified according to the dominant cow's milk protein of either whey or casein. Casein dominant formulas are based on whole cow milk protein and have a casein:whey ratio of approximately 80:20. Whey dominant formulas are modified so that the casein:whey ratio is

Table 6.1	Feeding method at around 6 to 10 weeks by initial feeding method		
Feeding method at 6 to 10 weeks	Initial feeding method		All babies
	Breastfed at birth	Not breastfed at birth	
	%	%	%
Breastfeeding exclusively	32	-	21
Breastfeeding and giving infant formula	27	-	18
Giving infant formula exclusively	42	100	62
Base	*3,410*	*1,770*	*5,181*

Table 6.2	Non-human milk given to breastfed babies at stages 1 and 2 (1985,1990 and 1995 Great Britain)					
Mothers breastfeeding at stage 1 or stage 2						
Whether non-human milk given	6-10 weeks			4-5 months		
	1985	1990	1995	1985	1990	1995
	%	%	%	%	%	%
Non-human milk given	34	39	46	24	27	43
Only breast milk given	66	61	54	76	73	57
Base	*1,720*	*1,764*	*1,954*	*1,192*	*1,182*	*1,236*

Table 6.3   **Non-human milk given to breastfed babies at stages 1 and 2 by country**
Mothers breastfeeding at stage 1 or stage 2

Whether non-human milk given	6-10 weeks				4-5 months			
	England and Wales	Scotland	Northern Ireland	United Kingdom	England and Wales	Scotland	Northern Ireland	United Kingdom
	%	%	%	%	%	%	%	%
Non-human milk given	46	42	50	46	43	38	44	43
Only breast milk given	54	58	50	54	57	62	56	57
Base	*1,825*	*569*	*310*	*1,988*	*1,150*	*383*	*137*	*1,252*

approximately 40:60, which is closer to that in human milk. Some manufacturers claim that casein dominant formulas are more satisfying for older babies, although there is no firm evidence. It is likely that these claims will influence mothers.

Although most formulas are manufactured from cow's milk, some are also available based on soy protein isolate as a protein source. These products may be used from birth but should not usually be a first choice unless there is a specific reason for excluding cow's milk products from the diet (Weaning and the Weaning Diet[1]).

Follow-on formulas, which are again based on cow's milk, may be used at later ages by mothers to provide the milk drink element in the mixed diets of older infants. They are not intended to be used as a sole source of nutrition and the report of the Working Group on the Weaning Diet recommends that follow-on milk should not be used as a replacement for breast milk or infant formula before the age of about six months.

The same report[1] recommends that whole cow's milk should only be used as a main milk drink after the age of one year. In addition, semi-skimmed milk is not suitable as a drink before the age of two years and fully skimmed cow's milk should not be introduced before the age of five years.

Figure 6.1 (Table 6.4) shows the types of formula used by mothers in Great Britain at each stage of the survey in 1995 and in earlier years. In 1995 the most common type of non-human milk given when babies were 6 to 10 weeks old was a whey dominant formula: 60% of mothers used a whey dominant formula compared with 37% using casein dominant. The relative importance of whey dominant formulas in the early weeks has increased over the last decade: 50% of mothers giving non-human milk were using whey dominant formulas in 1985 compared with 60% in 1995.

By the second stage of the survey, when babies were about four months old, the relative importance of casein and whey dominant formulas had reversed. In 1995, 54% of mothers in Great Britain giving manufactured baby milks were using a casein dominant formula at this stage and 40% were using a whey dominant formula. At about four months, 2% of babies were being given a follow-on formula and 1% were given cow's milk as their main non-human milk drink. Over the past ten years there has been a decline in the use of cow's milk at this stage, from 7% in 1985 to 1% in 1995. In addition, casein dominant formulas are now more commonly used than in 1985.

Between the second and third stages of the survey there was, as in previous years, a shift from the use of whey and casein dominant formulas to other milks. The 1995 survey showed much greater use of follow-on milks and a marked decrease in the use of cow's milk as the main non-human milk drink compared with 1990. One quarter of mothers giving non-human milk (25%) were using follow-on formulas compared with 5% in 1990 and the proportion giving their baby cow's milk had decreased from 42% to 16%. The age of introduction of cow's milk and its use in different forms in the diet is considered in more detail in section 6.4.

Table 6.4, Figure 6.1

There are some differences in the type of non-human milk used by mothers who are exclusively giving manufactured baby milk and those who combine human and non-human milk. As in 1990, mothers who were also breastfeeding were more likely to use whey dominant formulas during the first few months than were mothers who did not breastfeed. These formulas have a casein:whey ratio which is similar to that of human milk. In 1995, 82% of mothers in Great Britain who were also breastfeeding were giving whey dominant formulas when their baby was 6 to 10 weeks old compared with 54% of mothers who were not breast feeding. By the

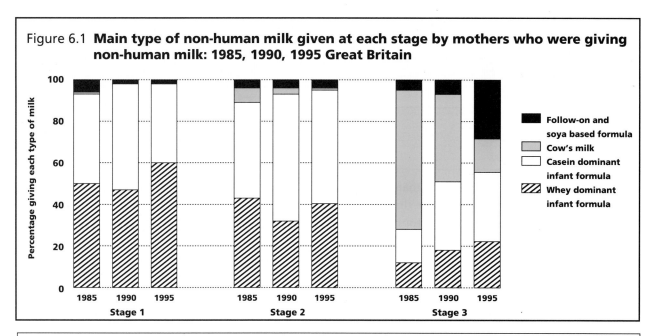

Figure 6.1 **Main type of non-human milk given at each stage by mothers who were giving non-human milk: 1985, 1990, 1995 Great Britain**

Table 6.4 Main type of non-human milk given at each stage by mothers who were giving non-human milk (1985, 1990 and 1995 Great Britain)

Mothers giving non-human milk at relevant stage

Type of non-human milk	6-10 weeks			4-5 months			8-9 months		
	1985	1990	1995	1985	1990	1995	1985	1990	1995
	%	%	%	%	%	%	%	%	%
Whey dominant	50	47	60	43	32	40	12	18	22
Casein dominant	43	51	37	46	61	54	16	33	33
Soya-based formula	}6	}2	}2	}4	2}4	2}4	}4	2}7	3}28
Follow-on formula					1	2		5	25
Cow's milk	0	0	0	7	3	1	67	42	16
Whole	0	0	0	6	3	1	60	39	14
Semi-skimmed	-	-	0	1	0	0	5	3	1
Skimmed	-	0	-	0	0	0	2	0	0
Other/inadequately described	-	0	1	1	1	1	1	0	1
Base	4,072	4,332	3,953	4,313	4,526	4,306	5,048	5,200	4,667

second stage of the survey, the use of whey dominant formulas was almost twice as common among mothers who combined breast feeding with giving non-human milk (70%) than among mothers who were exclusively giving non-human milk (36%). The use of whey dominant formulas has increased significantly among both groups since 1990.

By the third stage of the survey, when babies were about nine months old, mothers who were also breastfeeding were more likely than those who were not breastfeeding to be giving their baby cow's milk as their main milk drink. As mentioned previously, no information was collected on the frequency with which breastfeeding mothers gave additional milks. In 1995, 26% of mothers in Great Britain who were also breastfeeding their baby used cow's milk compared with 15% of those who were exclusively giving manufactured baby milk. However, the use of cow's milk at this age has decreased markedly for

both groups since 1990, from 68% and 41% respectively. This decrease was balanced by an increase in the use of follow-on formulas among both groups of mothers.

Table 6.5, Figure 6.2

There was some variation between countries in the type of non-human milk used at each stage of the survey. In the early months, mothers in England and Wales were more likely than those elsewhere to use a whey dominant formula. This was in part due to the greater proportion of mothers in England and Wales who were combining breast milk and manufactured baby milk but the effect was also seen among mothers who were exclusively giving infant formula milk at the first and second stages of the survey. Mothers in Scotland and Northern Ireland were therefore more likely than those in England and Wales to be using a casein dominant formula at stages one or two.

At nine months, mothers in England and Wales were

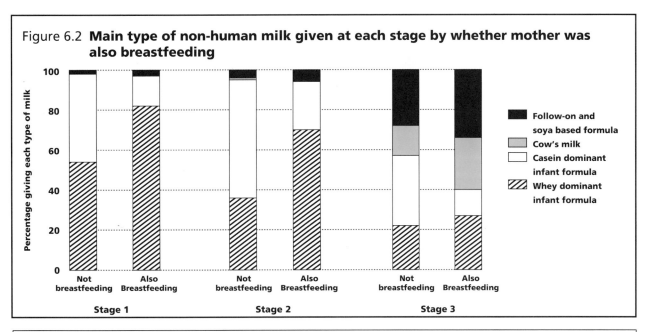

Figure 6.2 **Main type of non-human milk given at each stage by whether mother was also breastfeeding**

Table 6.5 **Main type of non-human milk given at each stage by whether mothers were also breastfeeding (1990 and 1995 Great Britain)**
Mothers giving non-human milk at relevant stage

Type of non-human milk	Mothers not breastfeeding at						Mothers who were also breastfeeding at					
	6-10 weeks		4-5 months		8-9 months		6-10 weeks		4-5 months		8-9 months	
	1990	1995	1990	1995	1990	1995	1990	1995	1990	1995	1990	1995
	%	%	%	%	%	%	%	%	%	%	%	%
Whey dominant	42	54	30	36	18	22	73	82	62	70	15	27
Casein dominant	56	44	63	58	34	35	23	15	29	24	8	12
Soya-based formula	}2	}2	3 }3	2 }4	3 }7	3 }27	}3	}2	5 }6	2 }4	2 }10	3 }32
Follow-on formula			0	2	4	24			0	2	7	29
Cow's milk	0	0	3	1	41	15	0	0	3	0	68	26
Other/inadequately described	0	1	1	1	0	1	1	1	1	1	0	2
Base	*3,649*	*3,063*	*4,200*	*3,780*	*4,867*	*4,351*	*683*	*890*	*326*	*526*	*333*	*317*

least likely to be giving their baby cow's milk as their main non-human milk drink (15% compared with at least 21% elsewhere) and were still more likely to be using a whey dominant formula (22% compared with 18% elsewhere).

Table 6.6

Use of ready-to-feed infant formula

Infant formulas are traditionally sold as dry powder to be reconstituted with water, but ready to feed bottles and cartons of formula are now also available. At all stages of the 1995 survey, only small proportions of mothers giving infant formula were using ready-to-feed formula: the percentage ranged from 3% to 6% at the different stages. These rates showed a modest increase over those reported in 1990. As in 1990, mothers who were also breastfeeding were more likely to use a ready-to-feed formula than those who exclusively gave infant formula. For example at six to ten weeks, 13% of mothers who also breastfed usually used a ready-to-

feed formula compared with 4% of mothers who exclusively gave manufactured baby milk.

Table 6.7

Additions to formula

Mothers were asked for the first time in 1995 whether they ever added anything to the formula that they gave their baby. This question was designed to identify the proportion of mothers adding sugar or honey to the milk at an early age. The proportion of mothers who sometimes made additions to the milk increased from 6% when babies were about six to ten weeks old to 11% when they were nine months old. At all stages, about 1% or 2% of mothers added sugar or honey to the milk.

Table 6.8 details the various additions which were sometimes made by mothers. These showed some variation according to the baby's age. At the first stage, mothers were most likely to add gripe water or products to thicken the feed (2% of mothers giving

Table 6.6   Main type of non-human milk given at each stage by mothers who were giving non-human milk by country

Mothers giving non-human milk at relevant stage

Type of non-human milk	6-10 weeks				4-5 months				8-9 months			
	England and Wales	Scotland	Northern Ireland	United Kingdom	England and Wales	Scotland	Northern Ireland	United Kingdom	England and Wales	Scotland	Northern Ireland	United Kingdom
	%	%	%	%	%	%	%	%	%	%	%	%
Whey dominant	62	42	49	60	41	31	27	39	22	18	17	22
Casein dominant	36	55	49	38	53	63	60	54	33	36	34	33
Soya-based formula	}2	}2	}2	}2	3 }4	1 }4	4 }8	2 }4	3 }28	2 }25	4 }25	3 }28
Follow-on formula					2	3	4	2	25	23	22	25
Cow's milk	-	0	0	0	1	1	4	1	15	21	23	16
Other/inadequately described	1	1	0	1	1	0	1	1	1	1	1	1
Base	*3,587*	*1,523*	*1,318*	*4,076*	*3,940*	*1,626*	*1,398*	*4,461*	*4,267*	*1,780*	*1,432*	*4,826*

Table 6.7   The use of ready-to-feed infant formulas at different stages (1990 and 1995 Great Britain)

Mothers giving non-human milk at relevant stage

	6-10 weeks		4-5 months		8-9 months	
	1990	1995	1990	1995	1990	1995
	Percentage using ready to feed formula					
Mothers giving non-human milk exclusively	2	4	1	4	1	3
Mothers who were also breastfeeding	12	13	5	10	1	5
All mothers giving non-human milk	**3**	**6**	**2**	**4**	**1**	**3**
Bases:						
Mothers giving non-human milk exclusively	*3,649*	*3,057*	*4,200*	*3,780*	*4,867*	*4,325*
Mothers who were also breastfeeding	*683*	*872*	*326*	*529*	*333*	*315*
All mothers giving non-human milk	*4,332*	*3,930*	*4,526*	*4,300*	*5,200*	*4,639*

Table 6.8   Additions made to milk in bottles at different stages

Mothers giving non-human milk at relevant stage

Additions to milk in bottle	6-10 weeks	4-5 months	8-9 months
	Percentage adding		
Sugar or honey	1	1	2
Tea	0	0	4
Rusk	1	3	1
Baby rice or cereals	1	1	0
Ovaltine, horlicks etc	-	0	2
Gripe water, thickeners	2	1	0
Vitamins	1	1	2
Medicines	0	0	0
Other additions	1	0	0
All additions	**6**	**8**	**11**
Base	*4,099*	*4,446*	*4,846*

manufactured baby milks) but these were less common at later stages. Other additions at six to ten weeks were vitamins and small amounts of rusk or baby rice, although these were only used by 1% of all mothers giving manufactured baby milk. Rusks were more commonly added at the second stage. By the time babies were about nine months old, tea was the most common addition (4% of mothers giving manufactured baby milk) and other food drinks such as ovaltine, horlicks, coffee and milk shakes were also more likely to be added than at earlier stages.

Table 6.8

6.3 Choice of brand of formula

The infant formula that a mother uses will often be influenced by the brand and type of formula provided in hospital. In 1995, women who gave infant formula from birth were asked if they were given a choice of the brand of infant formula that they wished to use. Across the United Kingdom, 92% of mothers who gave manufactured baby milks from birth said that they were given a choice of formula, and there was little variation by country in this rate.

Table 6.9

After leaving hospital, mothers were asked if they had changed the brand and type of formula milk that they were using. In 1995, 35% of mothers in Great Britain who were using infant formula at around six to ten weeks had changed the type of formula they were using. This continues the downward trend from 41% in 1990 and 44% in 1985.

As in previous years, the most common reason for changing the formula used was because the mother thought the baby was still hungry or not satisfied (76%). Mothers also changed milk because their baby was being sick (14%), was constipated (7%), or because of a suspected allergy (3%). Four per cent of mothers answered that they wanted to use a brand or type of formula other than the one given in hospital.

Table 6.10

Mothers in Scotland and Northern Ireland were more likely to change the type of formula because they perceived their baby was still hungry (84% and 88% of reasons given compared to 75% in England and Wales). This may correspond with the greater proportion of mothers using casein dominant formulas in those countries

Table 6.11

Table 6.9 Whether mothers were given a choice of infant formula in hospital by country

Mothers who gave infant formula from birth

	England and Wales	Scotland	Northern Ireland	United Kingdom
	%	%	%	%
Mother given a choice	92	89	93	92
Mother not given a choice	8	11	7	8
Base	*1,492*	*834*	*817*	*1,770*

Table 6.10 Reasons given by mothers for changing type of infant formula (1985, 1990 and 1995 Great Britain)

Mothers who changed type of infant formula

Reasons for changing infant formula	1985	1990	1995
		Percentage giving reason	
Still hungry/not satisfied	69	79	76
Kept being sick	18	15	14
Constipation	10	10	7
Allergy	3	3	3
Preferred a different brand from the one given in hospital *	-	-	4
Other reason	10	7	9
Base	*2,427*	*1,956*	*1,354*

Percentages do not add up to 100 as some mothers gave more than one reason for a particular change.
* Code introduced in 1995

Table 6.11 Reasons given for changing type of infant formula by country

Mothers who changed type of infant formula

Reasons for changing infant formula	England and Wales	Scotland	Northern Ireland	United Kingdom
		Percentage giving reason		
Still hungry/not satisfied	75	84	88	76
Kept being sick	14	12	9	14
Constipation	7	8	6	7
Allergy	4	2	3	3
Preferred a different brand from the one given in hospital*	4	3	2	3
Other reason	10	4	4	9
Base	*1,203*	*673*	*538*	*1,414*

Percentages do not add up to 100 as some mothers gave more than one reason for a particular change.
* Code introduced in 1995

6.4 The use of cow's milk

As seen in Table 6.4, less than 0.5% of mothers were giving their baby cow's milk as their main non-human milk drink at stage one of the survey. This proportion showed little change by stage two (1%) and had increased to 16% by stage three, when babies were about nine months old. On the third stage questionnaire, mothers were asked if they were giving cow's milk to their baby as a secondary drink, and whether they were using it to mix solid food. If cow's milk was being given as a drink, mothers were also asked whether they usually used whole milk, semi-skimmed or skimmed milk.

In 1995, 61% of mothers were giving their baby cow's milk in some form by the time the baby was about nine months old. This continues the decline in the use of cow's milk seen between 1985 (88%) and 1990 (76%).

There was a particularly marked decrease between 1990 and 1995 in the proportion of mothers using cow's milk as the main non-human milk (from 40% to 15%). Part of this fall may be attributable to the younger average age of babies at the third stage of the 1995 survey compared with previous surveys although, as shown in Table 6.13, the usage has declined at all ages up to nine months. The proportion of mothers who used cow's milk to mix their baby's food at stage three also decreased between 1990 and 1995 (from 68% to 52%). In contrast, a higher proportion of mothers were giving cow's milk as a secondary drink (30% in 1995 compared with 17% in 1990), so that the use of cow's milk in any form had not decreased as steeply as might be expected from the fall in its use as the main milk drink.

As mentioned in Section 6.2, the recent COMA report on the weaning diet[1] recommends that skimmed and semi-skimmed milks are not suitable for infants of the age covered by this survey. In 1995, almost all mothers who were giving their babies cow's milk as their main drink were giving whole milk and the use of semi-skimmed and skimmed milks had decreased (from 7% in 1985 to 3% in 1990 and 1% in 1995). However, more babies (4%) were being given semi-skimmed or skimmed cow's milk as a secondary drink so that, overall, there was little change between 1990 and 1995 in the proportion of all babies who were being given fat-reduced cow's milk (5% in 1995 compared with 6% in 1990).

Table 6.12

Table 6.12 Cow's milk given at stage 3 (1985, 1990 and 1995 Great Britain)

Way in which cow's milk was given	1985	1990	1995
	Percentage of babies given cow's milk		
As main milk	64	40	15
Whole	57	37	13
Semi-skimmed	5	3	1
Skimmed	2	0	0
As a secondary drink	15	17	30
Whole	11	14	25
Semi-skimmed	3	3	4
Skimmed	1	0	0
To mix food	78	68	52
All using cow's milk	88	76	61
Base	*5,223*	*5,413*	*5,017*

Percentages do not add up to 100 as some mothers gave cow's milk in more than one way

The proportion of mothers who gave their baby cow's milk as their main milk was lowest in England and Wales (14%) and highest in Northern Ireland (23%). A similar pattern was also seen for the use of cow's milk as a secondary drink or to mix food and, taking all uses together, mothers in England and Wales were least likely to be giving cow's milk in any form (60% compared with at least 66% elsewhere).

Table 6.13

Table 6.13 Cow's milk given at stage 3 by country

Way in which cow's milk was given	England and Wales	Scotland	Northern Ireland	United Kingdom
	Percentage of babies given cow's milk			
As main milk	14	20	23	15
Whole	13	18	21	14
Semi-skimmed	1	2	2	1
Skimmed	0	0	0	0
As a secondary drink	30	31	33	30
Whole	25	25	28	25
Semi-skimmed	4	6	5	4
Skimmed	0	0	0	0
To mix food	52	55	57	53
All using cow's milk	60	66	67	61
Base	*4,598*	*1,863*	*1,476*	*5,181*

Percentages do not add up to 100 as some mothers gave cow's milk in more than one way

At stage three of the survey, mothers were asked at what age they had first given cow's milk, either as a drink or to mix solid food. Thus we can examine the age at which cow's milk was first introduced into the child's diet. As shown in Table 6.14, mothers had rarely introduced cow's milk before their babies were five months old. Overall, 5% of mothers had introduced cow's milk by the age of five months and they were mainly using it to mix solid foods. About 1% of mothers were using it as the main milk drink and 1% of mothers were giving it as a secondary drink. Mothers were most likely to have introduced cow's milk at about seven or eight months so, by the time babies were eight months old, 40% of mothers were using cow's milk to mix food and 19% were giving it as a secondary drink.

At all ages, mothers were less likely than in 1990 to be using cow's milk as a main drink or to mix food. For example, at six months old, 2% of babies were being given cow's milk as their main milk drink in 1995 compared with 11% in 1990, and 14% of mothers were using cow's milk to mix food compared with 26% in 1990. Although the use of cow's milk as a secondary drink has increased between 1990 and 1995, the age of introduction has not changed substantially. In both years, about 4% of mothers had introduced cow's milk as a secondary drink before six months of age and usage then increased fairly steadily up to nine months of age.

Table 6.14

6.5 Help with the cost of milk

At the time of the survey, families receiving Income Support or Job Seekers income related benefits were entitled to tokens, available from early pregnancy to when the child is five years old, which may be exchanged for free cow's milk. During the baby's first year, the tokens may alternatively be exchanged

Table 6.14 Age by which mothers had introduced cow's milk for different uses (1990 and 1995 Great Britain)

Introduced by:	To mix food		As main drink		As secondary drink		All uses	
	1990	1995	1990	1995	1990	1995	1990	1995
	Proportion of mothers who had introduced cow's milk by given age							
6 weeks	0	0	1	0	0	0	1	0
3 months	1	1	1	0	0	0	3	1
4 months	5	2	2	0	0	0	7	3
5 months	9	5	3	1	1	1	11	5
6 months	26	14	11	2	3	4	30	17
7 months	39	26	19	5	6	10	44	30
8 months	54	40	29	9	10	19	61	46
9 months	63	48	36	13	13	27	71	57
Base	*5,413*	*5,017*	*5,413*	*5,017*	*5,413*	*5,017*	*5,413*	*5,017*

for free infant formula. Breastfeeding mothers may take the entitlement in the form of cow's milk to drink themselves. Table 6.15 shows the proportion of mothers who said that they were receiving tokens at the second and third stages of the survey. About one quarter of mothers were receiving tokens at each stage and the proportions were slightly higher than in 1990. At stage two, when babies were about four months old, 27% of mothers were receiving milk tokens in 1995 compared with 23% in 1990. As the survey did not include a question about receipt of benefits, it is not possible to investigate the take up of milk tokens among eligible families.

Table 6.15

Looking at the United Kingdom as a whole, about three quarters (73%) of mothers who received tokens exchanged them at a child health clinic. They were also commonly exchanged at shops other than supermarkets (16%) or with the milkman (11%). The pattern differed in Northern Ireland with a much smaller percentage (46%) being exchanged at a clinic and more (42%) at small shops.

Table 6.16

Mothers who were exclusively breastfeeding, and presumably exchanging tokens for cow's milk, tended to exchange them with the milkman (47%) or at the supermarket (44%). Over three quarters (78%) of mothers who were exclusively giving non-human milk exchanged tokens for infant formula at the child health clinic and a further 17% at small shops. (Only 2% of mothers were giving cow's milk at stage 2).

Table 6.17

6.6 Problems with giving manufactured baby milk

Mothers who did not breastfeed are less likely to report problems feeding their baby than those who did breastfeed. However, there are still a variety of difficulties that a mother may have, particularly if it is her first child.

As the majority of mothers will use infant formula at some stage it is important to teach new mothers how to make up a bottle of infant formula in order to reduce the chance of feeding problems. In 1995, 70% of mothers of first babies in Great Britain attended antenatal classes. Most mothers who attended classes were given a talk on feeding their baby, although less than half were instructed on how to make up a bottle of formula milk. Thus about one quarter (27%) of mothers were shown how to make up a bottle at classes. Mothers who intended to give infant formula were more likely to be shown how to make up a bottle. However, as mothers who intended to breastfeed were much more likely to attend antenatal classes than those who did not intend to

Table 6.15 Whether mothers received milk tokens at stages 2 and 3 (1985, 1990 and 1995 Great Britain)

Whether mother received milk tokens	4-5 months			8-9 months		
	1985	1990	1995	1985	1990	1995
	%	%	%	%	%	%
Received tokens	30	23	27	28	22	24
Did not receive tokens	70	77	73	72	78	76
Base	5,223	5,413	5,017	5,223	5,413	5,017

Table 6.16 Where mothers usually exchanged milk tokens at stage 2 by country
Mothers who received tokens at stage 2

Where mother usually exchanged milk tokens	England and Wales	Scotland	Northern Ireland	United Kingdom
	Percentage exchanging tokens			
Child health clinic	74	82	46	73
With the milkman	12	5	15	11
At a supermarket	7	4	2	7
At another type of shop	16	11	42	16
Somewhere else/ not stated	3	3	2	3
Base	1,222	506	424	1,382

Percentages do not add up to 100 as some mothers exchanged at more than one place.

Table 6.17 Where mothers usually exchanged milk tokens by feeding method
Mothers who received tokens at stage 2

Where mother usually exchanged milk tokens	Breastfed	Breast and non-human milk	Not breastfed	Total
	Percentage exchanging tokens			
Child health clinic	7	62	78	73
With the milkman	47	19	8	11
At a supermarket	44	18	4	7
At another type of shop	9	14	17	16
Somewhere else/ not stated	0	2	3	3
Base	79	68	1,236	1,382

Percentages do not add up to 100 as some mothers exchanged at more than one place.

breastfeed, a higher proportion of all first time mothers who intended to breastfeed were shown how to make up a bottle (30% compared with 18%).

Table 6.18

Problems giving infant formula from a bottle in hospital

There was little change between 1990 and 1995 in the proportion of mothers experiencing problems giving infant formula in a bottle to their baby while in hospital. Seventeen percent of mothers in the United Kingdom who bottle fed from birth reported feeding problems and, as in previous years, mothers of first babies were more likely to have problems than women having their second or later child (21% compared with 15%). The most common problem was that the baby was ill or in special care, mentioned by 36% of mothers who had feeding problems in hospital. In addition, one quarter of mothers reported that the baby would not suck or rejected the bottle (25%) or that the baby was vomiting

(25%). More than one tenth (13%) of mothers who had feeding problems also mentioned that the baby fell asleep during feeds or was slow feeding.

Table 6.19

Mothers who had problems feeding their baby were asked whether they were able to get help in the hospital. Eighty nine percent said that they were able to get help, and the majority received help from a midwife (56%) or nurse (45%). Around one fifth of the mothers received help or advice from a doctor.

Table 6.20

Problems giving infant formula from a bottle at home

Forty-two per cent of mothers were exclusively giving infant formula in a bottle when they left hospital and a further 8% had introduced infant formula as well as breastfeeding. Of these mothers who were giving infant formula, 17% reported problems feeding their baby after they had returned home. By this stage the problems described were different to those reported while the mother was still in hospital: the baby being ill or problems because the baby rejected the bottle were much less common at this stage. Instead, the most common problem reported in the first weeks at home was that babies appeared to be hungry or were not gaining weight (35%). The other main problems were that the baby suffered from vomiting (22%) or wind (20%). One fifth (22%) of these mothers who had problems mentioned difficulties related to breastfeeding and these were more common among mothers of first than later babies.

Table 6.21

As in previous years, the vast majority of mothers who had problems with giving infant formula at home received professional help or other advice. All mothers were most likely to receive advice from a health visitor or midwife. However, mothers of first babies were more likely to talk to friends and relatives (27% compared with 12%).

Table 6.22

Table 6.18 Sources of information on infant feeding for mothers of first babies by intended feeding method

	Intended feeding method		
	Infant formula	Breast or breast and infant formula	All first babies*
	Percentage who:		
Attended antenatal classes	44	79	70
Attended a talk on feeding at a class	35	68	59
Taught how to make up a bottle at a class	18	30	27
Base	*514*	*1,639*	*2,335*

* Includes some mothers who were undecided

Table 6.19 Feeding problems reported by mothers who used infant formula from birth by birth order

Mothers who used infant formula from birth who had problems feeding their baby

Problem	First births	Later births	All babies
	Percentage experiencing problem		
Baby seemed hungry/not gaining weight	3	4	4
Baby falling asleep/slow feeding	11	15	13
Baby rejected bottle/wouldn't suck	28	23	25
Baby didn't like formula	3	4	4
Baby ill	31	41	36
Baby vomiting	26	24	25
Baby had wind	6	4	5
Problems relating to breastfeeding	8	4	6
Problem not specified	3	3	3
Other	9	13	11
Base	*135*	*159*	*295*

Percentages do not add up to 100 as some mothers experienced more than one type of problem

Notes

1 Department of Health *Weaning and the Weaning Diet. Report of the working Group on the Weaning Diet of the Committee on Medical Aspects of Food Policy.* Report on Health and Social Subjects No 45. HMSO (London: 1994)

Table 6.20 Source of advice for mothers experiencing problems with feeding infant formula in hospital by birth order

Mothers who used infant formula from birth who had problems feeding their baby

Source of advice	First births	Later births	All babies
	Percentage naming the source		
Midwife	60	53	56
Nurse	44	47	45
Doctor	13	25	19
Other	2	4	2
Did not receive help	10	12	11
Base	*135*	*159*	*295*

Percentages do not add up to 100 as some mothers received advice from more than one source

Table 6.21 Feeding problems after leaving hospital reported by mothers giving infant formula after leaving hospital by birth order

Mothers using infant formula when they left hospital who had problems feeding their baby

Problem	First births	Later births	All babies
	Percentage experiencing problem		
Baby seemed hungry/ not gaining weight	37	33	35
Baby falling asleep/ slow feeding	10	11	11
Baby rejected bottle/ wouldn't suck	6	9	7
Baby didn't like formula	4	6	5
Baby ill	3	3	3
Baby vomiting	19	25	22
Baby had wind	21	19	20
Baby was constipated	6	3	4
Problems relating to breastfeeding*	28	17	22
Problem not specified	2	4	4
Other	6	6	6
Base	*194*	*220*	*413*

Percentages do not add up to 100 as some mothers experienced more than one type of problem

* Some mothers were combining breastfeeding and giving infant formula

Table 6.22 Source of advice for mothers experiencing problems with giving infant formula at home by birth order

Mothers using infant formula when they left hospital who had problems feeding their baby

Source of advice	First births	Later births	All babies
	Percentage naming the source		
Doctor/GP	25	28	26
Health Visitor	56	61	59
Midwife	46	50	48
Nurse	4	5	5
Friend or relative	27	12	19
Books, leaflets, magazines	8	3	5
Other	6	2	4
Did not receive help	8	8	8
Base	*194*	*220*	*413*

Percentages do not add up to 100 as some mothers received advice from more than one source

7 Feeding after the early weeks

Summary

- Seventeen per cent of mothers had had problems feeding their baby at stage two and 13% at stage three. Breastfeeding mothers were more likely to have experienced problems than bottle feeders.

- The majority (81%) of mothers who reported having had feeding problems at stage two had been given help or advice, generally from a health visitor (76%), the family doctor (38%) or friends and relatives (30%).

- The reasons for having given up breastfeeding varied with the duration of breastfeeding. In the early weeks, insufficient milk or that the baby seemed hungry were the most frequently mentioned reasons. In later months mothers were more likely to mention returning to work or that they had breastfed for as long as intended.

- When the babies were four to five months old, 28% of mothers were in paid work, and a further 16% were on maternity leave. By stage three, 43% of mothers were in paid work, and only 2% were on maternity leave.

- Nearly all mothers (99%) had seen a health visitor by the time they completed the questionnaire when their baby was six to ten weeks old and two thirds of mothers (66%) said that their baby had had a development check-up.

- At stage two the majority of mothers (86%) said they took their baby to the child health clinic, and just over a third (36%) took their baby to their family doctor for advice or regular check-ups.

- Over one quarter (28%) of mothers had had problems finding somewhere to feed their babies in public places and a further fifth (22%) had never tried feeding in public places.

7.1 Introduction

The previous chapters have looked at some of the characteristics of breast and bottle feeding mothers, at feeding problems they experienced in the early weeks and at sources of help and advice in dealing with these problems. This chapter is concerned with the circumstances of mothers beyond the initial weeks, looking at feeding problems experienced at the second and third stages of the survey, reasons for giving up breastfeeding and contact with health professionals. Information is also presented on mothers' attitudes to feeding in public places.

7.2 Problems with feeding

Problems experienced with breast and infant formula feeding in the first few weeks have been reported in Sections 5.5 and 6.6 respectively. At later stages of the survey mothers were again asked about any problems with feeding and about who had given them help or advice.

At the second stage of the survey, 17% of mothers said that they had had problems feeding their baby since completing the previous questionnaire. This proportion was unchanged since 1990. Mothers who were breastfeeding when their baby was four or five months old were more likely to have experienced problems: 19% compared with 16% of mothers who were not breastfeeding.

At stage three, 13% of mothers reported a feeding problem since completing the previous

questionnaire, and again this proportion was unchanged since 1990. As at earlier stages, mothers who were breastfeeding at stage three were more likely to have experienced a feeding problem than other mothers (17% and 12% respectively).

Table 7.1

At stage two, first time mothers were as likely as other mothers to report feeding problems, but by stage three, first time mothers were more likely to experience feeding problems (14% compared with 11% of other mothers).

Table 7.2

At both stages, mothers who had reported feeding problems were asked to describe them, and their responses are presented in Table 7.3. Overall, when babies were up to four or five months old, the most frequently reported problems were that the baby disliked the milk and that he or she appeared to be hungry. Some mothers mentioned problems with feeding solid food: 15% said that their baby would not take solids, and 4% said they would only take certain solids.

Breastfeeding mothers experienced slightly different problems from bottle feeders. Over two fifths (44%) of breastfeeding mothers who reported problems said that their baby appeared to dislike the milk, although as they were not asked to specify the kind of milk disliked it is not known whether their baby disliked breast milk or another kind of milk. In comparison, 13% of mothers only giving infant formula said that their baby appeared to dislike the

Table 7.1 Whether mothers experienced feeding problems when babies were about four months old (stage 2), and nine months old (stage 3) (1990 and 1995 Great Britain)

Whether mother had feeding problem	4-5 months						8-9 months					
	Breastfed		Not breastfed		All babies		Breastfed		Not breastfed		All babies	
	1990	1995	1990	1995	1990	1995	1990	1995	1990	1995	1990	1995
	%	%	%	%	%	%	%	%	%	%	%	%
Had feeding problem	21	19	16	16	17	17	15	17	11	12	12	13
No problem	79	81	84	84	83	83	85	83	89	88	88	87
Base	*1,182*	*1,233*	*4,200*	*3,774*	*5,413*	*5,017*	*530*	*648*	*4,867*	*4,351*	*5,413*	*5,017*

Table 7.2 Whether mothers experienced feeding problems when babies were about four months old (stage 2), and nine months old (stage 3) by birth order (1995 Great Britain)

Whether mother had feeding problem	4-5 months			8-9 months		
	First births	Later births	All babies	First births	Later births	All babies
	%	%	%	%	%	%
Had feeding problem	17	17	17	14	11	13
No problem	83	83	83	86	89	87
Base	*2,277*	*2,730*	*5,017*	*2,277*	*2,730*	*5,017*

milk. The most common problem reported by mothers who were not breastfeeding at stage two was that the baby appeared to be hungry (20%). Breastfeeders were less likely than non-breastfeeders to say that their baby had been ill (3% compared with 13%) or suffered from vomiting (4% and 15%).

By the time the babies were eight to nine months old, problems with feeding solids were more common. The most frequently mentioned problem was that the baby would not take solids (mentioned by 24% of mothers who had a problem), followed by the baby only taking certain solids (22%). One fifth of mothers (22%) said that their baby had been ill. As at stage two, breastfeeding mothers were more likely to say that their baby did not like the milk (15% compared with 8% of mothers who were not breastfeeding) and they were less likely to say that their baby would only take certain solids (13% compared with 24%).

Table 7.3

Help or advice with feeding problems

Mothers who reported having had feeding problems were asked if anyone had given them help or advice. The majority of mothers said that they had received help or advice — 81% at stage two and 71% at stage three.

The sources of help and advice were similar at both stages. At stage two, three quarters (76%) of mothers received advice from a health visitor, 38% spoke to their family doctor and 30% received advice from

friends and relatives. Scottish mothers were the most likely to receive help from their health visitor. Northern Irish mothers were more likely than others to consult their family doctor. Contact with health professionals is discussed further in Section 7.5.

Table 7.4

Table 7.5 compares the sources of advice for breastfeeding and for bottle feeding mothers. At stage two, breastfeeding mothers were more likely than bottle feeders to get advice from friends and relatives, or to consult books, leaflets and magazines, and less likely to visit their family doctor. The differences between breast and bottle feeders were not significant at stage three. At both stages first time mothers were more likely than mothers of later births to take advice from friends and relatives or to consult books, leaflets and magazines and they were less likely to visit their family doctor.

Tables 7.5 and 7.6, Figure 7.1

Mothers who were breastfeeding when their baby was six to ten weeks old, were specifically asked at the four month stage if anyone had given them help or advice on breastfeeding. One fifth of mothers (19%) said that they had been given help or advice. As already seen for help with feeding problems (Table 7.5), mothers were most likely to have received advice on breastfeeding from a health visitor (75%). More than a quarter (27%) said that they had received help from friends or relatives.

Table 7.7

Table 7.3	Feeding problems experienced by mothers when babies were about four months old (stage 2), and nine months old (stage 3) by whether baby was breastfed (1990 and 1995 Great Britain)

Mothers who reported feeding problems

Feeding problem	4-5 months						8-9 months					
	Breastfed		Not breastfed		All babies		Breastfed		Not breastfed		All babies	
	1990	1995	1990	1995	1990	1995	1990	1995	1990	1995	1990	1995
						Percentage having problem						
Baby hungry	20	15	15	20	16	19	5	4	2	4	3	4
Baby ill	15	3	24	13	21	10	25	19	34	23	33	22
Baby did not like milk	25	44	11	13	15	22	2	15	4	8	4	9
Baby vomiting	5	4	13	15	11	12	0	8	7	13	6	12
Baby got too much/too little wind	4	5	5	8	5	7	2	1	1	0	1	1
Baby constipated	3	3	4	5	3	4	2	3	1	1	1	2
Sore/cracked nipples	4	11	1	2	1	5	5	4	-	0	1	1
Baby could not latch on	1	2	0	2	1	2	-	0	0	0	0	0
Baby would not take solids	9	13	12	16	11	15	13	28	11	23	11	24
Baby would only take certain solids	3	3	5	4	5	4	22	13	21	24	21	22
Baby went off food for a while	6	2	8	7	8	6	4	1	6	4	6	4
Other	23	14	15	20	17	19	30	17	21	17	22	17
Base	*242*	*235*	*660*	*603*	*903*	*838*	*81*	*105*	*545*	*498*	*626*	*605*

Percentages do not add up to 100 as some mothers experienced more than one type of feeding problem..

Table 7.4   **Source of advice on feeding problems when babies were about four months old (stage 2) and nine months old (stage 3) by country**
Mothers who sought advice on their feeding problems

Source of advice	4-5 months				8-9 months			
	England and Wales	Scotland	Northern Ireland	United Kingdom	England and Wales	Scotland	Northern Ireland	United Kingdom
	Percentage naming the source							
Health visitors	75	80	67	76	74	80	73	74
Friends and relatives	30	35	35	30	27	28	19	27
Family doctor	38	39	58	38	35	36	46	35
Midwife or nurse	9	7	13	9	..	..	..	..
Voluntary support group	4	4	1	4	2	2	0	2
Books/leaflets/magazines	12	14	11	12	12	6	7	12
TV/Radio	..	..	..	..	1	0	0	1
Other	2	3	2	2	7	3	5	6
Base	*639*	*220*	*155*	*705*	*429*	*126*	*93*	*467*

Percentages do not add up to 100 as some mothers received advice from more than one source.

Table 7.5   **Source of advice on feeding problems when babies were about four months old (stage 2), and nine months old (stage 3) by whether baby was breastfed**
Mothers who sought advice on their feeding problems

Source of advice	4-5 months			8-9 months		
	Breastfed	Not breastfed	All babies	Breastfed	Not breastfed	All babies
	Percentage naming the source					
Health visitors	79	74	76	75	74	74
Friends and relatives	40	26	30	30	26	27
Family doctor	22	44	38	29	36	35
Midwife or nurse	6	10	9	..	..	..
Voluntary support group	9	1	4	6	0	2
Books/leaflets/magazines	23	9	12	13	11	12
TV/Radio	..	..	..	0	1	1
Other	3	2	2	4	7	6
Base	*193*	*512*	*705*	*77*	*389*	*467*

Percentages do not add up to 100 as some mothers received advice from more than one source.

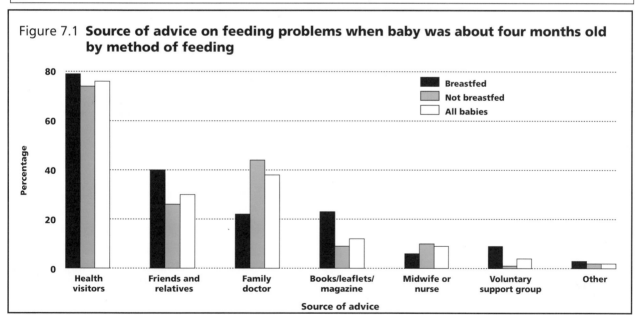

Figure 7.1 **Source of advice on feeding problems when baby was about four months old by method of feeding**

The most helpful source of advice

At the third stage of the survey, when babies were eight or nine months old, mothers were asked who or what had been the most helpful source of general advice on feeding since their baby was born. The source mentioned most frequently was a health visitor or nurse (61% of all mothers) followed by friends and relatives (50%) and books, leaflets and magazines (27%). Mothers in Northern Ireland were less likely to say the most helpful advice was from health visitors, perhaps reflecting the finding reported earlier in this chapter that Northern Irish mothers were less likely to receive advice from health visitors.

Table 7.8

Table 7.6 Source of advice on feeding problems when babies were about four months old (stage 2), and nine months old (stage 3) by birth order

Mothers who sought advice on their feeding problems

Source of advice	4-5 months			8-9 months		
	First births	Later births	All babies	First births	Later births	All babies
	Percentage naming the source					
Health visitors	77	74	76	75	74	74
Friends and relatives	41	21	30	37	16	27
Family doctor	33	43	38	26	45	35
Midwife or nurse	7	10	9	..	..	..
Voluntary support group	5	3	4	1	2	2
Books/leaflets/magazines	17	9	12	16	7	12
TV/Radio	..	..	..	2	0	1
Other	2	2	2	6	6	6
Base	*330*	*376*	*705*	*240*	*227*	*467*

Percentages do not add up to 100 as some mothers received advice from more than one source.

Table 7.7 Source of advice on breast feeding when babies were about four months old (stage 2) by country

Mothers who sought advice on their feeding problems

Source of advice	England and Wales	Scotland	Northern Ireland	United Kingdom
	Percentage naming the source			
Health visitors	75	82	71	75
Friends and relatives	26	27	37	27
Family doctor	13	11	12	12
Nurse	8	6	13	8
Voluntary support group	14	14	9	14
Books/leaflets/magazines	15	11	14	14
Other	2	3	0	2
Base	*344*	*117*	*59*	*377*

Percentages do not add up to 100 as some mothers received advice from more than one source.

Table 7.8 Most helpful source of advice on feeding since the birth of the baby by country

Source of advice	England and Wales	Scotland	Northern Ireland	United Kingdom
	Percentage naming the source			
Health visitor or nurse	62	60	57	61
Friends and relatives	50	52	55	50
Family doctor	9	9	9	9
Midwife	9	7	8	9
Voluntary support group	2	1	0	2
Books/leaflets/magazines	27	26	22	27
TV/Radio	1	1	1	1
Other	2	1	2	2
Base	*4,300*	*1,747*	*1,399*	*4,848*

Percentages do not add up to 100 as some mothers received advice from more than one source.

There were some differences between what first time mothers and mothers of later births reported as being the most helpful source of advice. First time mothers were more likely to mention friends and relatives (62% compared with 39% of mothers of later births) and to mention books, leaflets and magazines (32% compared with 23%).

Table 7.9

Table 7.9 Most helpful source of advice on feeding since the birth of the baby by birth order

Source of advice	First births	Later births	All babies
	Percentage naming the source		
Health visitor or nurse	61	62	61
Friends and relatives	62	39	50
Family doctor	8	10	9
Midwife	9	9	9
Voluntary support group	2	1	2
Books/leaflets/magazines	32	23	27
TV/Radio	1	1	1
Other	2	3	2
Base	*2,296*	*2,552*	*4,848*

Percentages do not add up to 100 as some mothers received advice from more than one source.

7.3 Reasons for stopping breastfeeding

The discussion of duration of breastfeeding in Chapter 2 showed that about one sixth (15%) of women who breastfed initially had given up within one week and 20% had given up within two weeks. After the initial two weeks, which were considered in detail in Chapter 5, the rate of giving up breastfeeding slowed: two thirds (65%) of mothers who had started breastfeeding were doing so when their babies were six weeks old and one third (32%) continued for more than six months. This section looks at the reasons that women gave for having given up breastfeeding and whether mothers would have liked to have breastfed for longer.

As shown in Table 7.10, the reasons for having given up varied with the duration of breastfeeding. During the first two weeks after birth, the three most frequently mentioned reasons, reported by between one fifth and two fifths of mothers who gave up, were insufficient milk or that the baby seemed hungry, that the mother had painful or engorged breasts, and that

Table 7.10 Reasons given by mothers for stopping breastfeeding by duration of breastfeeding
Breastfeeding mothers who stopped during the survey period

Reasons for stopping breastfeeding	Baby's age when breastfeeding ceased:							
	Less than 1 week	1 week, less than 2 weeks	2 weeks, less than 6 weeks	6 weeks, less than 3 months	3 months, less than 4 months	4 months, less than 6 months	6 months, less than 8 months	8 months or more
	Percentage giving reason							
Insufficient milk/baby seemed hungry	32	44	64	59	44	34	19	13
Baby would not suck/rejected breast	29	20	14	10	9	14	17	22
Painful breasts or nipples	28	36	18	8	3	1	1	3
Breastfeeding took too long/was tiring	11	16	20	18	14	13	4	12
Mother was ill	11	16	10	8	10	5	5	3
Did not like breastfeeding	10	5	4	3	1	0	2	2
Baby was ill	7	4	7	5	3	2	3	-
Domestic reasons	6	10	8	6	7	6	1	2
Difficult to judge how much baby had drunk	4	2	3	2	1	1	0	-
Baby could not be fed by others	3	1	2	4	8	4	7	6
Mother had inverted nipples	2	1	1	0	0	-	-	-
Embarrassment	1	2	2	3	0	1	-	1
Returning to work	1	1	3	19	33	38	25	18
Had breastfed as long as intended	1	-	1	2	6	14	28	28
Not convenient *				6	4	8	8	5
Baby was teething/ biting *						5	15	28
Other reasons	10	12	7	5	7	6	7	11
Base	480	164	522	344	243	203	266	119

* Code introduced at later waves of the survey
Percentages do not add up to 100 as some mothers mentioned more than one reason.

the baby would not suck or latch on to the breast.

Insufficient milk or the baby seeming to be hungry continued to be the main reason given by mothers who gave up at between two weeks and four months, mentioned by between 44% and 64% of women. The next most important reason varied over this period. One fifth (20%) of mothers who stopped breastfeeding at between two and six weeks said that breastfeeding took too long or was tiring; one third (33%) of those giving up at three to four months mentioned that they were returning to work. Mothers giving up at between two weeks and four months were less likely than those giving up in the first two weeks to mention painful breasts, that the baby would not suck/rejected the breast, or that they did not like breastfeeding.

The effect of returning to work continued to be an important influence on mother's feeding decisions above the age of four months. Almost two fifths (38%) of mothers who gave up at four to six months and one quarter (25%) of those giving up at six to eight months mentioned their return to work. At this stage, insufficient milk or that the baby seemed to be hungry continued to decline in importance whereas mothers were increasingly likely to say that they had breastfed for as long as they intended (28% of those who gave up at between six and eight months). Mothers who gave up at six months or more were also more likely to mention that the baby was biting or teething (28% of those giving up at eight months or more) and, as in the early weeks, that the baby would not suck or rejected the breast (22%).

Table 7.10

Whether mothers would have liked to breastfeed for longer

The reasons mothers gave for having stopped breastfeeding suggest that very few mothers who breastfed for less than three months had given up because they planned to stop at this stage. Above three months, mothers were increasingly likely to say that they had breastfed for as long as intended: the proportion rose from 6% of women who gave up at between three and four months to 28% of those giving up at six months or more.

Mothers who had given up breastfeeding were also specifically asked whether they would have liked to have continued for longer. The vast majority (89% or more) of mothers who gave up within six weeks of the birth would have liked to have breastfed for longer. This proportion fell to about three quarters (74%) of those giving up at six weeks to three months and one half (48%) of those giving up at four to six months. These results confirm the view from the previous table

Table 7.11 Whether mothers would have liked to have breastfed longer by duration of breastfeeding
Breastfeeding mothers who stopped during the survey period

Baby's age when breastfeeding ceased	Percentage of mothers who would have liked to breastfeed longer	Base
Breastfed for:		
less than 1 week	90	477
1 week, less than 2 weeks	91	163
2 weeks, less than 6 weeks	89	528
6 weeks, less than 3 months	74	348
3 months, less than 4 months	59	247
4 months, less than 6 months	48	208
6 months, less than 8 months	36	267
8 months or more	32	117

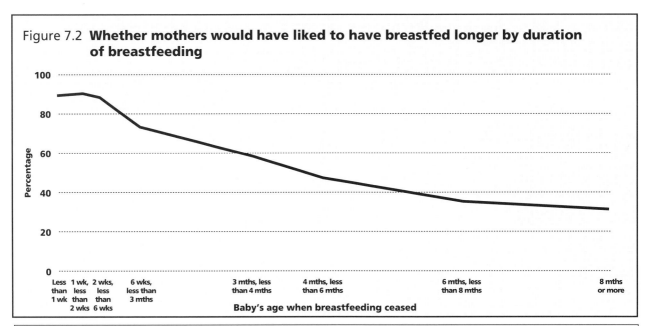

Figure 7.2 **Whether mothers would have liked to have breastfed longer by duration of breastfeeding**

Table 7.12 **Whether mothers would breastfeed another baby by duration of breastfeeding**
All breastfeeding mothers

	Baby's age when breastfeeding ceased				All mothers who breastfed
	Less than 1 week	1 week, less than 2 weeks	2 weeks, less than 6 weeks	6 weeks or more	
	%	%	%	%	%
If had another baby					
- would breastfeed again	56	74	86	95	86
- would not breastfeed	30	19	10	1	8
- no answer given	15	8	4	4	6
Base	*496*	*168*	*534*	*1,961*	*3,410*

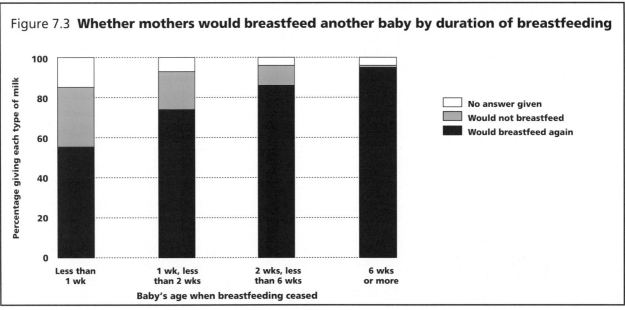

Figure 7.3 **Whether mothers would breastfeed another baby by duration of breastfeeding**

that women who start to breastfeed are generally committed to this method of feeding but are then deterred by problems or other circumstances.

Table 7.11, Figure 7.2

Whether mothers would breastfeed another baby
The mother's experience in breastfeeding her current baby was associated with her feeding intentions for future babies. Just over one half (56%) of mothers who had given up breastfeeding within the first week said that they would breastfeed another baby and almost one third (30%) said that they would not breastfeed. The comparable figures for mothers who had continued breastfeeding for six weeks were 95% who would breastfeed again and just 1% who would not. So, mothers who had initially

experienced difficulties with breastfeeding were, at this early stage, less inclined to repeat this experience if they had another child.

Table 7.12, Figure 7.3

7.4 Employment status of mothers

As seen in the previous section, returning to work was one of the main reasons given by mothers who gave up breastfeeding at between three and eight months (mentioned by between 25% and 38% of mothers who stopped at these ages). Each stage of the Infant Feeding Survey included a question about the mother's current employment status and the results are summarised here.

At the first stage of the survey in 1995, when babies were about six to ten weeks old, 8% of mothers were in paid work, one third (34%) were on paid

maternity leave and 5% were on unpaid maternity leave. More than half of mothers (54%) were neither working nor on maternity leave. Between 1990 and 1995 the proportion of mothers on paid maternity leave increased from 21% to 34%, matched by a fall in the proportion classified as not working (from 66% to 54%).

Table 7.13, Figure 7.4

Table 7.14 gives details of the employment status of mothers at each stage of the survey by country. By the time of the second stage interview, when babies were four to five months old, most mothers who had been on paid maternity leave had returned to work: 28% of mothers were in paid work at this stage compared with 7% at the first stage interview. Mothers in Northern Ireland were less likely than those elsewhere to be economically inactive. At stage one they were more likely than mothers in England, Wales and Scotland to be on paid maternity leave (42% compared with 33% to 35%) and at later stages they were more likely to be in paid work (40% compared with 28% to 31% at stage two). These differences in employment status may have contributed to the shorter duration of breastfeeding among mothers in Northern Ireland (as shown in Table 2.17).

Table 7.14

When the babies were eight to nine months old, mothers in paid employment who were breastfeeding were asked how they usually fed their baby when they were at work. The majority (59%) said their baby had other milk while they were at work, 5% expressed breast milk for the baby, 8% said they were able to take their baby to work, and the remainder had some other arrangement. Compared with 1990, mothers in 1995 were more likely to give their baby some other milk (39% in 1990).

Table 7.15

7.5 Contact with health professionals

As part of the stage one questionnaire, mothers were asked whether a health visitor had been to see them since their baby was born and, if so, how old the baby was at the first visit. Nearly all mothers (99%) had seen a health visitor by the time they completed the questionnaire when their baby was six to ten weeks old. Two thirds (64%) of mothers were first visited when their baby was between 10 and 14 days old, and

Table 7.13 Mother's working status when the babies were between 6 and 10 weeks old (1980, 1985, 1990 and 1995 Great Britain)

Mother's working status	1980	1985	1990	1995
	%	%	%	%
Working	4	5	8	7
On maternity leave - paid	⎤ 8	6	21	34
unpaid	⎦	6	5	5
Not working	88	83	66	54
Base	*4,224*	*5,223*	*5,413*	*5,017*

Table 7.14 Mother's working status at stages 1, 2 and 3 by country

Mother's working status	England and Wales	Scotland	Northern Ireland	United Kingdom
6-10 weeks				
	%	%	%	%
Working	6	10	8	7
On maternity leave - paid	35	33	42	35
unpaid	5	7	4	5
Not working	54	51	46	53
Base	*4,587*	*1,860*	*1,470*	*5,181*
4-5 months				
	%	%	%	%
Working	28	31	40	28
On maternity leave - paid	4	3	4	4
unpaid	12	12	5	12
Not working	57	54	52	56
Base	*4,587*	*1,860*	*1,470*	*5,181*
8-9 months				
	%	%	%	%
Working	43	45	48	43
On (unpaid) maternity leave†	2	2	1	2
Not working	55	52	50	55
Base	*4,587*	*1,860*	*1,470*	*5,181*

† Includes a small number of mothers on paid maternity leave.

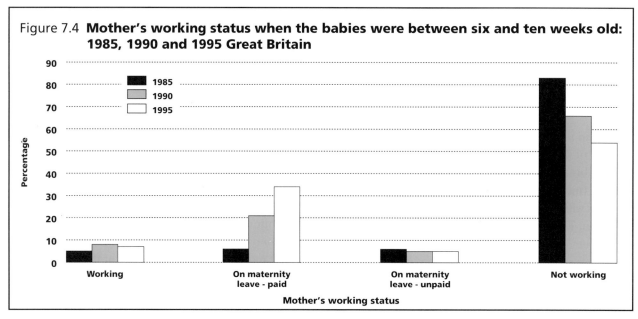

Figure 7.4 **Mother's working status when the babies were between six and ten weeks old: 1985, 1990 and 1995 Great Britain**

Table 7.15 **How baby was usually fed while the mother was working at stage 3 (1990 and 1995 Great Britain)**

Working mothers breastfeeding at stage 3

How baby is usually fed	1990	1995
	Proportion of mothers using method	
Baby has other milk	39	59
Baby has expressed breast milk	4	5
Baby taken to work to breastfeed	6	8
Other arrangement	51	32
Base	*129*	*209*

Percentages do not add up to 100 as some mothers used more than one method of feeding.

babies were, on average, 12.2 days old at the time of the first visit. Compared with the other constituent countries of the United Kingdom, mothers in Scotland tended to have been visited when their baby was younger (10.7 days on average, compared with 12.3 days for babies in England and Wales).

Table 7.16

Two thirds of mothers (66%) said that their baby had had a development check-up by stage one of the survey, when he or she was aged six to ten weeks old, varying from 60% in the South West of England and Wales to 90% in Scotland. Most babies (61%) had the development check-up at the family doctor's and a further 31% at the child health clinic or hospital. Fewer than one tenth (8%) of babies had the check-up at home. Babies in Northern Ireland were most likely to have had their development check-up at home (27% compared with 4% in Scotland and 8% in England and Wales).

Tables 7.17 and 7.18

At stage two of the survey, when babies were four or five months old, mothers were asked if they took their baby to a child health clinic or to their family doctor for advice or regular check-ups. The majority (86%) said they took their baby to the child health clinic, and just over a third (36%) took their baby to their family doctor for advice or regular check-ups.

Table 7.16 **Age of baby when health visitor visited mother and baby by country**

Babies who had been visited

Age of baby	England and Wales	Scotland	Northern Ireland	United Kingdom
	%	%	%	%
Less than 10 days	19	25	21	19
10 days	23	25	22	23
11 days	12	19	9	13
12 or 13 days	16	14	16	16
14 days	12	8	15	12
15 days or older	18	9	17	17
Mean age of baby (days)	12.3	10.7	11.9	12.2
Median age of baby (days)	11.0	10.0	11.0	11.0
Standard deviation	6.1	4.8	5.1	6.0
Base	*4,442*	*1,807*	*1,432*	*5,007*

Table 7.17 **Whether baby had had a development check-up by stage 1 by region and country**

Region and country of residence	Proportion who had had development check-up by stage 1	*Base*
London & South East	65	*1,800*
South West & Wales	60	*680*
Midlands & East Anglia	67	*900*
North	63	*1,184*
England and Wales	64	*4,564*
Scotland	90	*1,851*
Northern Ireland	70	*1,466*
United Kingdom	66	*5,143*

Table 7.18 Where baby had the development check-up by region and country
Babies who had had a development check-up

Where baby had development check-up	London and South East	South West and Wales	Midlands and East Anglia	North	England and Wales	Scotland	Northern Ireland	United Kingdom
	%	%	%	%	%	%	%	%
Child health clinic/hospital	32	29	23	34	30	35	31	31
Family doctor/GP	63	61	66	57	62	61	41	61
At home	6	10	11	8	8	4	27	8
Base	*1,170*	*409*	*598*	*732*	*2,910*	*1,644*	*1,024*	*3,393*

Mothers in Northern Ireland were less likely to go to a child health clinic (71%) and more likely to go to their family doctor (45%) than mothers in England and Wales or Scotland.

Table 7.19

Most mothers took their baby to the child health clinic either about once a fortnight (33%) or about once a month (47%). As well as being less likely to visit a child health clinic, mothers in Northern Ireland also tended to visit less frequently. One quarter (26%) visited less often than once a month compared with 12% of mothers in England and Wales.

Mothers visited their family doctor for advice or regular check-ups less often than visiting a child health clinic. One tenth of mothers (11%) who visited their family doctor, took their baby about once a fortnight or more often, whereas 40% of mothers who went to a child health clinic visited with a similar frequency.

Table 7.20

7.6 Feeding in Public Places

At the second stage of the survey, mothers were asked a number of questions about feeding their baby in public places.

Just over one quarter (28%) of mothers said that they had had problems finding somewhere to feed their babies in public places. One fifth (22%) had never tried feeding in public places. Breastfeeders were more likely than bottle feeders to have had problems: 40% compared with 24%. Breastfeeding

Table 7.19 Whether mother took baby to child health clinic or family doctor for advice or regular check-ups by country (stage 2)

Country	Proportion who took baby to child health clinic	Proportion who took baby to family doctor	Base
England and Wales	87	36	*4,589*
Scotland	87	35	*1,861*
Northern Ireland	71	45	*1,473*
United Kingdom	86	36	*5,181*

Some mothers took their baby to both the child health clinic and the family doctor.

Table 7.20 How often mother took baby to child health clinic or family doctor for advice or regular check-ups by country (stage 2)

Frequency	England and Wales	Scotland	Northern Ireland	United Kingdom
Frequency of attending child health clinic	%	%	%	%
Once a week	7	6	6	7
Once a fortnight	34	25	16	33
Once a month	46	52	52	47
Less than once a month	12	17	26	13
Base: mothers who attended child health clinic	*3,988*	*1,624*	*1,049*	*4,456*
Frequency of attending family doctor	%	%	%	%
Once a week	2	1	1	2
Once a fortnight	9	7	6	9
Once a month	39	39	41	39
Less than once a month	50	52	51	50
Base: mothers who attended family doctor	*1,626*	*637*	*646*	*1,841*

mothers in 1995 were both more likely to have tried to feed in public than in 1990 (89% compared with 83%) and were less likely to have had problems (40% compared with 44%). There were no differences between 1990 and 1995 for bottle feeding mothers.

Table 7.21

Table 7.21 Whether mothers ever had any problems finding somewhere to feed their babies in public places by method of feeding at stage 2 (1990 and 1995 Great Britain)

	Breastfeeders		Bottle feeders		All mothers	
	1990	1995	1990	1995	1990	1995
	%	%	%	%	%	%
Had problems	44	40	25	24	30	28
Did not have problems	39	49	51	50	49	50
Do not feed in public places	17	11	24	26	22	22
Base	*1,764*	*1,228*	*3,649*	*3,737*	*5,413*	*5,017*

Table 7.22 Where mothers prefer to breastfeed when in a public place

Mother who had ever breastfed

	Proportion stating
	%
Prefer a mother and baby room	29
Prefer to breastfeed without going to a special place	10
No preference	11
Never breastfed in public places	50
Base	*3,563*

Mothers were specifically asked if they had ever breastfed in a public place and if so, where they preferred to go. Table 7.22 shows that one half (50%) of mothers who had breastfed their baby had never tried to breastfeed in a public place. Twenty nine percent of mothers preferred to feed in a mother and baby room, and 10% preferred to breastfeed without going to any special place.

Table 7.22

Finally, mothers were asked where they thought it was important to have facilities for feeding babies and three places were specifically prompted in the question — shops/shopping centres, restaurants and public toilets. Present day practice in infant feeding: third report[1] stresses that 'it is important that mothers should feel free to feed their babies when and where this becomes necessary' and 'urges social, community, educational, commercial and other concerns to take a positive approach' (p17). In 1995, nearly all mothers (97%) said they thought shops and shopping centres should provide facilities, four fifths (80%) mentioned restaurants, and a third (33%) thought there should be feeding facilities in public toilets. A minority of mothers also mentioned stations and airports (3%) and places of entertainment such as parks and museums (5%). More mothers in 1995 than in 1990 thought it important to have facilities for feeding babies in restaurants (80% compared with 63%).

Table 7.23

Table 7.23 Places that mothers thought should provide facilities for feeding babies (1990 and 1995 Great Britain)

	Breastfeeders		Bottle feeders		All mothers	
	1990	1995	1990	1995	1990	1995
	Percentage mentioning each place					
Shops/shopping centres	96	98	93	96	94	97
Restaurants	64	78	63	81	63	80
Public toilets	39	41	30	31	32	33
Stations and airports	3	6	2	2	3	3
Places of entertainment eg parks, museums	3	7	2	4	3	5
Other public places	7	7	5	4	7	4
Base	*1,167*	*1,224*	*4,072*	*3,733*	*5,239*	*4,957*

Percentages do not add up to 100 as some mothers mentioned more than one place.

Notes and references

1　Department of Health. *Present day practice in infant feeding: third report.* Report on Health and Social Subjects 32　HMSO (London: 1988)

8 Additional drinks and supplementary vitamins

Summary

- The proportion of mothers giving additional water or drinks other than milk at six to ten weeks old declined from 79% in 1990 to 54% in 1995.

- Mothers who were not breastfeeding were more likely to have given additional drinks at stage one (69%) than breastfeeding mothers (30%).

- Water and unsweetened baby drinks were the most commonly mentioned additional drinks given by mothers at all stages.

- The proportion of babies being given additional vitamins at each stage of the survey was lower in 1995 than in 1990. At about four months the proportion fell from 19% in 1990 to 9% in 1995.

- Between 1990 and 1995 there was little change in the proportion of breastfeeding mothers taking vitamin or iron supplements (31%) at stage one.

Table 8.4	Additions to the water given at each stage of the survey (1985 and 1995 Great Britain)*					
Whether sugar/honey added to water	6-10 weeks		4-5 months		8-9 months	
	1985	1995	1985	1995	1985	1995
			Percentage of all mothers			
Water with sugar/honey added	12	7	9	4	5	3
Base	5,223	5,017	5,223	5,017	5,223	5,017

* Specific question about addition of sugar and honey was not asked in 1990

76% of mothers who were giving additional drinks at six to ten weeks and 86% at about four months gave this reason. The other reasons given by at least one third of mothers at stage one of the survey were to help digestive problems, constipation or to settle the baby. At about four months, a quarter (26%) of mothers who gave additional drinks (other than water) did so because the baby was constipated, and a fifth (21%) to settle the baby.

Table 8.5

Table 8.5	Reasons for giving additional drinks at stages 1 and 2 of the survey (1990 and 1995 Great Britain)			
Reasons for giving additional drinks	6-10 weeks		4-5 months	
	1990	1995	1990	1995
	Percentage giving reason			
Because baby is thirsty	80	76	85	86
To give baby extra vitamins	8	12	20	15
To help baby's digestion	34	33	41	8
Baby was constipated	27	42	2	26
To settle the baby*	-	32	-	21
Other reason	7	3	11	9
Base	4,203	1,011†	4,661	2,980†

Percentages do not add up to 100 as some mothers gave more than one reason.
* Code introduced in 1995
† Asked only of mothers giving drinks other than water in 1995

Use of a cup or beaker

The Weaning and the Weaning Diet Report[1] recommends that 'from six months of age, infants should be introduced to drinking from a cup'. When they were aged about nine months old, over three quarters (78%) of the babies had drunk from a cup or beaker with a spout. Babies in Scotland were more likely to have done so (86%) than those in Northern Ireland (81%) or England and Wales (78%). In all the separate countries, babies who were bottlefed were less likely than those who were breastfed to have ever drunk from a cup or beaker.

Table 8.6

Table 8.7 shows the age at which babies first used a cup or beaker. A third (36%) had used a cup or beaker by six months, and this had risen to three fifths (61%) by seven months.

Table 8.7

Table 8.6	Whether baby had ever drunk from a cup or beaker with a spout by 8 to 9 months by country and whether baby was breastfed			
Feeding method at stage 3	England and Wales	Scotland	Northern Ireland	United Kingdom
	Percentage who had ever drunk from cup or beaker with spout			
Breastfed	92	94	88	92
Combination of breast and non-human milk	93	97	93	93
Not breastfed	75	85	81	76
All babies *	78	86	81	78
Bases				
Breastfed	302	73	38	323
Combination of breast and non-human milk	296	130	44	330
Not breastfed	3,974	1,656	1,389	4,501
All babies *	4,598	1,863	1,497	5,181

* Includes some babies who received no milk.

Table 8.7	Age by which babies had used a cup or beaker with a spout by country			
Babies who had ever used a cup				
	England and Wales	Scotland	Northern Ireland	United Kingdom
	Percentage introducing cup by			
4 months	7	6	6	7
5 months	15	15	13	15
6 months	36	36	32	36
7 months	61	61	62	61
8 months	77	76	80	77
8 months	96	95	96	96
Over 8-9 months	100	100	100	100
Base	3,552	1,603	1,198	3,927

8.2 Supplementary vitamins

Certain infants such as premature babies or babies of mothers with vitamin deficiencies may not be receiving required nutrition levels through breast or formula milks. They may require the early use of supplements of Vitamins A, C and D. Otherwise, the COMA Report on Weaning and the Weaning Diet[1] recommends that vitamin supplements should be given to children aged from six months. Babies who are consuming 500ml of infant formula or follow-on formula a day do not need vitamin supplementation because these manufactured products are fortified.

Table 8.8 Supplementary vitamins given to babies at about 6 to 10 weeks old by feeding method (1985, 1990 and 1995 Great Britain)

Whether supplementary vitamins given at stage 1	Breastfed			Not breastfed			All babies		
	1985	1990	1995	1985	1990	1995	1985	1990	1995
	%	%	%	%	%	%	%	%	%
Received vitamins	34	14	6	23	11	6	27	12	6
Did not receive vitamins	66	86	94	77	89	94	73	88	94
Base	*1,719*	*1,764*	*1,954*	*3,503*	*3,649*	*3,063*	*5,223*	*5,413*	*5,017*

Table 8.9 Supplementary vitamins given to babies of about 4 to 5 months by method of feeding (1985, 1990 and 1995 Great Britain)

Whether supplementary vitamins given at stage 2	Breastfed			Bottle fed:						All babies*		
				liquid cow's milk			infant formula					
	1985	1990	1995	1985	1990	1995	1985	1990	1995	1985	1990	1995
	%	%	%	%	%	%	%	%	%	%	%	%
Received vitamins	45	22	10	44	38	18	32	18	9	35	19	9
Did not receive vitamins	55	78	90	56	62	82	68	82	91	65	81	91
Base	*1,187*	*1,182*	*1,252*	*239*	*121*	*49*	*3,701*	*4,039*	*3,860*	*5,223*	*5,413*	*5,017*

* Includes some babies who received only non-human milk for which the type was not known.

Table 8.10 Supplementary vitamins given to babies of about 8 to 9 months by method of feeding (1985, 1990 and 1995 Great Britain)

Whether supplementary vitamins given at stage 3	Breastfed			Bottle fed:						All babies*		
				liquid cow's milk			infant formula					
	1985	1990	1995	1985	1990	1995	1985	1990	1995	1985	1990	1995
	%	%	%	%	%	%	%	%	%	%	%	%
Received vitamins	45	33	27	45	37	25	37	25	14	42	30	17
Did not receive vitamins	55	67	73	55	63	75	63	75	86	58	70	83
Base	*462*	*530*	*648*	*3,072*	*2,015*	*649*	*1,508*	*2,762*	*3,664*	*5,223*	*5,413*	*5,017*

* Includes some babies who received only non-human milk for which the type was not known, or received no milk.

Use of vitamins for the baby

The proportion of babies being given vitamins at six to ten weeks old has continued to fall from 12% in 1990 to 6% in 1995. Unlike in previous years, breastfeeding mothers were no more likely to give supplementary vitamins than were bottle feeding mothers. Similarly, at about four months, the proportion of babies being given vitamins decreased from 19% in 1990 to 9% in 1995 and this decline occurred among all babies, irrespective of the type of milk they were given. By about nine months, 17% of babies were receiving extra vitamins, again a decrease since 1990. Babies having infant formula were the least likely to have vitamin supplements at about nine months (14% compared with 27% of breastfed babies and 25% of those having liquid cow's milk as their main drink).

Figures 8.2-8.4, Tables 8.8-8.10

Mothers in Northern Ireland were the least likely to be giving babies vitamin supplements at six weeks old — only 3% did so compared with 6% in England and Wales and 8% in Scotland. At about four months Scottish mothers were most likely to give vitamins —

13% compared with 8% or 9% of mothers elsewhere. The proportion of mothers giving babies vitamin supplements decreased between 1990 and 1995 in all the countries of the United Kingdom at both stage one and stage two.

Table 8.11

Of those who were giving vitamins at any of the three stages, the majority used Department of Health Children's Vitamin Drops that they either bought, received free or on prescription from the Child Health Clinic. At six weeks mothers were more likely to receive their vitamins free of charge or on prescription, however at later stages the mothers were more likely to buy their babies' vitamins — 55% of mothers giving vitamins at six weeks received them free or on prescription, compared with 34% and 22% at about four and nine months respectively.

A smaller proportion of mothers in 1995 gave their babies Children's Vitamin Drops at every stage compared with 1990, and therefore a higher proportion gave other types of vitamins. For

89

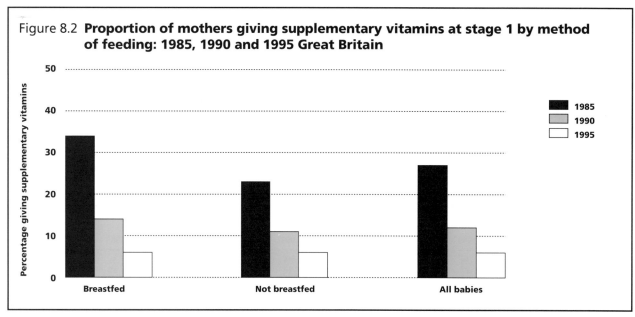

Figure 8.2 **Proportion of mothers giving supplementary vitamins at stage 1 by method of feeding: 1985, 1990 and 1995 Great Britain**

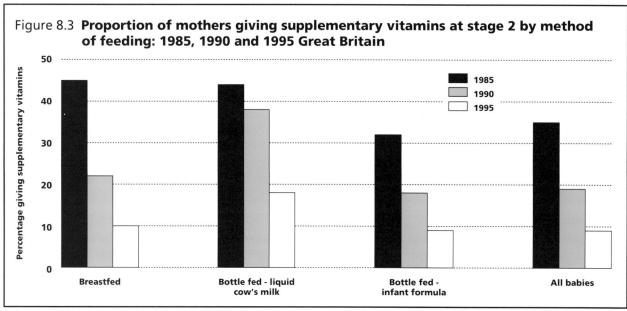

Figure 8.3 **Proportion of mothers giving supplementary vitamins at stage 2 by method of feeding: 1985, 1990 and 1995 Great Britain**

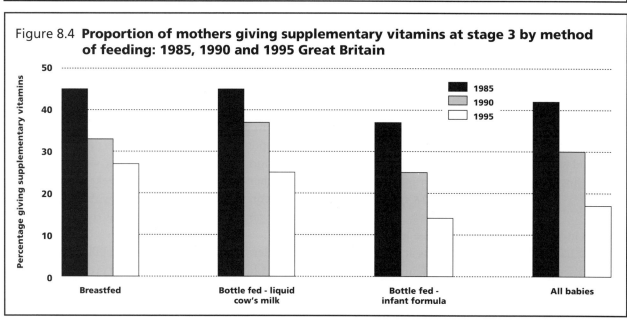

Figure 8.4 **Proportion of mothers giving supplementary vitamins at stage 3 by method of feeding: 1985, 1990 and 1995 Great Britain**

Table 8.11 Proportion of mothers giving extra vitamins at stages 1 and 2 by country (1990 and 1995 United Kingdom)

Extra vitamins given	England and Wales		Scotland		Northern Ireland		United Kingdom	
	1990	1995	1990	1995	1990	1995	1990	1995
	Percentage giving extra vitamins							
At six to ten weeks	11	6	21	8	6	3	12	6
At four to five months	18	9	28	13	21	8	19	10
Base	*4,942*	*4,598*	*1,981*	*1,863*	*1,497*	*1,476*	*5,533*	*5,181*

Table 8.12 Types of vitamins given at each stage of the survey (1990 and 1995 Great Britain)
Mothers giving supplementary vitamins

Type of vitamins	6-10 weeks		4-5 months		8-9 months	
	1990	1995	1990	1995	1990	1995
	%	%	%	%	%	%
Children's Vitamin Drops:	84	70	87	73	83	78
bought at clinic	56	30	65	42	67	52
free/prescribed at clinic	23	35	16	22	10	19
obtained elsewhere	5	5	5	9	7	7
Other brands:	16	30	13	27	17	22
bought	6	10	7	15	14	19
prescribed	10	20	6	12	3	3
Base	*650*	*282*	*1,020*	*452*	*1,637*	*845*

example, the proportion using other types of vitamins increased from 16% in 1990 to 30% in 1995 at stage one, from 13% to 27% at stage two and from 17% to 22% at stage three.

Table 8.12

Use of vitamins for the mother

Present day practice in infant feeding: third report[2] states that the vitamin content of human milk is sufficient for the infant's requirements provided the mother has a plentiful supply. It therefore recommends that all women should receive vitamins supplements during lactation.

At about six to ten weeks 31% of breastfeeding mothers were taking supplementary vitamins and iron tablets, falling to 26% at about four months and about nine months. These proportions have remained almost unchanged between 1990 and 1995.

Table 8.13

Table 8.14 shows that mothers in Social Class III manual were least likely to take vitamin supplements at each stage. The decline in the proportion of breastfeeding mothers taking vitamins between stage one and later stages was only evident in Social Class V/no partner/unclassified group.

Table 8.14

Table 8.13 Percentage of breastfeeding mothers who took supplementary vitamins at each stage of the survey (1990 and 1995 Great Britain)
Breastfeeding mothers

Stage	1990	1995
	Percentage taking vitamins	
6-10 weeks	29	31
4-5 months	27	26
8-9 months	23	26
Bases		
6-10 weeks	*1,764*	*1,942*
4-5 months	*1,183*	*1,236*
8-9 months	*530*	*644*

Table 8.14 Percentage of breastfeeding mothers who took supplementary vitamins at each stage of the survey by social class as defined by current or last occupation of husband/partner (1995 Great Britain)
Breastfeeding mothers

Social class	6-10 weeks	4-5 months	8-9 months
	Percentage taking vitamins		
I	35	31	37
II	30	29	27
IIINM	35	24	28
IIIM	26	19	19
IV	31	24	31
V, no partner and Unclassified	33	26	20
All	31	26	26
Bases			
I	*237*	*171*	*93*
II	*669*	*461*	*223*
IIINM	*166*	*105*	*61*
IIIM	*387*	*228*	*119*
IV	*162*	*98*	*55*
V, no partner and Unclassified	*321*	*171*	*91*
All	*1,942*	*1,236*	*644*

Notes and references

1 Department of Health. *Weaning and The Weaning Diet, Report of the Working Group on the Weaning Diet of the Committee on Medical Aspects of Food Policy* Report on Health and Social Subjects 45, HMSO (London: 1994)

2 Department of Health and Social Security. *Present day practice in infant feeding: third report.* Report on Health and Social Subjects 32. HMSO (London: 1988)

9 Solid foods

Summary

- In 1995, a smaller proportion of mothers had introduced solid foods by three months old than in previous years (55% compared with 68% in 1990).

- The age of introduction of solid food varied by method of feeding, region and country of residence, birth weight, social class of mother's husband/partner, smoking habits during and before pregnancy and alcohol consumption before pregnancy.

- Eight per cent of mothers said they had never given their baby meat: of these, half said it was because their baby was not ready for meat, a third intended to give their baby a vegetarian diet and 8% (30 mothers in all) mentioned BSE/CJD as a reason.

- Only 20% of non-meat eating babies received vitamin supplements.

- Nearly half of babies at stage two were usually given a drink containing vitamin C with their solid food.

- Mothers at stage three most frequently took account of 'general nutrition', 'variety of tastes and textures' and 'baby's preferences' when choosing solid food. They also tended to avoid sugar, salt and beef.

- About a tenth of mothers at stage three said they had found it difficult to wean their baby onto solid food, and nearly half of these mothers said their baby would only take certain solids.

9.1 Age of introduction of solid food

The COMA Report of the Working Group on the Weaning Diet[1] recommends that 'the majority of infants should not be given solid foods before the age of four months, and a mixed diet should be offered by six months' (p1).

In 1995, only a very small proportion of mothers (7%) had introduced any solid food by the time their babies were six weeks old. This was lower than the proportions recorded in 1990 (9%) and 1985 (11%). By three months, over half of mothers had introduced solids (55%), a lower proportion than in 1990 (68%). Although the vast majority of babies had been given solid foods by four months this was again slightly lower than in 1990 (91% and 94% respectively). These changes reflect the recommendations prevailing at the time of the different surveys: in 1990 advice came from the Present day practice in infant feeding: third report[2] which acknowledged that some infants might begin weaning at the age of three months. However, many mothers are still starting solid food earlier than is generally thought desirable.

Table 9.1 and Figure 9.1

As in previous years, mothers of babies who were not breastfed were more likely to have given solid foods by six weeks than were breastfeeding mothers (9% compared with 1%) and the proportion doing so had fallen between 1985 and 1995 in both feeding method groups. In 1995, breastfeeding mothers (both exclusively and in conjunction with infant formula) tended to introduce solid food later than others even at four months when the vast majority of mothers who were not breastfeeding had introduced solids (93%) only 84% of exclusively breastfeeding mothers had done so.

Tables 9.2 and 9.3

Table 9.4 shows the age at which mothers in the countries of the United Kingdom first introduced their babies to solid food. Scottish mothers tended to introduce solid food earliest, followed by those in Northern Ireland. In particular, 22% of Scottish mothers had introduced solid food at eight weeks, compared with 18% of mothers in Northern Ireland and 12% in England and Wales. By four months 91% or 92% of mothers in all countries had introduced solids.

Table 9.4 and Figure 9.2

Region

In 1995, as in previous years, mothers in Scotland and the North of England were the most likely to have introduced solid food by three months (64%

Table 9.1	Age at introduction of solid food (1980, 1985, 1990 and 1995 Great Britain)			
Solid food introduced by	1980	1985	1990	1995
		Percentage giving solid food		
4 weeks	4	3	3	2
6 weeks	14	11	9	7
8 weeks	24	24	19	13
3 months	56	62	68	55
4 months	89	90	94	91
6 months	98	99	99	99
9 months	99	100	100	100
*Base**	*4,224*	*5,223*	*5,413*	*4,997*

* Excludes some cases where the age at introduction of solid food was not known.

Figure 9.1 **Age at introduction of solid food: 1980, 1985, 1990 and 1995 Great Britain**

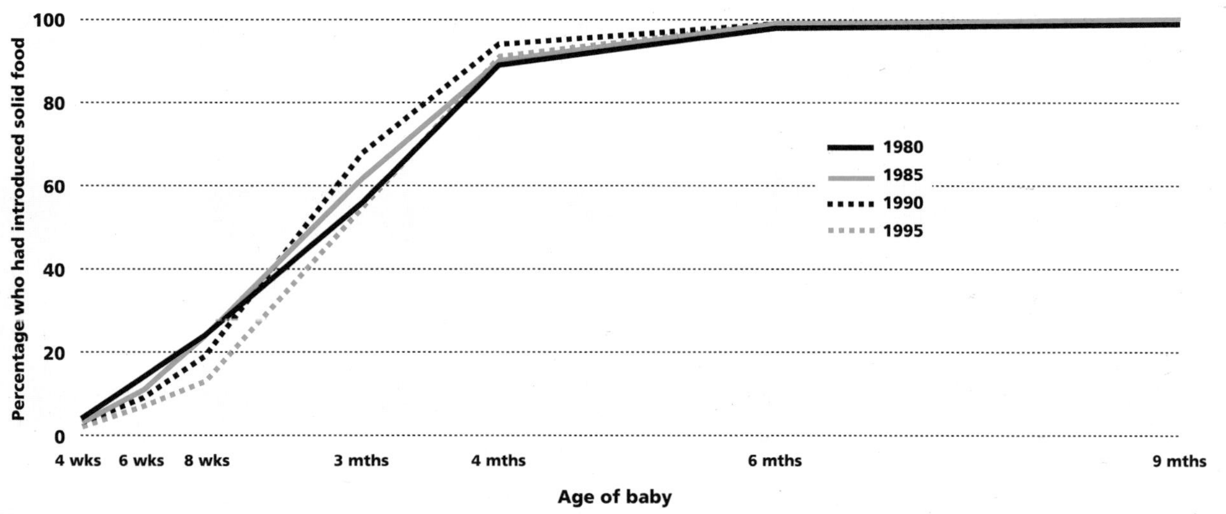

Table 9.2 Proportion of babies who had been given solid food by six weeks according to method of feeding (1985, 1990 and 1995 Great Britain)

Method of feeding at six weeks	1985	1990	1995	1985	1990	1995
	Percentage given solid food				*Bases*	
Breastfed	4	2	1	1,711	1,764	1,171
Not breastfed	14	12	9	3,483	3,649	3,795
Total *	**11**	**9**	**7**	**5,194**	**5,413**	**4,997**

* Excludes some cases where the age at introduction of solid food was not known.

Table 9.3 Age at introduction of solid food by method of feeding at relevant stage

Solid food introduced by	Breastfed	Breastfed and manufactured baby milk	Not breastfed	Total
	Percentage giving solid food			
4 weeks	0	0	3	2
6 weeks	1	1	9	7
8 weeks	2	4	17	13
3 months	30	38	63	55
4 months	84	88	93	91
6 months	97	98	100	99
9 months	100	100	100	100
Base*†	*648*	*522*	*3,795*	*5,160*

* Excludes some cases where the age at introduction of solid food was not known.
† Stage 2 base.

Table 9.4 Age at introduction of solid food by country

Solid food introduced by	England and Wales	Scotland	Northern Ireland	United Kingdom
	Percentage giving solid food			
4 weeks	2	2	2	2
6 weeks	7	8	8	7
8 weeks	12	22	18	13
3 months	54	64	63	56
4 months	91	91	92	91
6 months	99	99	100	99
9 months	100	100	100	100
Base*	*4,569*	*1,856*	*1,464*	*5,160*

* Excludes some cases where the age at introduction of solid food was not known.

and 62%) and those in London and the South East the least likely (46%). This pattern was apparent even after allowing for differences in breastfeeding prevalence in the different regions (Table 9.6).

The decrease in the proportion of mothers giving solid food at three months between 1990 and 1995 was found in all regions.

Tables 9.5 and 9.6

Birthweight

In investigating which babies are introduced to solids at an earlier age, it is not possible to look directly at whether bigger babies are more physically advanced and have a more demanding appetite which is more difficult to satisfy: no information was collected on the current weight or length of the baby at the time the questionnaires were completed. However, as babies growing normally will grow at a rate related to their birthweight, this has been used as an indicator of weight in later infancy.

The pattern was similar to that found in 1990, with mothers of higher birthweight babies tending to introduce solid food at an earlier age. For example, 58% of the mothers of babies weighing 3,500

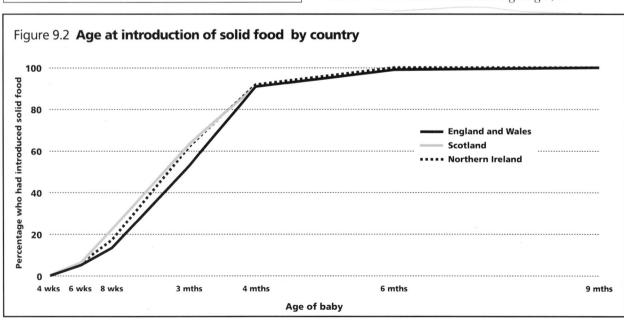

Figure 9.2 Age at introduction of solid food by country

Table 9.5 Age at introduction of solid food by region (1990 and 1995 Great Britain)

Solid food introduced by	Region										All babies	
	London and South East		South West and Wales		Midlands and East Anglia		North		Scotland			
	1990	1995	1990	1995	1990	1995	1990	1995	1990	1995	1990	1995
	Percentage giving solid food											
4 weeks	2	2	3	2	3	3	3	1	5	2	3	2
6 weeks	6	5	8	8	9	9	10	8	15	8	9	7
8 weeks	14	8	18	14	20	16	22	14	29	22	19	13
3 months	59	46	67	56	72	59	74	62	76	64	68	55
4 months	92	89	95	92	95	94	95	93	95	91	94	91
6 months	99	99	100	99	99	100	100	100	100	99	99	99
9 months	100	100	100	100	100	100	100	100	100	100	100	100
*Base**	*1,665*	*1,780*	*641*	*704*	*1,028*	*903*	*1,437*	*1,191*	*458*	*419*	*5,229*	*4,997*

* Excludes some cases where the age at introduction of solid food was not known.

Table 9.6 Age at introduction of solid food by region and method of feeding at relevant stage (1995 Great Britain)

Solid food introduced by	London and South East	South West and Wales	Midlands and East Anglia	North	Scotland	Great Britain
Breastfed††	*Percentage giving solid food*					
4 weeks	0	1	1	0	0	0
6 weeks	0	2	1	1	2	1
8 weeks	2	4	2	3	6	2
3 months	26	34	38	42	38	33
4 months	83	86	89	90	84	85
6 months	96	99	97	97	98	97
9 months	100	100	100	99	100	100
*Base**:	*269*	*109*	*103*	*115*	*46*	*641*
Not Breastfed	*Percentage giving solid food*					
4 weeks	2	3	4	2	3	3
6 weeks	7	10	11	9	10	9
8 weeks	11	18	20	17	26	16
3 months	54	64	66	67	70	62
4 months	91	95	95	94	92	93
6 months	99	100	100	100	100	100
9 months	100	100	100	100	100	100
*Base**†	*1,507*	*595*	*799*	*1,074*	*372*	*4,348*

* Excludes some cases where the age at introduction of solid food was not known
†† Includes mothers who breastfed and gave manufactured baby milk
† Stage 2 base

grammes or more at birth had introduced solid food by three months, compared with 44% of babies weighing less than 2,500 grammes. By four months these had increased to 92% and 82% respectively. The decrease in the proportion of mothers who had given solid food by three months between 1990 and 1995 was evident among babies of differing birthweights.

Table 9.7

Social class (as defined by the current occupation of the husband or partner)

The relationship between age at introduction of solids and social class of the mothers' husband or partner found in previous surveys, was also present in 1995. At three months, 35% of mothers in Social Class I had given solid food, increasing to 68% of mothers in Social Class V and 69% of mothers with no partner. The differences at four months were less marked, with mothers in Social Class I being the least likely to have introduced solids (88%) and those in Social Class V the

most likely (94%). These results might be explained by the lower prevalence of breastfeeding among mothers in the lower social class groups. Table 9.9 shows the age of introduction of solids by whether the baby was breast fed or not and whether the mother's husband or partner was in a non-manual or manual job. Mothers from manual groups were more likely than their non-manual counterparts to have introduced solid food at three months among both breastfeeders and those not breastfeeding (but not among those who both breastfed and gave infant formula). For example, 39% of breastfeeding mothers from a manual background had introduced solids at three months compared with 24% of their non-manual counterparts.

The overall picture of a decrease in the proportion of mothers giving solid food at three months between 1990 and 1995 was found in all social class groups (Table 9.8).

Tables 9.8 and 9.9

Table 9.7 Age at introduction of solid food by birthweight (1990 and 1995 Great Britain)

Solid food introduced by	Birthweight of baby								All babies	
	Less than 2500g		2500-2999g		3000-3499g		3500g or more			
	1990	1995	1990	1995	1990	1995	1990	1995	1990	1995
	Percentage giving solid food									
4 weeks	2	1	2	2	3	2	3	2	3	2
6 weeks	7	5	6	6	9	7	10	8	9	7
8 weeks	15	8	16	12	18	12	22	15	19	13
3 months	59	44	66	53	67	55	72	58	68	55
4 months	89	82	92	91	94	92	96	92	94	91
6 months	98	97	99	100	99	100	100	99	99	99
9 months	100	100	100	100	100	100	100	100	100	100
Base*	*295*	*310*	*884*	*862*	*1,987*	*1,752*	*2,063*	*2,049*	*5,229*	*4,997*

* Excludes some cases where the age at introduction of solid food was not known.

Table 9.8 Age at introduction of solid food by social class as defined by current or last occupation of husband/partner (1990 and 1995 Great Britain)

Solid food introduced by	Social class																Total	
	I		II		IIINM		IIIM		IV		V		No partner		Unclassified			
	1990	1995	1990	1995	1990	1995	1990	1995	1990	1995	1990	1995	1990	1995	1990	1995	1990	1995
	Percentage giving solid food																	
4 weeks	1	0	1	1	2	0	3	2	2	3	6	4	4	4	4	3	3	2
6 weeks	2	2	5	4	8	5	10	7	10	8	15	9	14	13	10	10	9	7
8 weeks	9	3	13	7	17	10	20	14	22	13	24	19	28	24	20	17	19	13
3 months	57	35	61	45	70	54	69	59	73	58	72	68	76	69	68	60	68	55
4 months	91	88	92	88	96	91	94	93	96	92	95	94	95	93	94	93	94	91
6 months	100	98	99	100	99	100	99	99	100	100	99	99	99	99	99	99	99	99
9 months	100	100	100	100	100	100	100	100	100	100	100	100	100	100	100	100	100	100
Base*	*385*	*341*	*1,007*	*1,296*	*412*	*390*	*1,556*	*1,237*	*726*	*537*	*115*	*180*	*728*	*735*	*300*	*282*	*5,229*	*4,997*

* Excludes some cases where the age at introduction of solid food was not known.

Table 9.9 Age at introduction of solid food by whether husband/partner's current or last occupation was non-manual or manual and method of feeding at relevant stage (1995 Great Britain)

Solid food introduced by	Non-manual	Manual	No partner/ Unclassified	Total
	Percentage giving solid food			
Breastfed only				
4 weeks	0	0	0	0
6 weeks	1	1	0	1
8 weeks	1	2	1	2
3 months	24	39	36	29
4 months	82	89	84	84
6 months	95	96	100	97
9 months	99	100	100	100
Base*†	*389*	*184*	*67*	*641*
	Percentage giving solid food			
Combination of breastfed and manufactured baby milk				
4 weeks	0	0	0	0
6 weeks	1	0	0	1
8 weeks	4	3	6	4
3 months	35	42	42	38
4 months	55	90	96	88
6 months	100	96	98	95
9 months	100	100	100	100
Base*†	*306*	*138*	*71*	*516*
	Percentage giving solid food			
Not breastfed				
4 weeks	1	3	5	3
6 weeks	5	9	14	9
8 weeks	10	17	24	16
3 months	54	64	70	62
4 months	92	94	94	93
6 months	100	99	99	100
9 months	100	100	100	100
Base*†	*1,229*	*1,536*	*885*	*3,650*

* Excludes some cases where the age at introduction of solid food was not known.
† Stage 2 base.

Smoking and drinking during pregnancy

Mothers who smoked during pregnancy were more likely to have introduced solid food by three months than those who did not smoke (66% and 52% respectively), although the difference was not statistically significant by four months. This relationship may be confounded by social class as smoking is strongly related to social class. However, the number of smokers within each social class group was too small to enable any further analysis. The reduction between 1990 and 1995 in the proportion of mothers who had introduced food by three months was found among both smokers and non-smokers.

Table 9.10

Table 9.11 shows the age at introduction of solid food by alcohol consumption during pregnancy. Non-drinkers are those women who did not drink any alcohol during pregnancy; light drinkers are those women who drank less than one unit of alcohol a week; and drinkers are those who drank one or more units of alcohol a week. Unlike 1990, drinking habits during pregnancy did not affect the introduction of solid foods at any age, even when social class was taken into account.

Table 9.11

Table 9.10 Age at introduction of solid food by smoking status during pregnancy (1990 and 1995 Great Britain)

Solid food introduced by	Smoking status during pregnancy					
	1995			1990		
	Non-smoker	Smoker	Total	Non-smoker	Smoker	Total
	Percentage giving solid food					
4 weeks	2	3	2	2	5	3
6 weeks	6	11	7	7	14	9
8 weeks	11	20	13	16	27	19
3 months	52	66	55	66	75	68
4 months	91	93	91	94	95	94
6 months	99	100	99	99	100	99
9 months	100	100	100	100	100	100
*Base**	*3,916*	*1,081*	*4,997*	*3,800*	*1,429*	*5,229*

* Excludes some cases where the age at introduction of solid food was not known.

Table 9.11 Age at introduction of solid food by whether mother drank alcohol during pregnancy (1990 and 1995 Great Britain)

Solid food introduced by	Drinking status during pregnancy					
	1995			1990		
	Non-drinker	Light drinker*	Drinker†	Non-drinker	Light drinker*	Drinker†
	Percentage giving solid food					
4 weeks	2	2	2	3	2	3
6 weeks	7	7	7	9	9	9
8 weeks	13	13	12	18	19	21
3 months	56	55	55	66	69	71
4 months	91	91	92	93	95	94
6 months	98	100	100	99	100	99
9 months	100	100	100	100	100	100
*Base***	*1,603*	*2,343*	*1,015*	*1,646*	*2,487*	*1,097*

* Light drinkers are defined as women who drank less than one unit of alcohol a week during pregnancy
† Drinkers are defined as women who drank one unit of alcohol a week during pregnancy.
** Excludes some cases where the age at introduction of solid food was not known.

9.2 Solid foods given at different ages

At each stage, mothers were asked to list all the cereal, rusks or solid food the baby had eaten on the day before they completed the questionnaire. The mothers were asked to describe each food fully, giving the brand name or saying if it was homemade. For commercial baby food, mothers ticked a column to show whether it was dried or tinned/jarred. Office coders coded this information from a large range of precodes, which tended to summarise each meal or snack, rather than defining each ingredient in the food. Some foods, therefore, may appear to be under-represented as they were eaten as part of a main dish not coded separately. For example, a homemade meal consisting of chicken, potatoes and carrots, would have been coded in 1995 as a meat based meal, whereas in 1990 the three separate ingredients would have each been allocated a code. For this reason, comparisons between the types of food given in 1990 and 1995 are only presented for cereals, rusks, babyfood and the broad categories of homemade and other foods which were coded in the same way in both the survey years.

In 1995, nearly three quarters (71%) of mothers had given cereal the day before they completed the stage one questionnaire, and a further 31% had given rusks. Compared with 1990, fewer mothers had given rusks (48% in 1990) and a higher proportion had given cereals (53%). Similar proportions of mothers had given dried, tinned or jarred baby food when their baby was aged six to ten weeks in both survey years.

By about four months, mothers were more likely to have given non-rice cereals, commercially prepared babyfood and homemade food than at stage one. Mothers were more likely to give tinned or jarred babyfood which is ready to eat (50%) rather than dried babyfoods which require mixing with water or milk before serving (38%). Compared with 1990, mothers at the four month stage were less likely to give dried babyfood and more likely to give non-rice cereal, tinned or jarred babyfood and homemade food. For example, 38% gave dried babyfood in 1995 while 49% did so in 1990, 56% gave non-rice cereal in 1995 as opposed to 44% in 1990, and 41% gave homemade food in 1995 compared with 27% in 1990.

The vast majority of babies aged about nine months had been given cereal (83%), or homemade food (79%) the day before the questionnaire was completed. Nearly two thirds (63%) had been given some form of commercially prepared babyfood, and a quarter (25%) had been given rusks. The category 'other foods', given by 82% of mothers, covers all types of commercially prepared adult food. It is encouraging that the majority of mothers gave home made food at about nine months as the COMA Report of the Working Group on the Weaning Diet[1] suggests that it is important to give home prepared foods as part of weaning, in order to accustom the infant to a greater range of flavours and textures than manufactured foods can provide.

By the nine month stage there was very little difference in the pattern of babyfoods given in 1990 and 1995, although mothers in 1995 were slightly less likely to give dried babyfood and slightly more likely to give tinned or jarred babyfood than in 1990.

Table 9.12

A detailed breakdown of the types of homemade and commercially prepared adult food given on the day before the stage two and stage three questionnaires were completed are presented in Table 9.13. As discussed above, the categories are not directly comparable with those in previous surveys and so the table only presents results for 1995.

At about four months, the most popular foods given were vegetables (20%) and fruit (19%). One tenth (10%) of mothers had given their baby a meat based meal and 5% had given yoghurt or fromage frais the previous day. Only 2% of mothers had given bread or toast the previous day, but by nine months this had risen to 35%. This reflects the advice given to

mothers to avoid gluten (found in cereals such as wheat used in breadmaking) before the infant is six months in order to reduce the risk of coeliac disease (COMA Report of the Working Group on the Weaning Diet, p71).

By about nine months, nearly half of mothers had given yoghurt or fromage frais (47%), 34% had given fresh fruit and 17% had given another type of dessert on the previous day. Meat based meals were the most popular type of combination meal: 40% of babies had had a meat based meal, 10% a fish based meal, and 9% a vegetable based meal.

Table 9.13

In the stage three questionnaire in 1995 mothers were asked how often they gave their baby different types of foods. The results are presented in Table 9.14 which shows that the majority of mothers gave their baby some food containing carbohydrates at least once a day (86% gave cereal or rusk, and 46%

Table 9.13 Proportion of mothers who had given different kinds of food on one day at stages 2 and 3

All mothers who had given solid food yesterday

Type of food	Baby aged:	
	4-5 months	8-9 months
	Percentage giving each food	
Yoghurt	5	47
Fresh fruit	19	34
Other dessert	2	17
Dried fruit or nuts	2	1
Egg	1	4
Cheese and dairy produce	2	11
Meat based meal	10	40
Fish based meal	2	10
Vegetable based meal	2	9
Potatoes	14	19
Other vegetables	20	23
Bread/toast and sandwiches	2	35
Other foods	2	21
Base	4,898	5,060

Table 9.12 Proportion of mothers who had given different kinds of food on one day at each stage of the survey (1990 and 1995 Great Britain)

All mothers who had given solid food yesterday

Type of food	6-10 weeks		4-5 months		8-9 months	
	1990	1995	1990	1995	1990	1995
			Percentage giving each food			
Rice cereal*	37	53	13	14	4	2
Other cereal*	15	18	44	56	82	81
Rusk	48	31	35	33	24	25
Dried babyfood†	} 36	15	49	38	20	18
Tinned or jarred babyfood†		18	46	50	42	45
Homemade food	4	5	27	41	..	79
Other food	1	1	13	14	..	82
Base	1,263	647	5,097	4,740	5,272	4,901

* Baby or adult cereal.
† Commercially prepared tinned or dried food.

gave bread) and about half gave dairy products (55%), puddings or desserts (49%), or cooked vegetables (47%) every day.

The majority of mothers gave most of the different food types at least once a week. For example, 94% gave cooked vegetables, 91% gave potatoes, 89% gave dairy products, 81% gave puddings or desserts and 80% gave meat at least once a week.

Over half of mothers (57%) never gave their baby raw vegetables, nearly half (47%) never gave eggs and 32% never gave sweets or chocolates. Foods which are avoided and the reasons why, will be looked at in more detail in Section 9.3.

Table 9.14

Consumption of meat

Meat and meat products are rich in haem iron which is readily absorbable by infants. The Department of Health therefore recommends that foods containing haem iron should be introduced by six to eight months (COMA Report of the Working Group on the Weaning Diet, p41).[1] In order to look at the

consumption of meat at stage three when the babies were about nine months old, mothers were asked whether their baby had ever had meat, how often they gave meat, and those who did not give meat were asked why they were not doing so.

Fourteen percent of mothers said that they never usually give meat nowadays, but only 8% had never given their baby meat (Tables 9.14 and 9.15). Overall, 92% of babies in 1995 had had meat at least once, a fall of two percentage points compared with 1990. Unlike in 1990, there was no significant differences between babies from different social classes.

Table 9.15

Nearly a third of mothers who had ever given meat gave their baby meat every day (32%) and 73% gave meat at least three times a week. This is lower than in 1990, when 40% of mothers gave meat every day and 76% gave meat at least three times a week. As in 1990, there were some social class differences with babies from higher social classes eating meat more frequently: babies from Social Class I were the most likely to eat meat at least three times a week (80%)

Table 9.14 Frequency with which mothers gave different types of food at stage 3

Frequency with which food given	%	Frequency with which food given	%
Cereal or rusk		**Raw vegetables**	
At least once a day	86	At least once a day	5
At least once a week	10	At least once a week	21
Less than once a week	2	Less than once a week	18
Never	2	Never	57
Rice or pasta		**Cooked vegetables**	
At least once a day	12	At least once a day	47
At least once a week	63	At least once a week	47
Less than once a week	12	Less than once a week	3
Never	13	Never	5
Bread		**Raw fruit**	
At least once a day	46	At least once a day	30
At least once a week	36	At least once a week	42
Less than once a week	8	Less than once a week	11
Never	11	Never	17
Meat		**Cooked fruit**	
At least once a day	29	At least once a day	15
At least once a week	51	At least once a week	39
Less than once a week	7	Less than once a week	18
Never	14	Never	28
Fish		**Cheese, yoghurt, fromage frais**	
At least once a day	4	At least once a day	55
At least once a week	51	At least once a week	34
Less than once a week	21	Less than once a week	5
Never	25	Never	6
Eggs		**Puddings or desserts**	
At least once a day	2	At least once a day	49
At least once a week	26	At least once a week	32
Less than once a week	26	Less than once a week	10
Never	47		9
Potatoes		**Sweets or chocolate**	
At least once a day	31	At least once a day	7
At least once a week	60	At least once a week	33
Less than once a week	5	Less than once a week	28
Never	4	Never	32
Peas, beans, lentils, chickpeas			
At least once a day	12		
At least once a week	54		
Less than once a week	14		
Never	19		
Base	*5,180*	*Base*	*5,180*

Table 9.15 Proportion of mothers who had given meat at stage 3 by social class as defined by current or last occupation of husband/partner (1990 and 1995 Great Britain)

Babies who were given solid food at 8-9 months

Social class	1990	1995	1990	1995
	Percentage who had given meat at 8-9 months		Base	
I	97	91	*397*	*337*
II	95	94	*1,047*	*1,296*
IIINM	96	94	*427*	*389*
IIIM	94	93	*1,608*	*1,233*
IV	93	92	*739*	*535*
V	91	95	*117*	*177*
No partner	92	91	*313*	*735*
Unclassified	91	89	*755*	*279*
Total	**94**	**92**	*5,404*	*5,017*

There were some social class differences in the reasons given for not offering meat. Mothers in Social Classes I and II were more likely to say they intended to give their baby a vegetarian diet than mothers in Social Class V or those who did not live with their husband/partner (45% and 17% respectively) and less likely to say that their baby was not ready for meat (41% and 59% respectively). Mothers in Social Classes III and IV were more likely to intend to give their baby a vegetarian diet and less likely to say their baby was not ready for meat in 1995 than in 1990, but there were no other statistically significant differences between the two survey years.

Table 9.17

and those whose mothers were not living with their husband or partner were the least likely (68%).

Table 9.16

Mothers who had not given their baby meat at all were asked why, and the reasons given are shown in Table 9.17. About half of the mothers (51%) said that their baby was not ready to eat meat, and almost a third (31%) intended to give a vegetarian diet. A large number of mothers had ticked the 'some other reason box on the questionnaire and then written in the reason. These were examined by office coders, and the majority of the answers mentioned bovine spongiform encephalitis (BSE) or Creutzfeldt-Jakob disease (CJD). Overall, 8% of mothers who did not offer meat, gave BSE/CJD as the reason.

The proportion of mothers who said that their baby was not ready to eat meat at nine months has decreased from 67% in 1990 to 51% in 1995. However, the increase over the five-year period in the proportion intending to give their baby a vegetarian diet was not statistically significant.

The COMA Report of the Working Group on the Weaning Diet[1] states that it is important for babies having vegetarian diets to have high levels of vitamin C as this enhances the absorption of iron present in non-meat sources of iron. One method of ensuring this vitamin C is received is by giving vitamin supplements. Only 20% of babies who did not have meat in their diets were receiving extra vitamins directly or were breastfed by mothers who took vitamin supplements. Babies from Social Class IV were the least likely to receive extra vitamins (7%) and those from Social Classes I and II or from Social Class V or whose mother did not live with their husband/partner were the most likely (22% and 26%).

Table 9.18

Giving drinks containing vitamin C

The COMA Report also suggests that vitamin C enriched fruit drinks consumed with a meal may be useful to aid the absorption of iron from a meal. Table 9.19 shows that at stage two when the babies were aged about four months, just under half (47%)

Table 9.16 Frequency of consumption of meat at stage 3 by social class as defined by current or last occupation of husband/partner (1990 and 1995 Great Britain)

Babies who had ever had meat

Frequency of consumption of meat	Social class																Total	
	I		II		IIINM		IIIM		IV		V		No partner		Unclassified			
	1990	1995	1990	1995	1990	1995	1990	1995	1990	1995	1990	1995	1990	1995	1990	1995	1990	1995
Every day	42	37	40	33	41	31	40	31	40	34	36	31	38	30	35	28	40	32
At least three times a week	82	80	78	74	81	76	78	72	73	73	68	70	68	68	72	68	76	73
At least once a week	95	95	94	92	95	94	96	93	94	92	92	92	92	91	93	90	94	93
Less often than once a week	4	4	5	6	4	5	4	6	6	6	6	7	7	7	6	10	5	6
Baby not having meat at the moment	1	1	1	2	1	0	0	1	1	2	2	1	1	2	0	1	1	1
Base	*385*	*309*	*986*	*1,213*	*409*	*364*	*1,514*	*1,142*	*686*	*490*	*106*	*168*	*694*	*666*	*286*	*247*	*5,067*	*4,599*

Table 9.17 Reasons for not offering meat by social class as defined by current or last occupation of husband/partner (1990 and 1995 Great Britain)

Babies who had never had meat

Reasons for not offering meat	Social class								Total	
	I and II		IIINM and IIIM		IV		V, no partner, Unclassified			
	1990	1995	1990	1995	1990	1995	1990	1995	1990	1995
	Percentage giving reason									
Baby does not like meat	5	3	9	6	9	11	7	16	8	8
Baby is not ready to eat meat	40	41	73	53	80	51	74	59	67	51
Baby given a vegetarian diet	51	45	18	30	10	32	17	17	24	31
BSE/CJD *	..	9	..	10	..	2	..	8	..	8
Other reasons	5	4	3	0	5	4	2	3	4	2
Base	*77*	*109*	*116*	*110*	*53*	*44*	*99*	*106*	*345*	*369*

Percentages do not add up to 100 as some mothers gave more than one reason
* code introduced in 1995.

Table 9.18 Whether babies who did not eat meat were given extra vitamins by social class as defined by current or last occupation of husband/partner

Babies who had never had meat

Whether baby was given extra vitamins	Social class				Total
	I and II	IIINM and IIIM	IV	V, no partner, Unclassified	
	%	%	%	%	%
Had extra vitamins	22	18	7	26	20
Did not have extra vitamins	78	82	93	74	80
Base	*119*	*124*	*46*	*119*	*408*

of mothers in the United Kingdom gave a drink containing vitamin C with their babies' solids. There was very little difference between the different countries of the United Kingdom.

Mothers who were not breastfeeding were more likely to give drinks containing vitamin C at mealtimes than exclusively breastfeeding mothers (52% and 31% respectively).

Table 9.19

Using milk to mix food

Mothers who had introduced solid food were asked if they used milk to mix up their babies' food and if so, which type of milk. At stage two, when the babies were four months old, the majority of mothers used infant formula milk to mix their babies' food (88%), 8% used cow's milk and the remainder used expressed breast milk or something else. By stage three, when the babies were about nine months old, nearly three quarters (74%) used cow's milk to mix their food, a quarter (26%) used infant formula milk and 17% used a follow-on formula milk.

There were some differences between the constituent countries of the United Kingdom at both stages; in particular mothers in Northern Ireland were less likely to use infant formula milk and more

Table 9.19 Proportion of mothers who gave drinks containing vitamin C with solids at stage 2 by country and whether baby was breastfed

Babies who were given solid food at 4-5 months

Whether mother gave drinks containing vitamin C with solids and method of feeding	England and Wales	Scotland	Northern Ireland	United Kingdom
	%	%	%	%
Breastfed only				
Yes, usually	12	19	16	13
Yes, sometimes	18	23	19	18
No, never	70	58	66	69
Base	*600*	*230*	*69*	*660*
	%	%	%	%
Combination of breastfed and manufactured baby milk				
Yes, usually	14	13	15	14
Yes, sometimes	28	23	29	21
No, never	66	65	56	66
Base	*481*	*143*	*59*	*520*
	%	%	%	%
Not breastfed				
Yes, usually	23	24	25	23
Yes, sometimes	29	29	26	29
No, never	48	47	49	48
Base	*3,349*	*1,454*	*1,315*	*3,822*
	%	%	%	%
All				
Yes, usually	21	23	24	21
Yes, sometimes	26	28	26	26
No, never	53	50	50	53
Base	*4,431*	*1,827*	*1,444*	*5,002*

Table 9.20 **Type of milk used to mix up food at stages 2 and 3 by country**
Mothers who used milk to mix up their babies' food.

Type of milk used to mix up solid food	England and Wales	Scotland	Northern Ireland	United Kingdom
	Percentage using:			
4-5 months				
Cow's milk	7	11	19	8
Infant formula milk	89	85	80	88
Expressed breast milk	5	4	1	4
Something else	1	0	2	1
Base	*2,441*	*1,005*	*857*	*2,762*
	Percentage using:			
8-9 months				
Cow's milk	74	77	79	74
Infant formula milk	26	23	24	26
Follow-on formula milk	17	16	12	17
Expressed breast milk	1	1	1	1
Something else	1	1	0	1
Base	*3,236*	*1,327*	*1,048*	*3,650*

Percentages do not add up to 100 as some mothers used more than one type of milk.

likely to use cow's milk at stage two and were less likely to use follow-on formula milk at stage three than other mothers.

Table 9.20

Although 23% of breast feeding mothers used expressed breast milk to mix up the food at stage two, three times as many (69%) used infant formula milk. Similarly, at stage three, only 7% of breast feeding mothers used expressed breast milk — the majority used cow's milk (76%), infant formula milk (18%) or follow-on milk (18%).

Table 9.21

Table 9.21 **Type of milk used to mix up food at stages 2 and 3 by method of feeding**
Mothers who used milk to mix up their babies' food.

Type of milk used to mix up solid food	Breastfed *	Not breastfed	All mothers
	Percentage using:		
4-5 months			
Cow's milk	8	8	8
Infant formula milk	69	93	88
Expressed breast milk	23	0	4
Something else	2	1	1
Base	*536*	*2,226*	*2,762*
	Percentage using:		
8-9 months			
Cow's milk	76	74	74
Infant formula milk	18	27	26
Follow-on formula milk	18	16	17
Expressed breast milk	7	0	1
Something else	3	1	1
Base	*484*	*3,162*	*3,646*

Percentages do not add up to 100 as some mothers used more than one type of milk.
* Includes mothers who breastfed and gave manufactured baby milk

9.3 Influences on the choice of solid food

In the stage two and stage three questionnaires, mothers were asked what they took into account when deciding what types of solid food to give their baby. As in previous years, this was an open question without any prompting or precodes and many mothers mentioned more than one factor. Table 9.22 shows the answers grouped as being related to nutritional factors or not. General nutrition, which included comments such as 'balanced diet', 'calories' or 'mixed diet', was mentioned by 25% of mothers when their baby was four months and 48% when their baby was about nine months old. Sugar content, vitamin content and mention of other ingredients such as fruit and vegetables or vegetarian food, were the next most common nutritional considerations at both stages, although the proportion mentioning sugar content fell from 24% at stage two to 17% at stage three. Salt content and additives were each mentioned by 12% of mothers at stage two, but by fewer mothers at stage three (9% and 6% respectively).

Of the non-nutritional factors, variety of tastes and textures was the most common thing mentioned at

Table 9.22 **What mothers took into account when deciding what solid foods to give (1990 and 1995 Great Britain)**
Babies who were given solid food at relevant stage

	4-5 months		8-9 months	
	1990	1995	1990	1995
	Percentage mentioning each factor			
Nutritional factors				
Nutrition generally eg 'balanced diet', 'food value'	25	25	43	48
Sugar content	21	24	18	17
Additives	12	12	10	6
Vitamins	12	18	20	18
Salt content	11	12	13	9
Gluten content	9	9	1	1
Protein content	2	2	8	6
Fat content	2	1	8	4
Mineral content	2	6	6	6
Carbohydrate content	0	1	2	3
Other ingredient content * eg fruit and veg	..	20	..	19
Non-nutritional factors				
Variety	31	36	35	34
Baby's preferences	24	21	25	24
Home cooked	9	13	17	15
Ease of preparation	9	10	8	10
Price	6	8	4	3
Baby's age	5	6	0	9
Other eg size of packet, shelf-life	38	27	57	20
Base	*5,316*	*4,408*	*5,404*	*4,494*

Percentages do not add up to 100 as some mothers gave more than one reason.
* Code introduced in 1995.

both stages (by 36% of mothers at stage two and 34% at stage three), followed by baby's preferences.

There were some changes between 1990 and 1995 at stage two: mothers in 1995 were more likely to mention sugar content, vitamin content, variety and whether the food was home cooked, and less likely to mention baby's preferences. When the babies were about nine months old, mothers in 1995 were more likely to mention nutrition generally, and less likely to mention additives and salt content.

Table 9.22

The stage three questionnaire went on to ask mothers if they avoided giving their baby foods with particular ingredients, and if so which ingredients and why. Mothers recorded the ingredients and reasons, and the answers were coded later by office coders. Fifty nine per cent of mothers in Great Britain said that they avoided particular ingredients, an increase since 1990 of eight percentage points.

The types of ingredients avoided are presented in Table 9.23. Sugar and salt were both commonly avoided (by 40% and 25% of mothers respectively), which reflects the findings in the previous table that mothers considered sugar and salt content when choosing food for their babies. Forty percent of mothers who avoided a particular ingredient (26% of all mothers) said that they avoided beef, 14% avoided nuts and 12% avoided eggs. In 1990, the proportion avoiding beef, eggs and nuts were not presented separately, but a smaller proportion of mothers avoided sugar, salt, additives and colourings in 1995 than in 1990.

Table 9.23

As in 1990, the majority of mothers gave fairly general reasons for avoiding ingredients. Nearly half (44%) said that they avoided ingredients because they were not beneficial, and 20% because they were harmful. Of the more specific reasons, publicity (mentioned by 42% of mothers), 'bad for teeth' (25%) and allergies (26%) were the most commonly mentioned.

Compared with 1990, mothers were more likely to mention allergies and publicity as a reason for avoiding particular ingredients, and less likely to mention the other reasons.

Table 9.24

Table 9.23 Ingredients avoided by mothers who gave solid food at stage 3 (1990 and 1995 Great Britain)

Mothers who avoided ingredients

Ingredients avoided	1990	1995
	Percentage avoiding each ingredient	
Sugar	53	40
Salt	45	25
Additives	19	9
Colourings	11	4
Preservatives	5	2
Fat	8	4
Flavourings	3	0
Other additives	1	2
Beef *	..	40
Eggs *	..	12
Nuts *	..	14
Spices *	..	7
Other specific foodstuffs	64	37
Other	0	3
Base	*2,649*	*2,940*

* Code introduced in 1995 previously included in other specific foodstuffs.
Percentages do not add up to 100 as some mothers avoided more than one ingredient

Table 9.24 Reasons for avoiding particular ingredients at stage 3 (1990 and 1995 Great Britain)

Mothers who avoided ingredients

Reasons for avoiding particular ingredients	1990	1995
	Percentage giving reason	
Not beneficial	47	44
Harmful	33	20
Other problems	18	9
Bad for teeth	27	25
Hyperactivity	16	4
Allergies	16	26
Developed a sweet tooth	7	5
Publicity	8	42
Other reasons	7	11
Base	*2,532*	*2,873*

Percentages do not add up to 100 as some mothers avoided more than one ingredient.

Table 9.25 Variety of solid food baby generally eats at stage 3 by feeding method

Babies who were given solid food at 8-9 months

Variety of solid food baby generally eats	Feeding method (milk)			Total *
	Breastmilk only	Breastmilk and manufactured milk	Manufactured baby milk	
	%	%	%	%
Eats most things	54	64	67	66
Eats a reasonable variety of things	40	28	28	29
Fussy or faddy eater	6	8	5	5
Base	*320*	*329*	*4,488*	*5,145*

* Includes some babies who received no milk.

The COMA Report[1] recommends that 'by the age of one year the diet should be mixed and varied' (p64). Mothers were asked in the stage three questionnaire to describe the variety of food their baby aged about nine months generally ate, using a set of precoded answers. Two thirds (66%) said that their baby ate most things, and only 5% described their baby as a fussy eater.

Mothers who were exclusively breastfeeding their baby were less likely than others to say that their baby ate most things: 54% compared with 64% of mothers who gave both breastmilk and manufactured milk and 67% of mothers who gave only manufactured baby milk.

Table 9.25

9.4 Preparing and feeding solid food

Mothers were asked at stage three whether their baby had ever fed him or herself from a spoon, and only a minority (17%) had done so. Babies in Northern Ireland were less likely to have used a spoon than other babies: 10% had done so, compared with 17% of babies in England and Wales and 19% of Scottish babies.

Table 9.26

Table 9.26 Proportion of babies who had used a spoon at stage 3 by country
Babies who were given solid food at 8-9 months

Whether baby had used a spoon	England and Wales	Scotland	Northern Ireland	United Kingdom
	%	%	%	%
Used a spoon	17	19	10	17
Not used a spoon	83	81	90	83
Base	*4,569*	*1,856*	*1,464*	*5,160*

Table 9.27 Way in which mother prepared solid foods at stage 3 by country
Babies who were given homemade solid food at 8-9 months

Way in which mother prepared solid foods	England and Wales	Scotland	Northern Ireland	United Kingdom
	Percentage using method			
Mashes the food	56	59	72	57
Sieves, blends or liquidises food into puree	26	19	20	25
Cut up the food finely	19	21	10	19
Mince the food up	4	4	2	4
Some other method	1	1	1	1
Base	*4,300*	*1,758*	*1,399*	*4,851*

Percentages do not add up to 100 as some mothers gave more than one method.

Table 9.28 Proportion of mothers who had found it difficult weaning baby onto solid food at stage 3 by country
Babies who were given solid food at 8-9 months

Whether mother had found it difficult weaning baby	England and Wales	Scotland	Northern Ireland	United Kingdom
	%	%	%	%
Yes, found it difficult	11	10	9	11
No, did not find it difficult	89	90	91	89
Base	*4,569*	*1,856*	*1,464*	*5,160*

The COMA Report[1] recommends that food consistency should progress from pureed through minced/mashed to finely chopped at about nine to twelve months (p65). Table 9.27 shows that at about nine months, over half (57%) of mothers mashed their baby's food and 19% cut it up finely. A quarter (25%) of mothers were pureeing their baby's food. There were some differences in the ways in which mothers prepared solid foods in the constituent countries of the United Kingdom. In particular, mothers in Northern Ireland were more likely than other mothers to mash the food, and less likely to puree it or to cut it up finely.

Table 9.27

9.5 Difficulties with weaning

When their babies were about nine months old, mothers who had introduced solid food were asked if they had found it difficult weaning their baby onto solid food. About a tenth (11%) said that they had found it difficult, a proportion that did not vary significantly between the constituent countries of the United Kingdom.

Table 9.28

Table 9.29 Proportion of mothers who found it difficult weaning baby onto solid food at stage 3 by method of feeding
Babies who were given solid food at 8-9 months

Whether mother had found it difficult weaning baby	Feeding method (milk)			Total *
	Breastmilk only	Breastmilk and manufactured milk	Manufactured baby milk	
	%	%	%	%
Yes, found it difficult	18	13	10	11
No, did not find it difficult	82	87	90	89
Base	*321*	*329*	*4,493*	*5,160*

* Includes some babies who received no milk.

Table 9.29 shows that breastfeeding mothers found it more difficult to wean their baby than other mothers (18% compared with 10% of bottle feeders). This reflects the finding that breast feeding mothers were also more likely to say their babies did not eat most things (Table 9.25).

Table 9.29

Mothers who said they had found it difficult were then asked in what way they had found it difficult. A set of precoded answers were presented, and if the mother ticked some other reason they were asked to

Table 9.30 Difficulties with weaning reported by mothers at stage 3 by country

Mothers who found it difficult to wean their baby

Difficulty with weaning baby onto solid food	England and Wales	Scotland	Northern Ireland	United Kingdom
	Percentage reporting difficulty			
Baby would only take certain solids	48	45	47	48
Baby prefers drinks to food	30	33	32	31
Baby was disinterested in food	30	22	18	29
Baby would not take solids	27	27	26	27
Baby vomiting	17	18	22	17
Colic	5	3	6	5
Some other reason	3	1	2	3
Base	*509*	*187*	*136*	*566*

Percentages do not add up to 100 as some mothers reported more than one difficulty.

write the reason in on the questionnaire. The most frequently mentioned difficulty was that the baby would only take certain solids (mentioned by 48% of mothers who had found weaning difficult). The baby preferring drinks to food, the baby being disinterested in food and the baby not taking solids were all mentioned by over a quarter of these mothers (31%, 29% and 27% respectively). The difficulties varied very little between the constituent countries of the United Kingdom: the only significant difference was that mothers in England and Wales were more likely to say that their baby was disinterested in food than their counterparts in Scotland and Northern Ireland.

Table 9.30

References

1   Department of Health. *Weaning and the Weaning Diet Report of the Working Group on the Weaning Diet of the Committee on Medical Aspects of Food Policy* HMSO (London: 1994)

2   Department of Health and Social Security. *Present day practice in infant feeding: third report;* Report on Health and Social Subjects 32 HMSO (London: 1988)

Appendices

Table I.1   Distribution of the population and the sample by whether single or multiple birth and country (1995)

Single or multiple birth	England and Wales		Scotland		Northern Ireland	
	Population	Survey	Population	Survey	Population	Survey
	%	%	%	%	%	%
Singleton	99	98	99	98	99	99
Twin	1	2	1	2	1	1
Triplet or higher order birth	0	0	0	0	0	-
Base:	639,071*	4,575	59,213*	1,850	23,663*	1,468

* Number of maternities resulting in at least one live birth.

Table I.2   Distribution of the population and the sample by sex of the baby and country (1995)

Sex of the baby	England and Wales		Scotland		Northern Ireland	
	Population	Survey	Population	Survey	Population	Survey
	%	%	%	%	%	%
Male	51	52	51	50	52	54
Female	49	48	49	50	48	46
Base:	648,138*	4,598	60,051*	1,863	23,860*	1,476

* Number of live births.

Table I.3   Distribution of the sample by weight at birth in grammes, sex of the baby and country (1995)

Weight of baby at birth (grammes)	England and Wales			Scotland			Northern Ireland			United Kingdom		
	Boys	Girls	Total	Boys	Girls	Total	Boys	Girls	Total	Boys	Girls	Total
	%	%	%	%	%	%	%	%	%	%	%	%
Under 2,500g	6	7	6	7	7	7	5	4	5	6	7	6
2,500g but less than 3,000g	15	21	18	14	18	16	11	14	13	15	21	18
3,000g but less than 3,500g	34	38	36	34	39	37	32	36	34	34	38	36
3,500g but less than 4,000g	32	26	29	29	28	29	35	35	35	31	27	29
4,000g but less than 4,500g	11	7	9	13	7	10	14	9	12	11	7	9
4,500g or more	2	1	2	3	1	2	2	1221	2			
Mean	3,396	3,283	3,342	3,413	3,300	3,356	3,492	3,408	3,454	3,400	3,288	3,348
Std dev	594	563	582	638	544	595	557	497	532	597	560	582
Median	3,424	3,311	3,368	3,424	3,339	3,368	3,509	3,424	3,481	3,424	3,311	3,367
Base:	2,389	2,177	4,566	916	937	1,852	791	676	1,467	2,683	2,463	5,146

Table I.4   Distribution of the population and the sample by birth order (1985, 1990 and 1995 Great Britain)

Birth order	Population*			Surveys		
	1985	1990	1995	1985	1990	1995
	%	%	%	%	%	%
First birth	40	40	39	46	45	46
Second birth	36	37	37	33	32	33
Third birth	16	16	15	14	16	14
Fourth birth	⎱8	⎱8	5⎱8	5⎱7	5⎱8	5⎱8
Fifth or later birth			3	2	3	2
Base:	584,500	554,200	467,974	5,223	5,413	5,017

* Figures based on legitimate live births only.

Table I.5   Distribution of the population and the sample by mother's age (1985, 1990 and 1995 Great Britain)

Mother's age	Population*			Surveys		
	1985	1990	1995	1985	1990	1995
	%	%	%	%	%	%
Under 20	9	8	7	8	7	6
20-24	30	26	20	30	25	19
25-29	35	36	34	35	37	34
30-34	⎱27	⎱31	28⎱40	⎱27	⎱31	28⎱40
35 or over			12			12
Base:	723,100	772,073	708,189	5,223	5,413	5,017

* Figures based on all live births.

Table I.6   Distribution of the population and the sample by social class as defined by current or last occupation of husband/partner (1985, 1990 and 1995 Great Britain)

Social class	Population*			Surveys		
	1985	1990	1995	1985	1990	1995
	%	%	%	%	%	%
I & II	24	25	25	26	26	31
IIINM	9	8	7	8	8	8
All non-manual	**33**	**33**	**32**	**34**	**34**	**39**
IIIM	28	24	19	32	30	24
IV & V	16	12	11	19	16	14
All manual	**44**	**36**	**31**	**51**	**46**	**38**
Unclassified	4	3	3	4 ⎤ 15	6 ⎤ 20	6 ⎤ 22
No husband/partner†	..	..	..	11 ⎦	14 ⎦	16 ⎦
Illegitimate**	19	28	34	..	..	
Base:	*723,000*	*772,100*	*708,189*	*5,223*	*5,413*	*5,017*

* Figures based on all live births
† Births to mothers not living with their husband or partner
** Births to unmarried mothers
Note: Due to differences in definitions, the survey figures for births to mothers with no husband/partner are not directly comparable to the population figures for illegitimate births

Table 1.7   Distribution of the sample by mother's age, for first and later births (1985, 1990 and 1995 Great Britain)

Mother's age	First births			Later births			All babies*		
	1985	1990	1995	1985	1990	1995	1985	1990	1995
	%	%	%	%	%	%	%	%	%
Under 20	16	13	12	2	2	1	8	7	6
20-24	38	31	26	23	20	14	30	25	19
25-29	31	36	34	38	39	34	35	37	34
30 or over			22			34			28
35 or over	{14}	{20}	6 {28}	{38}	{39}	17 {50}	{27}	{31}	12 {40}
Base:	*2,347*	*2,430*	*2,271*	*2,875*	*2,983*	*2,745*	*4,224*	*5,413*	*5,017*

* Includes some cases for whom the exact birth order was not known.

Table 1.8   Distribution of the sample by age at which mother completed full-time education, for first and later births (1985, 1990 and 1995 Great Britain)

Age at which mother completed full-time education	First births			Later births			All babies*		
	1985	1990	1995	1985	1990	1995	1985	1990	1995
	%	%	%	%	%	%	%	%	%
16 or under	56	49	40	63	57	48	60	54	45
17 or 18	30	35	37	23	30	33	26	32	35
Over 18	14	16	23	14	13	18	14	14	20
Base:	*2,347*	*2,430*	*2,271*	*2,875*	*2,983*	*2,745*	*5,223*	*5,413*	*5,017*

* Includes some cases for whom the exact birth order was not known.

Table I.9   Age of mothers of first babies by social class as defined by current or last occupation of husband or partner (1985, 1990 and 1995 Great Britain)

Mother's age	Social Class														
	I			II			IIINM			IIIM			IV and V		
	1985	1990	1995	1985	1990	1995	1985	1990	1995	1985	1990	1995	1985	1990	1995
	%	%	%	%	%	%	%	%	%	%	%	%			
Under 20	2	4	-	3	2	2	4	9	5	10	11	7	22	18	10
20-24	16	14	14	25	21	14	33	30	20	46	34	28	47	44	32
25-29	49	47	40	42	45	40	44	41	44	34	39	38	24	27	37
30-34			37			34			26			22			16
35 or over	{32}	{36}	8 {46}	{30}	{33}	10 {44}	{19}	{21}	6 {30}	{9}	{16}	5 {28}	{8}	{11}	5 {21}
Base:	*136*	*191*	*157*	*444*	*447*	*555*	*213*	*201*	*177*	*703*	*684*	*501*	*386*	*346*	*293*

Table I.10   Distribution of social class as defined by current or last occupation of husband/partner by age at which mother completed full-time education (1985, 1990 and 1995 Great Britain)

Social class	Mother's age at finishing full time education											
	16 or under			17 or 18			18 or over			All ages		
	1985	1990	1995	1985	1990	1995	1985	1990	1995	1985	1990	1995
	%	%	%	%	%	%	%	%	%	%	%	%
I	2	4	3	7	6	6	21	23	17	6	7	7
II	12	13	16	24	22	26	46	38	41	20	20	25
IINM	8	6	6	11	11	9	8	9	8	8	8	8
Total non manual	**21**	**23**	**26**	**42**	**39**	**42**	**75**	**70**	**66**	**34**	**35**	**39**
IIIM	37	34	28	31	31	26	13	15	13	32	30	24
IV	17	16	13	13	13	11	6	5	6	14	14	11
V	6	3	5	4	2	4	-	-	1	5	2	4
Total manual	**60**	**53**	**45**	**48**	**46**	**41**	**19**	**18**	**20**	**51**	**46**	**38**
Unclassified	5	6	7	2	6	5	4	5	6	4	6	6
No partner*	14	18	22	8	10	12	3	6	8	11	14	16
(combined)	19	24	29	10	15	18	6	11	13	15	20	22
Base:	*3,110*	*2,880*	*2,223*	*1,346*	*1,710*	*1,739*	*725*	*775*	*1,010*	*5,223*	*5,413*	*5,017*

* Births to mothers not living with their husband or partner
Note: Due to differences in definitions, the survey figures for births to mothers with no husband/partner are not directly comparable to the population figures for illegitimate births

Table I.11   Age of mothers of first babies at finishing full-time education (1985,1990 and 1995 Great Britain)

Mother's age	Mother's age at finishing full time education								
	16 or under			17 or 18			Over 18		
	1985	1990	1995	1985	1990	1995	1985	1990	1995
	%	%	%	%	%	%	%	%	%
Under 20	23	20	19	10	9	11	0	1	1
20-24	42	35	30	42	33	25	15	15	19
25-29	25	31	29	35	41	38	47	44	36
30-34	9	14	17	13	18	21	37	40	35
35 or over			6			5			9
(30-34/35+ combined)			22			25			44
Base:	*1,309*	*1,183*	*907*	*697*	*837*	*836*	*328*	*387*	*508*

Table I.12   Distribution of the sample by birth order and country (1990 and 1995)

Birth Order	England and Wales		Scotland		Northern Ireland	
	1990	1995	1990	1995	1990	1995
	%	%	%	%	%	%
First birth	45	45	48	47	38	39
Second birth	32	33	31	33	29	29
Third birth	16	14	14	14	17	19
Fourth birth	5	5	5	4	8	8
Fifth or later birth	2	3	2	2	8	5
Base:	*4,942*	*4,598*	*1,981*	*1,863*	*1,498*	*1,476*

Table I.13   Distribution of the sample by age at which mother completed full-time education, birth order and country (1990 and 1995)

Age at which mother completed full time education	First births																	
	England and Wales		Scotland		Northern Ireland		England and Wales		Scotland		Northern Ireland		England and Wales		Scotland		Northern Ireland	
	1990	1995	1990	1995	1990	1995	1990	1995	1990	1995	1990	1995	1990	1995	1990	1995	1990	1995
	%	%	%	%	%	%	%	%	%	%	%	%	%	%	%	%	%	%
16 or under	49	40	50	40	38	29	57	49	58	46	46	34	54	45	54	43	43	32
17 or 18	35	37	31	35	43	43	30	33	28	32	38	43	32	35	29	33	40	43
19 or over	16	22	19	25	20	28	13	18	15	22	16	22	14	20	17	23	18	24
Base:	*2,204*	*2,076*	*950*	*867*	*568*	*578*	*2,738*	*2,522*	*1,031*	*996*	*930*	*898*	*4,942*	*4,598*	*1,981*	*1,863*	*1,498*	*1,476*

Table I.14 **Distribution of the sample by mother's age, birth order and country (1990 and 1995)**

Mother's age	First births						Later births						All babies					
	England and Wales		Scotland		Northern Ireland		England and Wales		Scotland		Northern Ireland		England and Wales		Scotland		Northern Ireland	
	1990	1995	1990	1995	1990	1995	1990	1995	1990	1995	1990	1995	1990	1995	1990	1995	1990	1995
	%	%	%	%	%	%	%	%	%	%	%	%	%	%	%	%	%	%
Under 20	13	12	11	13	15	12	2	1	2	1	2	0	7	6	6	6	7	5
20-24	31	26	32	24	34	27	20	14	19	13	18	10	25	19	25	18	24	16
25-29	36	34	37	34	35	40	38	34	40	34	36	33	37	34	38	34	36	
30 or over	20	22⌐28	20	22⌐29	15	18⌐22	40	33⌐50	39	36⌐52	44	36⌐57	31	28⌐40	30	30⌐42	33	29⌐43
35 or over		6		7		4		17		16		21		12		12		14
Base:	2,204	2,076	950	869	568	578	2,738	2,522	1,031	998	930	898	4,942	4,598	1,981	1,863	1,498	1,476

Table I.15 **Distribution of the sample by social class as defined by current or last occupation of husband or partner and country (1990 and 1995)**

Social class	England and Wales		Scotland		Northern Ireland	
	1990	1995	1990	1995	1990	1995
	%	%	%	%	%	%
I	7	7	7	8	4	6
II	20	25	18	21	19	22
IIINM	8	8	8	7	7	11
All non-manual	**35**	**39**	**33**	**37**	**30**	**38**
IIIM	30	24	29	24	30	26
IV	14	10	13	12	9	8
V	2	4	3	4	4	4
All manual	**46**	**38**	**45**	**39**	**43**	**38**
Unclassified	6	6	6	6	8	7
No husband/partner	14	16	15	19	18	17
Base:	4,942	4,598	1,981	1,863	1,497	1,476

113

Appendix II
Sample design and weighting strategy

1 Sample design

The sample design in 1995 was similar to that of previous surveys.

In order to obtain a sufficiently large sample of births in Scotland and Northern Ireland for separate analysis, births in these two countries were given a greater chance of selection than those in England and Wales. The aim was to achieve interviews at stage three of the survey with about 1,600 mothers in each of Scotland and Northern Ireland and 4,000 mothers in England and Wales.

The 1995 survey continued the practice, established in 1985, of over-sampling births to mothers in Social Class V,[1] mothers who did not register a partner on the birth certificate and mothers whose social class could not be classified.[2] Previous surveys have shown strong associations between social class and infant feeding practices and over-sampling ensures that there are sufficient numbers for analysis as a separate group if necessary. Births to women in these categories were given twice the chance of selection of other births.

2 Drawing the sample in each country

The samples in each country were selected from births occurring in a given range of dates between August and October 1995 and were designed to be representative of all births in these periods. The number of days chosen varied between countries, and depended on the estimated number of births in each social class group which would be registered within the sampling period and other details of the sampling scheme in each country.

The dates were:

England and Wales	-	19 August to 22 September
Scotland	-	12 August to 10 September
Northern Ireland	-	12 August to 13 October

The sampling frame in each country consisted of all registrations for births on the selected dates that were received by the appropriate registration office[3] within a specified sampling period, up to a maximum of eight weeks after the birth.

England and Wales

A two-stage sample design was used in England and Wales. The 100 first-stage units were a sample of registration sub-districts or groups of smaller sub-districts. As far as possible these were the same sub-districts as used on the previous Infant Feeding Surveys. The original sub-districts used in the first survey in 1975 were selected with probability proportional to the number of births. At each subsequent survey, variation in birth rates between districts necessitated some changes to the selected sub-districts. The criteria used to determine which districts were dropped and which districts replaced them is called the Keyfitz procedure.[4] This method aims to ensure a probability of selection of each sub-district that reflects changes in birth rates while minimising the number of sampling units that need to be changed.

Within the selected sub-districts a systematic random sample of births was first selected. Social class was coded on the basis of the information about the father's occupation recorded on the birth registration. All births coded as Social Class V, where social class was unclassified or where no partner was recorded were selected for the survey sample. One in two of all other births were selected. This produced a total of 6,972 selected births in England and Wales.

Scotland and Northern Ireland

In Scotland and Northern Ireland the sample comprised all births between the specified dates to mothers in Social Class V, those with no partner or mothers whose social class could not be classified, plus one in two of all other births. This yielded a total of 2,908 births in Scotland and 2,434 births in Northern Ireland.

3 Re-weighting the results

Various weights were applied to data from the first and subsequent stages of the survey. These compensated for differences in the probability of selection for mothers in different social class groups and different countries, and for differential non-response at each stage of the survey. The stages of weighting were as follows.

i. *To correct for over-sampling of mothers in Social Class V, with no partner or whose social class was unclassifiable.*
   As babies born to mothers in this group were

given twice the chance of selection of others, the results were re-weighted by a factor of 0.5.

ii. *To correct for differential response by social class group at the first stage of the survey.*

First stage response in 1995 was considerably lower than in previous years (see Section 1.5). Information on the social class of the mother's husband or partner, based on registration data, was available for the full set sample, including non-respondents. Analysis showed that there was also a consistent pattern within each country of declining response through the range from Social Class I to Social Class V (Table II.1). This was corrected by weighting cases in each social class group within country by the inverse of the response rate for the group.

iii. *To correct for over sampling of births in Scotland and Northern Ireland.*

As births in Scotland and Northern Ireland were given a greater chance of selection than those in England and Wales, they were re-weighted to give the correct balance when showing results for Great Britain or United Kingdom. The weights were derived by comparing the proportion of sampled births in each country with the proportion of all births in 1995 in each country. The resulting weighting factors were 0.228 for births in Scotland and 0.113 for births in Northern Ireland (and 1.00 for England and Wales).

iv. *To correct for differential response by social class group, initial feeding method and by country at later stages of the survey.*

Response rates to the second and third stages of the survey continued to vary according to the mother's social class group, although to a lesser extent than at stage one, initial feeding method and also by country (Tables II.2 and II.3). In order to facilitate comparisons between different tables and parts of tables, the weights applied to data from the second and third stages were designed to give the same weighted sample sizes for each country as at the first wave. Hence estimates for the second and third stages of the survey are based on a smaller number of individuals than is suggested by the weighted base given, and so are subject to larger errors than those based on data from the first stage.

The weighted sample

Applying all these weights gives a total weighted sample of 5,181 questionnaires for the United Kingdom and 5,018 for Great Britain.

When the results for each country are shown separately, they are weighted only to compensate for differential non-response and the over sampling of the lower social class groups. This gives a total weighted sample size of 4,598 for England and Wales, 1,867 for Scotland and 1,476 for Northern Ireland.

Significance tests

Appendix III gives more detail of the calculation of standard errors and confidence intervals for survey estimates shown in the report tables. Unless otherwise stated, changes and differences mentioned in the text are statistically significant at the 95% confidence level. For data from stages two and three of the survey, the calculation of sampling errors and tests of significance are based on the actual number of questionnaires rather than the weighted totals.

Notes

1   As defined by current or last occupation of the husband/partner
2   Either because of inadequate information about the husband's or partner's job or because he had never worked.
3   Registration Division of ONS for England and Wales and the General Register Offices in Scotland and Northern Ireland.
4   Nathan Keyfitz. Sampling with probabilities proportional to size: adjustment for changes in the probabilities. *Journal of the American Association 46* (1951) pp105-109.

Table II.1 **First stage response rates by social class of husband/partner at registration and country**

Social class of husband or partner	England and Wales	Scotland	Northern Ireland
	Response rate (%)		
I	86	89	87
II	81	81	78
IIIN	76	73	79
IIIM	77	78	75
IV	74	73	71
V	70	72	63
No husband/partner*	63	57	64
Unclassified	80	70	63
All mothers	*75*	*74*	*72*

* Births to mothers not living with their husband or partner

Table II.2 **Response to wave 2 by social class as defined by current or last occupation of husband/partner at registration, whether the mother ever tried to breastfeed and country**

Social class of husband or partner	England and Wales		Scotland		Northern Ireland	
	Breastfed initially	Bottlefed from birth	Breastfed initially	Bottlefed from birth	Breastfed initially	Bottlefed from birth
			Response rate(%)			
I	89	82	94	84	94	96
II, III	89	85	89	84	96	96
IV & V, unclassified	88	81	88	78	92	91
No husband/partner *	76	74	86	65	88	92
All mothers	**88**	**82**	**89**	**80**	**95**	**94**

* Births to mothers not living with their husband or partner

Table II.3 **Response to wave 3 by social class as defined by current or last occupation of husband/partner at registration, whether the mother ever tried to breastfeed and country**

Social class of husband or partner	England and Wales		Scotland		Northern Ireland	
	Breastfed initially	Bottlefed from birth	Breastfed initially	Bottlefed from birth	Breastfed initially	Bottlefed from birth
			Response rate(%)			
I,II	86	79	88	71	88	91
III NM	84	86	76	74	88	88
III M	83	78	85	78	94	90
IV & V, unclassified	82	76	82	69	87	86
No husband/partner *	68	63	75	53	73	81
All mothers	**83**	**76**	**84**	**71**	**89**	**88**

* Births to mothers not living with their husband or partner

Appendix III
Sampling errors

1 Sources of error in surveys

Like all estimates based on samples, the results of the Infant Feeding Survey are subject to various possible sources of error. The total error in a survey estimate is the difference between the estimate derived from the data collected and the true value for the population. The total error can be divided into two main types: systematic error and random error.

Systematic error, or bias, covers those sources of error which will not average to zero over repeats of the survey. Bias may occur, for example, if certain sections of the population are omitted from the sampling frame, where non-respondents to the survey have different characteristics to respondents, or if interviewers systematically influence responses in one way or another. When carrying out a survey, substantial efforts are put into the avoidance of systematic errors but it is possible that some may still occur.

The most important component of random error is sampling error, which is the error that arises because the estimate is based on a sample survey rather than a full census of the population. The results obtained for any single sample may, by chance, vary from the true values for the population but the variation would be expected to average to zero over a number of repeats of the survey. The amount of variation depends on the size of the sample and the sample design and weighting method.

Random error may also arise from other sources, such as variation in the informant's interpretation of the questions, or interviewer variation. Efforts are made to minimise these effects through interviewer training and through pilot work.

2 Standard errors and confidence intervals

Although the estimate produced from a sample survey will rarely be identical to the population value, statistical theory allows us to measure the accuracy of any survey result. The standard error (or sampling error) can be estimated from the values obtained for the sample and this allows calculation of confidence intervals which give an indication of the range in which the true population value is likely to fall.

It is usual practice to refer to the 95% confidence interval around a survey value. This is calculated as 1.96 times the standard error on either side of the estimated percentage since, under a normal distribution, 95% of values lie within 1.96 standard errors of the mean value. If it were possible to repeat the survey under the same conditions many times, 95% of these confidence intervals would contain the population value. This does not guarantee that the intervals calculated for any particular sample will contain the population values but, when assessing the results of a single survey, it is usual to assume that there is only a 5% chance that the true population value falls outside the 95% confidence interval calculated for the survey estimate.

The 95% confidence interval for a sample percentage estimate, p, is given by the formula:

$$p +/- 1.96 \text{ x } se(p) \qquad (1)$$

where $se(p)$ represents the standard error of the percentage estimate. For results based on a simple random sample (srs), which has no clustering or stratification or weighting, estimating standard errors is straightforward. In the case of a percentage, the standard error is based on the percentage itself (p) and the subsample size (n):

$$se = \sqrt{p\ (1\text{-}p)/n} \qquad (2)$$

As described in Appendix II, the Infant Feeding Survey used a multi-stage sample design in England and Wales which involved both clustering and stratification. The samples in Scotland and Northern Ireland were simple random, but in all three countries the data were weighted to compensate for unequal sampling fractions and for differential response by social class.

In this case, therefore, the calculation of the standard error given at (2) above will be an underestimate of the true standard error of estimates for the sample in England and Wales, and hence also for Great Britain and the United Kingdom. The standard error needs to be multiplied by a design factor (deft) which allows for the complex sample design and for weighting. The design factor is simply the ratio of the standard error with a complex sample design to the standard error that would have been achieved with a simple random sample of the same size.

The true standard errors and design factors for selected Infant Feeding Survey measures are given in the following tables. For other estimates, the 95% confidence interval for a percentage from the Survey can be calculated as:

$$p +/- 1.96 \times \textit{deft} \times se(p) \qquad (3)$$

where $se(p)$ is the standard error assuming a simple random sample (see (2) above). An appropriate value of deft can be taken from those given in Tables III.1 to III.3 by selecting a variable which is likely to be clustered in the same way. It should be noted that design factors for estimates based on subsamples are generally smaller than those for estimates based on the total sample. In particular, design factors for characteristics of the sample in Scotland and Northern Ireland are around 1.00, because of the simple random sample design used in those countries. Design factors for estimates based on the sample in Great Britain will tend to be slightly smaller than those for the full United Kingdom sample.

Table III.1 Standard errors for incidence and duration of breastfeeding

Characteristic	Sample sub-group	Percentage (p)	Standard error	Design factor	Weighted base
Incidence of breastfeeding (UK)					
Country	England and Wales	67.6	1.06	1.64	4,598
	Scotland	55.2	1.04	0.96	1,863
	Northern Ireland	44.6	1.21	1.02	1,476
	Great Britain	66.5	0.98	1.79	5,017
	United Kingdom	65.8	0.96	1.93	5,181
Mothers in Great Britain					
Birth order	First birth	73.0	1.13	1.48	2,271
	Later birth	61.2	1.11	1.44	2,745
Mother's age (for first babies only)	Under 20	43.9	2.61	1.14	274
	20-24	63.9	1.98	1.22	585
	25-29	80.0	1.52	1.26	765
	30 and over	85.3	1.24	1.07	642
Age mother finished full-time education	16 or under	51.8	1.22	1.41	2,223
	17 or 18	72.5	1.14	1.27	1,739
	19 or over	88.8	0.89	1.09	1,010
Social class of husband or partner	I	89.9	1.57	1.17	337
	II	81.5	1.01	1.06	1,240
	III non-manual	71.8	2.28	1.15	385
	III manual	63.7	1.50	1.26	1,212
	IV	57.1	2.05	1.14	532
	V	50.3	3.45	1.27	179
	Unclassified	61.8	2.54	1.24	318
	No partner	47.3	2.03	1.53	815
Percentage of women who continued to breastfeed for at least 6 weeks after the birth					
Country	England and Wales	65.1	1.22	1.40	3,048
	Scotland	65.8	1.50	1.01	1,011
	Northern Ireland	55.7	1.85	0.98	645
	Great Britain	65.1	1.14	1.51	3,275
	United Kingdom	64.9	1.12	1.60	3,347
Mothers in Great Britain					
Birth order	First birth	60.2	1.46	1.35	1,644
	Later birth	70.1	1.41	1.37	1,631
Mother's age (for first babies only)	Under 20	41.0	4.86	1.19	116
	20-24	50.0	2.77	1.37	494
	25-29	61.3	1.53	1.16	1,129
	30 and over	74.7	1.39	1.38	1,530
Age mother finished full-time education	16 or under	52.8	1.72	1.25	1,105
	17 or 18	63.1	1.68	1.35	1,252
	19 or over	83.3	1.27	1.16	893
Social class of husband or partner	I	82.2	2.33	1.20	300
	II	72.9	1.48	1.15	1,025
	III non-manual	66.5	2.94	1.11	277
	III manual	57.6	1.73	1.03	761
	IV	58.6	2.67	1.02	298
	V	46.5	5.21	1.26	87
	Unclassified	61.8	3.05	1.05	178
	No partner	55.0	3.18	1.37	349
Percentage of women who continued to breastfeed for at least 4 months after the birth					
Country	England and Wales	41.8	1.16	1.29	3,048
	Scotland	44.7	1.55	1.00	1,011
	Northern Ireland	27.3	1.70	1.01	645
	Great Britain	42.0	1.08	1.39	3,275
	United Kingdom	41.7	1.06	1.48	3,347
Mothers in Great Britain					
Birth order	First birth	35.3	1.37	1.30	1,644
	Later birth	48.8	1.48	1.32	1,631
Mother's age (for first babies only)	Under 20	22.0	3.34	0.97	116
	20-24	25.8	2.34	1.32	494
	25-29	36.1	1.46	1.13	1,129
	30 and over	53.2	1.43	1.24	1,530
Age mother finished full-time education	16 or under	30.3	1.39	1.10	1,105
	17 or 18	37.4	1.44	1.16	1,252
	19 or over	63.1	1.78	1.25	893
Social class of husband or partner	I	63.0	3.18	1.30	300
	II	50.3	1.77	1.22	1,052
	III non-manual	42.5	3.43	1.23	377
	III manual	33.1	1.67	1.04	761
	IV	36.3	2.90	1.14	298
	V	25.5	4.78	1.33	87
	Unclassified	41.1	3.47	1.17	178
	No partner	28.4	2.77	1.32	349

Table III.2   Standard errors for selected measures for GB sample

Characteristic	Sample sub-group	Percentage (p)	Standard error	Design factor	Weighted base
Percentage of breastfeeding mothers who gave additional bottles at stage 1					
	Breastfeeding mothers	45.5	1.29	1.34	1,954
Percentage of breastfeeding mothers who gave additional bottles at stage 2					
	Breastfeeding mothers	42.8	1.40	1.10	1,236
Percentage of women who received milk tokens at stage 2					
		26.6	1.15	2.06	5,017
Percentage of women who received milk tokens at stage 3					
		24.0	1.08	1.91	5,017
Type of non-human milk given by bottle feeding mothers at stage 1					
Whey dominant	Mothers giving bottles	59.9	0.98	1.53	3,930
Casein dominant	Mothers giving bottles	37.3	0.98	1.55	3,930
Type of non-human milk given by bottle feeding mothers at stage 2					
Whey dominant	Mothers giving bottles	39.8	0.94	1.42	4,306
Casein dominant	Mothers giving bottles	54.3	0.98	1.44	4,306
Type of non-human milk given by bottle feeding mothers at stage 3					
Follow-on formula	Mothers giving bottles	24.8	0.87	1.47	4,667
Cow's milk	Mothers giving bottles	15.6	0.59	1.18	4,667

Table III.3 Standard errors for selected measures for UK sample

Characteristic	Sample sub-group	Percentage (p)	Standard error	Design factor	Weighted base
During pregnancy					
Attended antenatal classes		41.0	0.90	1.74	5,145
Took supplementary iron or vitamins		61.5	0.91	1.79	
Smoking					
Smoked before pregnancy		34.8	0.70	1.41	5,181
Smoked during pregnancy		23.4	0.64	1.44	5,181
Smoked at stage one		25.4	0.65	1.43	5,181
Gave up smoking during pregnancy	Smokers	33.3	0.98	1.21	1,803
Received advice on smoking	Smokers	85.6	0.98	1.62	1,795
Drinking					
Drank before pregnancy		86.1	0.83	2.28	5,165
Drank during pregnancy		65.7	0.94	1.88	5,162
Gave up drinking during pregnancy	Drinkers	23.8	0.60	1.24	4,446
Received advice on drinking	Drinkers	71.0	0.79	1.52	4,423
Percentage of women who planned to breastfeed					
Country	England & Wales	28.7	0.96	1.53	4,598
	Scotland	38.4	1.03	0.98	1,863
	Northern Ireland	48.2	1.19	1.00	1,476
	United Kingdom	30.0	0.86	1.79	5,181
Birth order (mothers in UK)	First birth	22.0	0.89	1.37	2,335
	Later birth	36.7	1.09	1.61	2,845
Percentage of women who received either *The Pregnancy Book* or *Birth to Five*					
Country	England & Wales	83.6	0.81	1.58	4,598
	Scotland	91.5	0.60	1.00	1,863
	Northern Ireland	76.2	1.02	1.01	1,476
	United Kingdom	84.0	0.72	1.88	5,181
Percentage of women who had problems finding somewhere to feed their babies in public places					
Method of feeding	Total	27.9	0.75	1.47	5,127
	Breastfed	40.3	1.76	1.45	1,244
	Not breastfed	23.9	0.68	1.26	3,884
Inroduction of solid foods					
Percentage of women who had given solid food to the baby by six weeks of age					
Country	England & Wales	6.9	0.43	1.11	4,398
	Scotland	8.4	0.67	1.02	1,817
	Northern Ireland	8.4	0.68	0.99	1,432
	United Kingdom	7.1	0.39	1.32	4,965
Method of feeding	Breastfed	0.8	0.22	0.94	1,171
	Not breastfed	9.0	0.47	1.29	3,795
Percentage of women who had given solid food to the baby by three months of age					
Country	England & Wales	54.5	1.06	1.39	4,398
	Scotland	63.8	1.12	0.98	1,817
	Northern Ireland	63.3	1.21	1.01	1,432
	United Kingdom	55.5	0.95	1.66	4,965
Method of feeding	Breastfed	33.2	1.71	1.43	1,171
	Not breastfed	62.4	0.92	1.48	3,795
Percentage of women who had given solid food to the baby by four months of age					
Country	England & Wales	91.4	0.41	0.96	4,398
	Scotland	90.6	0.70	1.01	1,817
	Northern Ireland	92.0	0.70	1.04	1,432
	United Kingdom	91.3	0.37	1.15	4,965
Method of feeding	Breastfed	85.5	0.90	1.01	1,171
	Not breastfed	93.1	0.37	1.15	3,795
Percentage of women who had given meat to baby at stage 3					
		91.7	0.44	1.35	5,162

Table III.3 (cont) **Standard errors for selected measures for UK sample**

Characteristic	Sample sub-group	Percentage (p)	Standard error	Design factor	Weighted base
Giving drinks and vitamins **Percentage of women who gave additional drinks to the baby at stage 1**					
Method of feeding	Total	54.5	0.91	1.74	5,181
	Breastfed	30.6	1.34	1.59	1,988
	Not breastfed	69.4	0.79	1.35	3,193
Percentage of women who gave vitamins to the baby at stage 1					
Method of feeding	Total	5.9	0.72	2.89	5,149
	Breastfed	5.5	1.07	2.56	1,972
	Not breastfed	6.2	0.61	1.99	3,177
Percentage of women who gave additional drinks to the baby at stage 2					
Country	England & Wales	76.4	0.82	1.29	4,598
	Scotland	77.1	1.00	1.01	1,863
	Northern Ireland	79.5	1.02	1.03	1,476
	United Kingdom	76.6	0.73	1.54	5,181
Percentage of women who gave vitamins to the baby at stage 2					
Method of feeding	Total	9.1	0.81	2.51	5,181
	Breastfed	9.6	0.96	1.32	1,252
	Not breastfed	9.0	0.83	2.30	3,929
Percentage of women who give drinks containing vitamin C with solid food to the baby at stage 2					
		20.7	0.64	1.40	5,037
Percentage of women who gave liquid cow's milk as a main drink at stage 3					
Country	England & Wales	14.1	0.59	1.08	4,598
	Scotland	19.9	1.00	1.00	1,863
	Northern Ireland	22.6	1.07	1.00	1,476
	United Kingdom	14.8	0.53	1.26	5,180
Percentage of women who gave liquid cow's milk as a secondary drink at stage 3					
Country	England & Wales	29.6	0.75	1.05	4,598
	Scotland	30.9	1.17	1.01	1,863
	Northern Ireland	32.8	1.21	1.01	1,476
	United Kingdom	29.8	0.67	1.24	5,180
Percentage of women who used liquid cow's milk to mix food at stage 3					
Country	England & Wales	52.0	0.90	1.15	4,598
	Scotland	55.1	1.25	1.00	1,863
	Northern Ireland	56.2	1.27	1.00	1,476
	United Kingdom	52.4	0.81	1.37	5,180
Percentage of women who used liquid cow's milk at stage 3					
Country	England & Wales	60.1	0.83	1.08	4,598
	Scotland	66.0	1.21	1.02	1,863
	Northern Ireland	67.3	1.21	1.01	1,476
	United Kingdom	60.8	0.74	1.29	5,180
Percentage of women who gave vitamins to the baby at stage 3					
		17.1	0.82	1.85	5,177
Additions to milk in bottles **Percentage of women who made additions to milk in bottles at stage 1**					
	Mothers giving bottles	6.4	0.37	1.28	4,045
Percentage of women who made additions to milk in bottles at stage 2					
	Mothers giving bottles	7.7	0.41	1.28	4,465
Percentage of women who made additions to milk in bottles at stage 3					
	Mothers giving bottles	11.3	0.47	1.22	4,844
Percentage of women who found it difficult to wean the baby at stage 3					
		11.0	0.46	1.23	5,162

Appendix IV
Coding frame for types of drinks

Plain or mineral water
Water from the tap
Boiled tap water
Mineral water (include "with a hint ofs..")
Purified water (bought from a shop)
Other water not otherwise specified

Water with sugar/honey added
Water with sugar added
Water with honey added

Baby drink with added sugar/glucose
Baby drink with added sugar/glucose specified

Baby drink unsweetened
Baby Ribena diluted concentrate
Baby Ribena ready to drink
Baby Ribena - not specified as ready to drink or concentrate
Diluted concentrate Baby juice drink
Ready to drink Baby juice drink
Other unsweetened baby drink - not specified as ready to drink or concentrate

Other baby drinks not otherwise specified
All other baby drinks not specified elsewhere

Herbal drinks (commercial)
Fennel
Orange and Clove
Camomile
Lemon, barley and camomile
Peach and herb
Hibiscus, apple and rosehip
Other commercial baby herbal drink

Homemade herbal or other drinks
Homemade herbal drinks with sugar/honey added
Homemade herbal drinks, unsweetened
All homemade herbal drinks not otherwise specified.
All other homemade drinks not otherwise specified

Adult drink with sugar/glucose
Diluted concentrate Ribena (not specified as baby)
Ready to drink Ribena (not specified as baby) including Ribena Spring
Ribena (not specified as baby) not specified as dilute or ready to drink
Sweetened fruit juice eg Britvic juices
Dilute concentrate squash drinks (not low calorie or diet)
Ready to drink squash drinks
Carbonated drinks
Other adult drinks with added sugar/glucose not specified as ready to drink or concentrate

Adult drinks with artificial sweetener
Dilute concentrate squash drinks with artificial sweetener
Ready to drink squash drinks with artificial sweetener
"Diet" carbonated drinks
Other drinks with artificial sweetener not specified as ready to drink or concentrate

Adult drinks unsweetened
Fresh fruit juice
Diluted squash sugar/artificial sweetener free
Ready to drink squash sugar/artificial sweetener free
Other unsweetened drink not specified as ready to drink or concentrate

Other adult drink not otherwise specified
All other unspecified adult drinks

Other drink
Fruit/herbal tea with no sugar/honey
Fruit/herbal tea with sugar/honey
Fruit or herbal tea not otherwise specified
Tea with milk, no sugar
Tea with milk and sugar/honey
Tea with sugar/honey, no milk
Tea with neither milk or sugar
Tea not otherwise specified
Milk shakes/Nesquik etc.
Hot chocolate
Ovaltine/Horlicks/Malted drinks
Other milk based drinks
Any other drink not elsewhere specified

Appendix V
Coding frames for types of foods given yesterday

A Table 9.12

Rice cereal
Baby rice (dried, tinned/jarred, other)
All adult rice products

Other cereal
Baby cereal (dried, tinned/jarred)
All types cooked at home (adult)
Porridge (adult, homemade or commercially prepared)
Pasta (adult)
Pasta with cheese (adult)
Pasta with vegetables (adult)
Other cereal products not otherwise specified (adult, homemade or commercially prepared)

Rusk

Dried babyfood
Savoury dried baby food
Dessert dried baby food
Other dried baby food

Tinned or jarred babyfood
Savoury tinned/jarred baby food
Dessert tinned/jarred baby food
Other tinned/jarred baby food

Homemade food
All fresh/homemade foods

Other food
All non-baby commercial (ready to eat/heat and serve) foods

B Table 9.13

Yoghurt
Yoghurt (homemade or commercially prepared)

Fresh fruit
Cooked fresh fruit
Raw fresh fruit

Other dessert
Homemade/commercially prepared rice pudding/semolina
Homemade/commercially prepared custard/egg custard
Other homemade desserts not otherwise specified
Ice cream
Instant Whip/Jellies
All other puddings/desserts not otherwise specified

Dried fruit or nuts
Nuts
Mixed dried fruit and nuts
Dried fruit
Fruit not otherwise specified

Egg
Whole egg
Egg yolk only

Cheese and dairy produce
Cheese
Cheese sauce
Other/mixed dairy products not otherwise specified

Meat based meal
Beef, Chicken/Turkey, Lamb, Pork, Bacon (including with vegetables/rice/pasta/pastry or pies)
Meat based stew/casserole/chili/spaghetti bolognese
Meat based soup (homemade or commercially prepared)
Meat based gravy
Meat based ready made meals (with veg/rice/pasta/pie/pastry) including sausages and beans
Meat pizza
Other meat/mixed meal

Fish based meal
Fish based meals (including with vegetables/rice/pasta/pastry or pies)
Fish fingers (including with vegetables/rice/pasta)
All types of fish

Fish based ready made meals (with veg/rice/pasta/pie/pastry)

Vegetable based meal
Vegetable based stew/casserole/pie/pastry
Vegetable based soup (homemade or commercially prepared)
Vegetable based gravy
Vegetable based ready made meals (with rice/pasta/pie/pastry)
Vegetable pizza

Potatoes
Potatoes (boiled, baked, fried with/without oil/butter - include oven chips etc.)

Other vegetables
All other types cooked
All other types raw
Tomato or other veg sauce
All other types of vegetable not otherwise specified
Baked beans
Other beans

Bread/toast
Slices of bread/bread and butter/margarine
Cheese sandwich
Egg sandwich
Meat sandwich
Vegetable sandwich
Yeast extract sandwich
Bread and jam/honey
Other sandwich not otherwise specified

Other foods
Other homemade food not otherwise specified
Soya protein
Ready made meals (sausages/burgers/mince)
Pizza n.e.s.
All other ready made meals not otherwise specified
Homemade cakes and biscuits
Commercially prepared biscuits or cakes
Sweets
Chocolate
Crisps/Savoury snacks
All other confectionery not otherwise specified
Soups n.e.s.
Commercial food products not otherwise specified

Appendix VI
Survey Documents

Five versions of the questionnaire were used, of which three are included here:

(a) the original questionnaire sent to all mothers at six weeks (stage 1);

(b) the questionnaire sent at four months to mothers who had been breastfeeding at the time of completing the first questionnaire (stage 2);

(c) the questionnaire sent at eight months to mothers who had been breastfeeding at the time of completing the second questionnaire (stage 3).

Those questionnaires not included here differed from the others only in questions omitted.

Eighteen different covering letters were used according to the stage of the survey, whether it was the initial approach or a reminder, and depending on whether the baby was born in England and Wales, Scotland or Northern Ireland. Three of the letters are included here:

(a) the initial letter at six weeks

(b) the initial letter at four months

(c) the initial letter at eight months

Survey letters

[serial number]

Date as postmark

Dear Madam

Survey of Infant Feeding

We contacted you several months ago asking for your help with a study of Infant Feeding which is being carried out by the Office of Population Censuses and Surveys (OPCS) on behalf of the UK Health Departments. On that occasion you kindly completed our questionnaire and I am writing to ask if you would help us again.

We are interested in finding out how the pattern of feeding changes as babies get older and I am enclosing a questionnaire about this which can be returned in the reply paid envelope provided.

If, for any reason, your baby is no longer with you, please tick the box on the front page of the questionnaire and return it to us so that we do not trouble you further.

OPCS is a Government department which carries out surveys for other UK departments and official bodies as well as organising the registration of births, deaths and marriages and the Census in England and Wales. All surveys carried out by OPCS rely on people's voluntary co-operation but we do hope that you will be able to take part. The information that you may give will be treated in strict confidence and will not be passed to any other Government department, business, members of the public or media.

If you have any questions about the survey or how to fill in the questionnaire please call me on 0500 600330 (you will not be charged for this call) or write to the above address. Thank you in anticipation for your help.

Yours faithfully

Hilary Such
Field Officer

IFS/W2/ORIG

On the 1 April 1996 OPCS will be merging with the Central Statistical Office to form the new Office for National Statistics. Our address and telephone number will remain the same but if we contact you again the letter will be headed as the new Office.

[serial number]

Date as postmark

Dear Madam

Survey of Infant Feeding

I am writing to ask for your help in a Survey of Infant Feeding that is being carried out by the Office of Population Censuses and Surveys (OPCS) on behalf of the Department of Health. This survey is carried out every five years to find out how feeding practices have changed over time.

We would like to hear from mothers of young babies about how they feed their babies. Since we cannot con act all mothers, we have selected names at random from the register of births and your name has been included by chance in this selection.

I realise how busy you are at the moment with a new baby but I would be very grateful if you could spare the time to fill in the enclosed questionnaire and return it in the envelope provided.

If, for any reason, your baby is no longer with you, please tick the box on the front page of the questionnaire and return it to us so that we do not trouble you further.

OPCS is a Government department responsible for organising the registration of births, deaths and marriages as well as the Census in England and Wales and which also carries out surveys for other departments and official bodies. All surveys carried out by OPCS rely on people's voluntary co-operation but we do hope that you will be able to take part. The information that you may give will be treated in strict confidence and will not be passed to any other Government department, business, members of the public or media. Information which led to your selection will not be retained and the results will not be used in any way in which they can be associated with your name or address.

If you have any questions about the survey or how to fill in the questionnaire please call Hilary Such, who is the Field Officer for this survey, on 0500 600330 (you will not be charged for this call) or write to the above address. Thank you in anticipation for your help.

Yours faithfully

Bill Jenkins
Deputy Head of Registration

IFS/W1-E.ORIG

[serial number]

Date as postmark

Dear Madam

Survey of Infant Feeding - Stage 3

We contacted you twice over the last 9 months asking for your help with a study of Infant Feeding which is being carried out on behalf of the UK Health Departments. On both occasions you kindly completed our questionnaire and I am writing to ask if you would help us again for a third time.

We are interested in finding out how the pattern of feeding changes as babies reach 9 to 10 months old and I am enclosing a questionnaire about this which can be returned in the reply paid envelope provided.

If, for any reason, your baby is no longer with you, please tick the box on the front page of the questionnaire and return it to us so that we do not trouble you further.

On the 1st April 1996, the Office of Population Censuses and Surveys merged with the Central Statistical Office to form the Office for National Statistics (ONS). ONS is the new Government department responsible for producing official social and economic statistics for the nation as well as organising the registration of births, deaths and marriages and the Census in England and Wales.

All surveys carried out by ONS rely on people's voluntary co-operation but we do hope that you will be able to take part. The information that you may give will be treated in strict confidence and will not be passed to any other Government department, business, members of the public or media.

If you have any questions about the survey or how to fill in the questionnaire please call me on 0500 600330 (you will not be charged for this call) or write to the above address. Thank you in anticipation for your help.

Yours faithfully

Hilary Such
Field Officer

IFS/W3/ORIG

Stage 1 questionnaire

3. Sometimes there will be some shaded boxes to the right of a question that look like this

   These are for use in the office and you should ignore them.

   Example: [ ]

4. Sometimes you are asked to give an age or a length of time in weeks and days or days and hours. Please follow the instructions very carefully.

   For example

   How old is your baby?

   If your baby is 6 weeks and 2 days old enter the number of whole weeks plus any additional days

   Please enter numbers in both boxes

   Example: [6] weeks and [2] days

5. Usually after answering each question you go on to the next one unless a box you have ticked has an arrow next to it with an instruction to go to another question

   Example: Yes [✓] → **Go to Q5**

   No [ ]

   By following the arrows carefully you will miss out some questions which do not apply, so the amount you have to fill in will make the questionnaire shorter than it looks.

6. If you cannot remember, do not know, or are unable to answer a particular question please write that in.

7. When you have finished please post the questionnaire to us as soon as possible in the reply-paid envelope provided, even if you were not able to answer all of it.

   We are very grateful for your help

cs-13871 V6

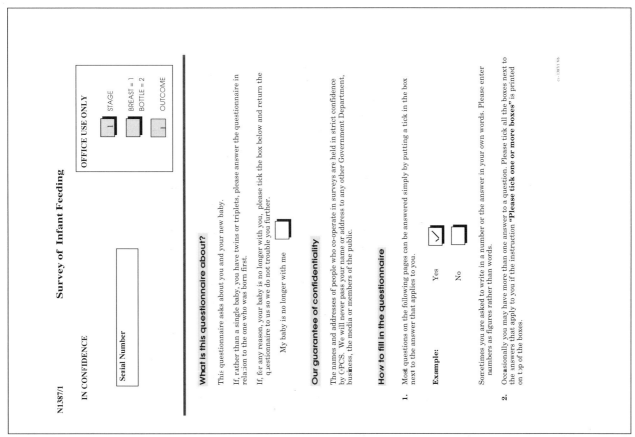

N1387/1   **Survey of Infant Feeding**

IN CONFIDENCE

OFFICE USE ONLY

STAGE [1]

BREAST = 1
BOTTLE = 2 [ ]

OUTCOME [ ]

Serial Number [ ]

What is this questionnaire about?

This questionnaire asks about you and your new baby.

If, rather than a single baby, you have twins or triplets, please answer the questionnaire in relation to the one who was born first.

If, for any reason, your baby is no longer with you, please tick the box below and return the questionnaire to us so we do not trouble you further.

My baby is no longer with me [ ]

Our guarantee of confidentiality

The names and addresses of people who co-operate in surveys are held in strict confidence by CPCS. We will never pass your name or address to any other Government Department, business, the media or members of the public.

How to fill in the questionnaire

1. Most questions on the following pages can be answered simply by putting a tick in the box next to the answer that applies to you.

   Example: Yes [✓]

   No [ ]

   Sometimes you are asked to write in a number or the answer in your own words. Please enter numbers as figures rather than words.

2. Occasionally you may have more than one answer to a question. Please tick all the boxes next to the answers that apply to you if the instruction **"Please tick one or more boxes"** is printed on top of the boxes.

cs-13871 V6

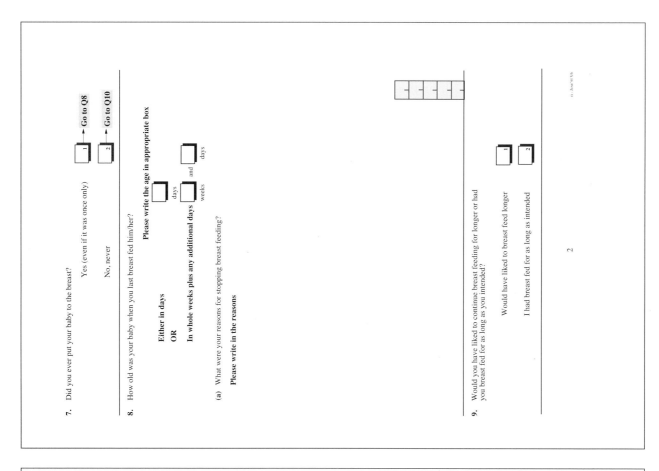

7. Did you ever put your baby to the breast?

Yes (even if it was once only) — 1 → **Go to Q8**

No, never — 2 → **Go to Q10**

8. How old was your baby when you last breast fed him/her?

Please write the age in appropriate box

Either in days [ ] days

OR

In whole weeks plus any additional days [ ] weeks and [ ] days

(a) What were your reasons for stopping breast feeding?

Please write in the reasons

9. Would you have liked to continue breast feeding for longer or had you breast fed for as long as you intended?

Would have liked to breast feed longer — 1

I had breast fed for as long as intended — 2

2

Section 1 - About your baby

First of all we would like to ask some general questions before finding out how you feed your baby at present.

1. What is your baby's first name? **Please write in below - 1 letter per box** [ ][ ][ ][ ][ ][ ][ ][ ]

2. How old is your baby? **Please write numbers in both boxes**

Write in how many whole weeks plus any additional days [ ] weeks and [ ] days

3. Is your baby a boy or a girl?

Boy — 1

Girl — 2

4. Is this your first baby?

Yes — 1

No — 2

5. Is your baby one of twins or triplets?

No, neither — 1

Yes, twin — 2

Yes, triplet — 3

If you have twins or triplets please complete this questionnaire with respect to the one that was born first.

Section 2 - About the milk that you give your baby

6. At the moment is your baby . . .

breast fed — 1 → **Go to (a)**

bottle fed — 2 → **Go to Q7**

or both? — 3 → **Go to Q10**

(a) Do you ever give your baby milk in a bottle at present (apart from expressed breast milk)?

Yes (even if only occasionally) — 1 → **Go to Q10**

No — 2 → **Go to Q16**

1

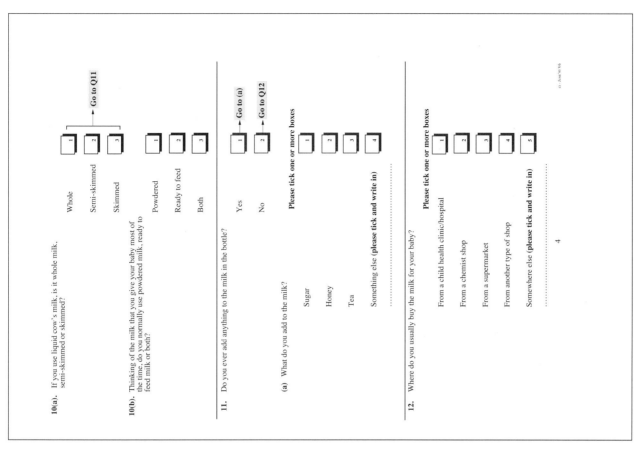

10(a). If you use liquid cow's milk, is it whole milk, semi-skimmed or skimmed?

- Whole [1]
- Semi-skimmed [2] → **Go to Q11**
- Skimmed [3]

10(b). Thinking of the milk that you give your baby most of the time, do you normally use powdered milk, ready to feed milk or both?

- Powdered [1]
- Ready to feed [2]
- Both [3]

11. Do you ever add anything to the milk in the bottle?

- Yes [1] → **Go to (a)**
- No [2] → **Go to Q12**

(a) What do you add to the milk?   **Please tick one or more boxes**

- Sugar [1]
- Honey [2]
- Tea [3]
- Something else (please tick and write in) [4]

....

12. Where do you usually buy the milk for your baby?   **Please tick one or more boxes**

- From a child health clinic/hospital [1]
- From a chemist shop [2]
- From a supermarket [3]
- From another type of shop [4]
- Somewhere else (please tick and write in) [5]

....

4

G - June '95 V6

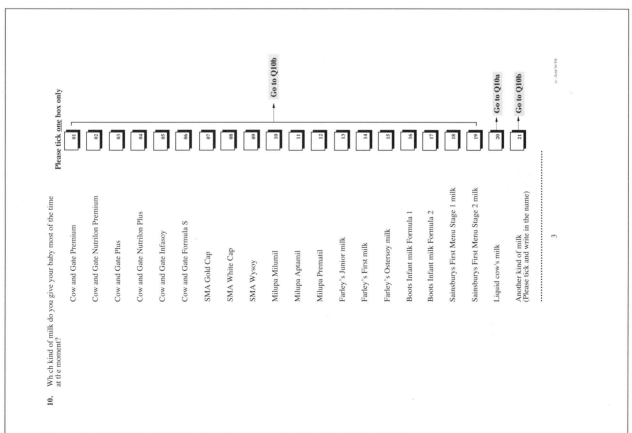

10. Which kind of milk do you give your baby most of the time, at the moment?

Please tick one box only

- Cow and Gate Premium [01]
- Cow and Gate Nutrilon Premium [02]
- Cow and Gate Plus [03]
- Cow and Gate Nutrilon Plus [04]
- Cow and Gate Infasoy [05]
- Cow and Gate Formula S [06]
- SMA Gold Cap [07]
- SMA White Cap [08]
- SMA Wysoy [09]
- Milupa Milumil [10] → **Go to Q10b**
- Milupa Aptamil [11]
- Milupa Prematil [12]
- Farley's Junior milk [13]
- Farley's First milk [14]
- Farley's Ostersoy milk [15]
- Boots Infant milk Formula 1 [16]
- Boots Infant milk Formula 2 [17]
- Sainsburys First Menu Stage 1 milk [18]
- Sainsburys First Menu Stage 2 milk [19]
- Liquid cow's milk [20] → **Go to Q10a**
- Another kind of milk (Please tick and write in the name) [21] → **Go to Q10b**

....

3

G - June '95 V6

13. Have you always used the milk mentioned at question 10 or have you changed type of milk at all (apart from changing from breast milk)?

Have always used the same type of milk [1] → Go to Q15

Have used other types of milk [2] → Go to Q14

14. Why did you change types of milk? **Please tick one or more boxes**

Baby was not satisfied/still hungry [1]

Baby kept being sick [2]

Baby was constipated [3]

Baby was allergic to the milk [4]

I preferred a different type to the one that I was given in hospital [5]

Other reason (please tick and write in the reason) [6]

....

15. Do you get milk tokens for free or reduced price milk?

Yes [1] → Go to (a)

No [2] → Go to Q16

(a) Where do you exchange the tokens for milk? **Please tick one or more boxes**

At a child health clinic/hospital [1]

With the milkman [2]

At a supermarket [3]

At another type of shop [4]

Somewhere else (please tick and write in) [5]

....

5

Section 3 About other drinks and food that you may give to your baby

16. Do you give your baby plain tap or mineral water to drink at the moment?

Yes [1] → Go to (a)

No [2] → Go to Q17

(a) Do you add sugar or honey to the water that you give to your baby? **Please tick one or more boxes**

Sugar [1]

Honey [2]

Neither [3]

17. Apart from plain tap or mineral water, are you giving your baby anything else to drink at the moment (such as fruit juice, squash or herbal drink)?

Yes [1] → Go to (a)

No [2] → Go to Q19

(a) Please list the drinks giving the brand name (or say if it is homemade) and the flavour and say if it is a special baby drink or not.

Brand (or homemade)	Flavour	Please tick if it is a baby drink

18. Do you give your baby drinks mainly **Please tick one or more boxes**

Because he/she is thirsty [1]

To give him/her extra vitamins [2]

To help his/her colic/wind [3]

To help his/her constipation [4]

To settle him/her [5]

Some other reason (please tick and write in the reason) [6]

....

6

Section 4 About vitamins for your baby and yourself

22. Do you give your baby any extra vitamins (apart from fruit drinks mentioned at question 17)?

Yes ☐1 ──► **Go to (a) and (b)**

No ☐2 ──► **Go to Q23**

(a) Do you use Children's Vitamin Drops from the child health clinic or another brand?

Children's Vitamin Drops ☐1

Other brand (**please tick and write in full name**) ☐2

....

(b) How do you usually get the vitamins?   **Please tick one box only**

Buy the vitamins myself at the child health clinic/hospital ☐1

Buy the vitamins somewhere else ☐2

Get the vitamins **free** at the child health clinic/hospital ☐3

Get vitamins **on prescription** ☐4

Other (**please tick and describe**) ☐5

....

8

ci-June'95 V6

---

19. Has your baby ever had any foods such as cereal, rusk or any other kind of solid food?

Yes ☐1 ──► **Go to (a)**

No ☐2 ──► **Go to Q22**

(a) How old was your baby when he/she first had any food apart from milk?

Please write in the age to the nearest whole week

Please write a number in the box

weeks old

20. At present, are you regularly giving your baby cereal, rusks or any other solid food?

Yes ☐1 ──► **Go to Q21**

No ☐2 ──► **Go to Q22**

21. Can you list all the cereal, rusks or solid food that your baby ate yesterday. Please describe each fully, giving the brand name and the stage (1 or 2) if relevant.

Didn't have solids yesterday ☐1 ──► **Go to Q22**

Type of food (and stage)	Brand (or home made)		

7

ci-June'95 V6

23. Are you taking any extra vitamin or iron supplements **yourself** either in tablet or powder form?

Yes ☐1 → **Go to (a) and (b)**

No ☐2 → **Go to Q24**

(a) What type of supplements are you taking?

Please tick one or more boxes

Iron only ☐1

Vitamins only ☐2

Vitamins and iron combined ☐3

Something else (**please tick and describe**) ☐4
....

(b) How do you usually get the vitamins or iron supplements?

Please tick one box only

Buy the vitamin or iron supplements myself at the child health clinic/hospital ☐1

Buy the vitamin or iron supplements somewhere else ☐2

Get the vitamin or iron supplements **free** at the child health clinic/hospital ☐3

Get the vitamin or iron supplements **on prescription** ☐4

Other (**please tick and describe**) ☐5
....

9

Section 5 About when you were pregnant

24. Thinking back to when you became pregnant, did you know that increasing your intake of folic acid can be good for you in the early stages of pregnancy?

Yes ☐1 → **Go to (a)**

No ☐2 → **Go to Q25**

(a) Did you change your diet or take supplements to increase your intake of folic acid in the first few months of your pregnancy?

Please tick one or more boxes

Yes, I changed my diet ☐1

Yes, I took supplements ☐2

No neither ☐3

25. When you were pregnant, did you take any extra vitamin or iron supplements either in tablet or powder form?

Yes ☐1 → **Go to (a)**

No ☐2 → **Go to Q26**

(a) What type of supplements did you take?

Please tick one or more boxes

Iron only ☐1

Vitamins only ☐2

Vitamins and iron combined ☐3

Something else (**please tick and describe**) ☐4
....

10

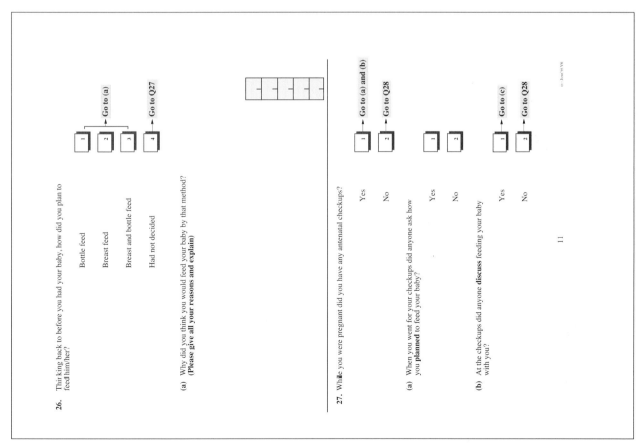

26. Thinking back to before you had your baby, how did you plan to feed him/her?

Bottle feed [1] ⎤
Breast feed [2] ⎬ → **Go to (a)**
Breast and bottle feed [3] ⎦
Had not decided [4] → **Go to Q27**

(a) Why did you think you would feed your baby by that method? **(Please give all your reasons and explain)**

27. While you were pregnant did you have any antenatal checkups?

Yes [1] → **Go to (a) and (b)**
No [2] → **Go to Q28**

(a) When you went for your checkups did anyone ask how you **planned** to feed your baby?

Yes [1] → **Go to (c)**
No [2] → **Go to Q28**

(b) At the checkups did anyone **discuss** feeding your baby with you?

Yes [1] → **Go to (c)**
No [2] → **Go to Q28**

11

(c) Who discussed feeding your baby with you?

Please tick one or more boxes

Doctor [1]
Health visitor [2]
Midwife [3]
Nurse [4]
Someone else **(Please tick and write in)** [5]

28. While you were pregnant with this baby did you go to any classes to prepare you for having the baby?

Yes [1] → **Go to (a) and (b)**
No [2] → **Go to Q29**

(a) Who were the classes organised by?

Please tick one or more boxes

A hospital [1]
A clinic/doctor's surgery/health centre [2]
Voluntary organisation (such as the National Childbirth Trust, La Leche League or the Association of Breastfeeding Mothers) [3]
Someone else **(Please tick and write in)** [4]

(b) Did you attend any classes that included talks or discussions about feeding babies?

Yes [1] → **Go to (c)**
No [2] → **Go to Q29**

(c) Were you taught how to make up bottles of milk at the classes you attended?

Yes [1]
No [2]

12

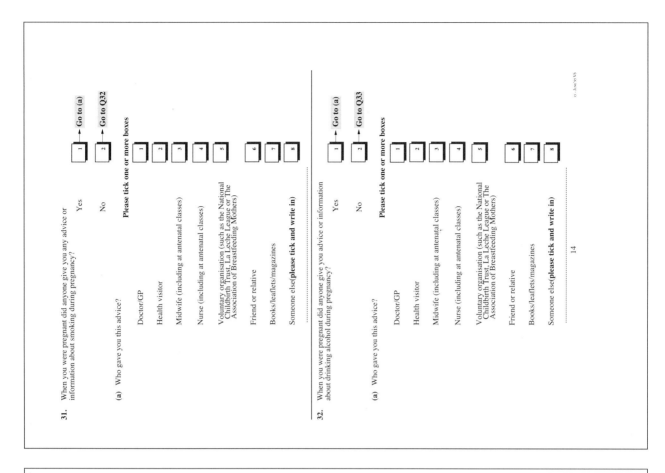

31. When you were pregnant did anyone give you any advice or information about smoking during pregnancy?

Yes ☐ 1 → **Go to (a)**

No ☐ 2 → **Go to Q32**

(a) Who gave you this advice?

Please tick one or more boxes

Doctor/GP ☐ 1

Health visitor ☐ 2

Midwife (including at antenatal classes) ☐ 3

Nurse (including at antenatal classes) ☐ 4

Voluntary organisation (such as the National Childbirth Trust, La Leche League or The Association of Breastfeeding Mothers) ☐ 5

Friend or relative ☐ 6

Books/leaflets/magazines ☐ 7

Someone else (**please tick and write in**) ☐ 8

32. When you were pregnant did anyone give you advice or information about drinking alcohol during pregnancy?

Yes ☐ 1 → **Go to (a)**

No ☐ 2 → **Go to Q33**

(a) Who gave you this advice?

Please tick one or more boxes

Doctor/GP ☐ 1

Health visitor ☐ 2

Midwife (including at antenatal classes) ☐ 3

Nurse (including at antenatal classes) ☐ 4

Voluntary organisation (such as the National Childbirth Trust, La Leche League or The Association of Breastfeeding Mothers) ☐ 5

Friend or relative ☐ 6

Books/leaflets/magazines ☐ 7

Someone else (**please tick and write in**) ☐ 8

14

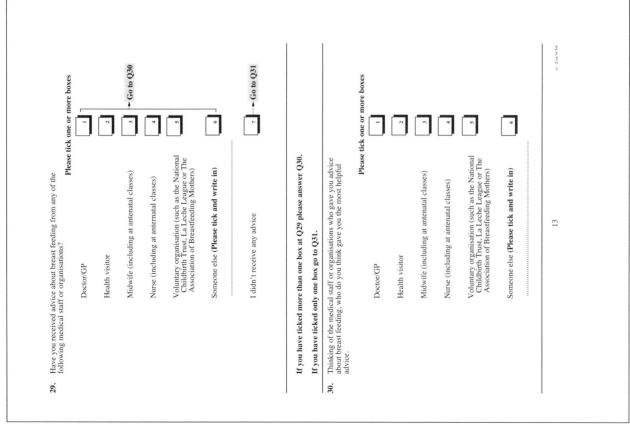

29. Have you received advice about breast feeding from any of the following medical staff or organisations?

Please tick one or more boxes

Doctor/GP ☐ 1

Health visitor ☐ 2

Midwife (including at antenatal classes) ☐ 3

Nurse (including at antenatal classes) ☐ 4

Voluntary organisation (such as the National Childbirth Trust, La Leche League or The Association of Breastfeeding Mothers) ☐ 5

Someone else (**Please tick and write in**) ☐ 6

→ **Go to Q30**

I didn't receive any advice ☐ 7 → **Go to Q31**

If you have ticked more than one box at Q29 please answer Q30.
If you have ticked only one box go to Q31.

30. Thinking of the medical staff or organisations who gave you advice about breast feeding, who do you think gave you the most helpful advice.

Please tick one or more boxes

Doctor/GP ☐ 1

Health visitor ☐ 2

Midwife (including at antenatal classes) ☐ 3

Nurse (including at antenatal classes) ☐ 4

Voluntary organisation (such as the National Childbirth Trust, La Leche League or The Association of Breastfeeding Mothers) ☐ 5

Someone else (**Please tick and write in**) ☐ 6

13

Section 6 About the birth of your baby

36. Was your baby born in hospital or at home?

In hospital ☐ 1 → **Go to (a)**

At home ☐ 2 → **Go to Q37**

(a) How long after the baby was born did you stay in hospital?

Please enter number in one box only

Either
How many **hours** did you spend in hospital ☐ hours

Or
How many **days** did you spend in hospital ☐ days

37. Thinking now of the birth itself, what type of delivery did you have?

Normal ☐ 1

Forceps ☐ 2

Vacuum extraction ☐ 3

Caesarean ☐ 4

38. While you were in labour were you given any of these?

Please tick one or more boxes

An epidural (spinal) injection ☐ 1

Another type of injection to lessen the pain (eg pethidine) ☐ 2

Gas and oxygen to breathe ☐ 3

A general anaesthetic (to make you unconscious) ☐ 4

Something else (**please tick and write in**) ☐ 5

....

Nothing at all ☐ 6

16

---

33. Did a midwife or health visitor see you at home in connection with your pregnancy before you had the baby?

Yes, midwife ☐ 1

Yes, health visitor ☐ 2

No, neither ☐ 3

34. Do you know any mothers with young babies?

Yes ☐ 1 → **Go to (a)**

No ☐ 2 → **Go to Q35**

(a) Would you say that most of the mothers you know with young babies bottle fed or breast fed?

Please tick one box only

Most of them bottle fed ☐ 1

Most of them breast fed ☐ 2

About half of them bottle fed and half of them breast fed ☐ 3

Don't know ☐ 4

35. Do you know whether you were breast fed or bottle fed when you were a baby?

Breast fed entirely ☐ 1

Bottle fed entirely ☐ 2

Both breast and bottle fed ☐ 3

Don't know ☐ 4

15

39. How much did your baby weigh when he/she was born?

Either What your baby weighed in **grams** [ ] gms

Or What your baby weighed in **pounds and ounces** [ ] lbs and [ ] ozs

40. About how long after your baby was born did you first hold him/her?

Please tick one box only

Immediately/within a few minutes [1]
Within an hour [2]
More than 1 hour, up to 12 hours [3]
More than 12 hours later [4]

41. After the birth were you alright or was anything the matter with you?

Alright [1] → **Go to Q42**
Something the matter [2] → **Go to (a)**

(a) Did this problem affect your ability to feed your baby the way you wanted to?

Yes [1]
No [2]

42. Was your baby put into special care at all, or put under a lamp for jaundice?

Please tick one or more boxes

Yes, put into special care [1] ⎫
Yes, put under a lamp [2] ⎬ → **Go to (a) and (b)**
No, neither [3] → **Go to Q43**

(a) For how long was your baby put into special care or put under a lamp?

One day or less [1]
Two or three days [2]
Four days or more [3]

17

(b) Did having your baby in special care or under a lamp affect your ability to feed your baby the way you wanted to?

Yes [1]
No [2]

43. The first time you fed your baby did anyone give you any advice or show you what to do?

Yes [1] → **Go to (a) and (b)**
No [2] → **Go to (c)**

(a) Who was this?

Please tick one or more boxes

Midwife [1] ⎫
Nurse [2] ⎪
Doctor [3] ⎬ → **Go to (b)**
Friend/relative [4] ⎪
Someone else (**please tick and write in**) [5] ⎭

....

(b) Was the advice helpful?

Yes [1] ⎫ → **Go to Q44**
No [2] ⎭

(c) Would you have liked any help or advice?

Yes [1]
No [2]

18

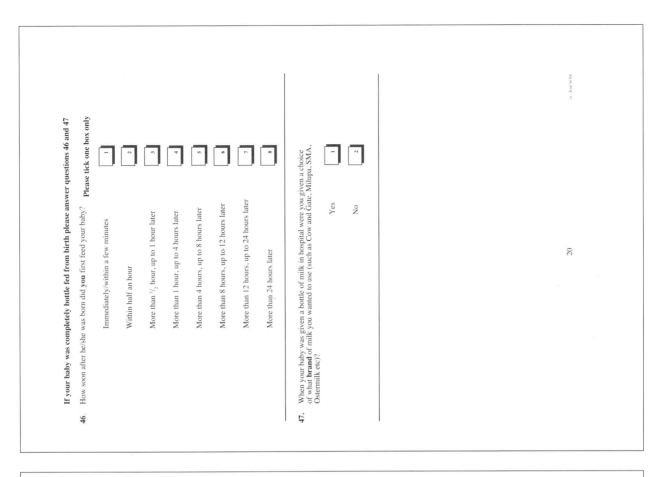

If your baby was completely bottle fed from birth please answer questions 46 and 47

46. How soon after he/she was born did **you** first feed your baby? **Please tick one box only**

- Immediately/within a few minutes ☐ 1
- Within half an hour ☐ 2
- More than 1/2 hour, up to 1 hour later ☐ 3
- More than 1 hour, up to 4 hours later ☐ 4
- More than 4 hours, up to 8 hours later ☐ 5
- More than 8 hours, up to 12 hours later ☐ 6
- More than 12 hours, up to 24 hours later ☐ 7
- More than 24 hours later ☐ 8

47. When your baby was given a bottle of milk in hospital were you given a choice of what **brand** of milk you wanted to use (such as Cow and Gate, Milupa, SMA, Ostermilk etc)?

- Yes ☐ 1
- No ☐ 2

20

G. June '95 V6

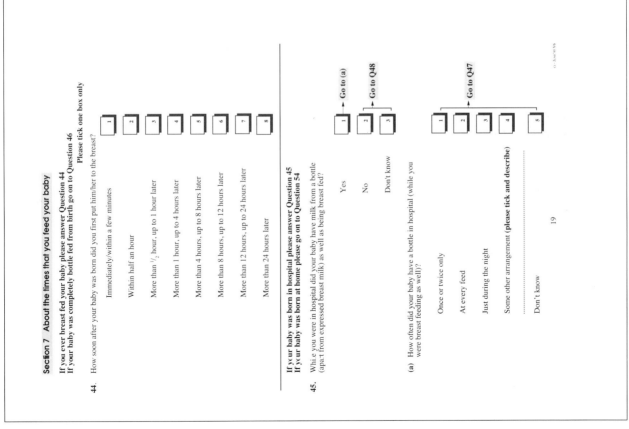

Section 7   About the times that you feed your baby

If you ever breast fed your baby please answer Question 44
If your baby was completely bottle fed from birth go on to Question 46

Please tick one box only

44. How soon after your baby was born did you first put him/her to the breast?

- Immediately/within a few minutes ☐ 1
- Within half an hour ☐ 2
- More than 1/2 hour, up to 1 hour later ☐ 3
- More than 1 hour, up to 4 hours later ☐ 4
- More than 4 hours, up to 8 hours later ☐ 6
- More than 8 hours, up to 12 hours later ☐ 7
- More than 12 hours, up to 24 hours later ☐ 8
- More than 24 hours later

If your baby was born in hospital please answer Question 45
If your baby was born at home please go on to Question 54

45. While you were in hospital did your baby have milk from a bottle (apart from expressed breast milk) as well as being breast fed?

- Yes ☐ 1 → **Go to (a)**
- No ☐ 2 → **Go to Q48**
- Don't know ☐ 3

(a) How often did your baby have a bottle in hospital (while you were breast feeding as well)?

- Once or twice only ☐ 1
- At every feed ☐ 2 → **Go to Q47**
- Just during the night ☐ 3
- Some other arrangement (please tick and describe) ☐ 4
  ....
- Don't know ☐ 5

19

G. June '95 V6

Section 8 About when you were in hospital

If your baby was born at home please go to Question 54

48. Did your baby stay beside you all the time you were in hospital?

Yes 1 → **Go to Q49**

No 2 → **Go to (a)**

(a) Even though he/she was not always beside you, did you always feed your baby yourself or did the midwives or nurses ever feed him/her?

Always fed baby myself 1 → **Go to Q49**

Midwives/nurses sometimes fed baby 2 → **Go to (b)**

(b) What did the midwives/nurses give your baby?

Please tick one or more boxes

Expressed breast milk 1

Manufactured baby milk 2

Dextrose or glucose water 3

Water 4

Don't know 5

21

---

49. Were there any problems feeding your baby while you were in hospital?

Yes 1 → **Go to (a)**

No 2 → **Go to Q51**

(a) What problems were there?
   (Please describe)

50. Did anyone give you any help or advice about this/these problems?

Yes 1 → **Go to (a)**

No 2 → **Go to Q51**

(a) Who helped or advised you?

Please tick one or more boxes

Midwife 1

Nurse 2

Doctor 3

Someone else (please tick and write in) 4

51. While you were in hospital were you always able to get help or advice when you needed it?

Yes - always 1

Yes - generally 2

No 3

22

56. Has your baby had a development check-up yet?

Yes ☐1 → **Go to (a)**

No ☐2 → **Go to Q57**

(a) Where did your baby have the development check-up?

At the child health clinic/hospital ☐1

At your family doctor's (GP) ☐2

At home ☐3

Somewhere else (**please tick and write in**) ☐4

....

57. Have you received help or advice from a voluntary organisation which helps new mothers (such as the National Childbirth Trust, La Leche League or the Association of Breast Feeding Mothers)?

Yes ☐1

No ☐2

58. Since you left hospital have you had any problems with feeding your baby?

(If your baby was born at home please answer about any feeding problems since the birth)

Yes ☐1 → **Go to (a)**

No ☐2 → **Go to Q60**

(a) What problems have you had? (**Please describe**)

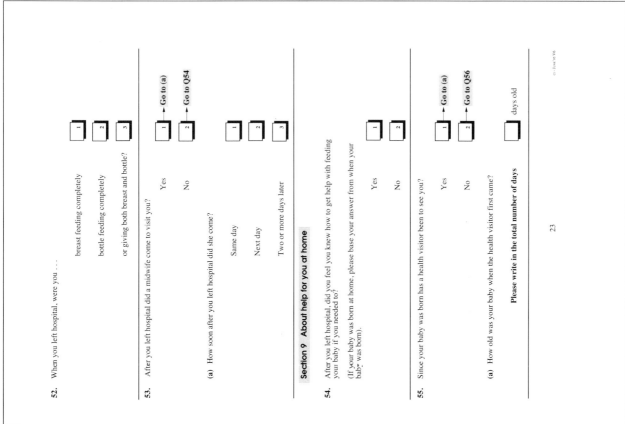

24

---

52. When you left hospital, were you . . .

breast feeding completely ☐1

bottle feeding completely ☐2

or giving both breast and bottle? ☐3

53. After you left hospital did a midwife come to visit you?

Yes ☐1 → **Go to (a)**

No ☐2 → **Go to Q54**

(a) How soon after you left hospital did she come?

Same day ☐1

Next day ☐2

Two or more days later ☐3

Section 9 About help for you at home

54. After you left hospital, did you feel you knew how to get help with feeding your baby if you needed to?

(If your baby was born at home, please base your answer from when your baby was born).

Yes ☐1

No ☐2

55. Since your baby was born has a health visitor been to see you?

Yes ☐1 → **Go to (a)**

No ☐2 → **Go to Q56**

(a) How old was your baby when the health visitor first came?

☐ days old

Please write in the total number of days

23

59. Did anyone give you any help or advice about this/these problems?

Yes ☐1 → **Go to (a)**
No ☐2 → **Go to Q60**

(a) Who helped or advised you?

Please tick one or more boxes

Doctor/GP ☐1
Health visitor ☐2
Midwife ☐3
Nurse ☐4
Friend or relative ☐5
Books/leaflets/magazines ☐6
Someone else **(please tick and write in)** ☐7

....

60. During your pregnancy or since the birth of your baby were you given a copy of either of these books?

Please tick one or more boxes

The Pregnancy Book (Health Education Authority) ☐1

The book called Birth to Five (Health Education Authority or Health Education Board for Scotland) ☐2

Section 10 About yourself

61. Have you ever smoked cigarettes?

Yes ☐1 → **Go to (a)**
No ☐2 → **Go to Q63**

(a) Do you smoke at all nowadays?

Yes ☐1 → **Go to Q62**
No ☐2 → **Go to (b)**

(b) Have you smoked at all in the past two years?

Yes ☐1 → **Go to Q62**
No ☐2 → **Go to Q63**

62 . **(a)** About how many cigarettes a day were you smoking **before you became pregnant?**

If the number smoked varied, please give an average

Please write in the number of cigarettes a day
(If none, write 0) ☐ → **Go to (b)**

(b) About how many cigarettes a day were you smoking **when you were pregnant?**

If the number smoked varied, please give an average ☐ → **Go to (c)**

(c) About how many cigarettes a day are you smoking **now?**

If the number smoked varies, please give an average ☐ → **Go to Q63**

63. Do you ever drink alcohol nowadays, including drinks you brew or make at home? **(Please exclude low or non alcoholic drinks)**

Yes ☐1 → **Go to Q65**
No ☐2 → **Go to Q64**

64. Have you drunk alcohol at all during the past two years?

Yes ☐1 → **Go to Q65**
No ☐2 → **Go to Q69**

67. During your pregnancy would you say you drank more, less or about the same amount of alcohol than before you were pregnant?

I drank **much more** during pregnancy than before	1	→ Go to (a)
I drank **more** during pregnancy than before	2	
I drank **about the same** during pregnancy as before	3	→ Go to Q68
I drank **less** during pregnancy than before	4	→ Go to (a)
I drank **much less** during pregnancy than before	5	

(a) Why did you change your drinking habits during pregnancy?

Please tick one or more boxes

Drinking alcohol made me feel sick	1
I disliked the taste of alcohol when I was pregnant	2
Alcohol cheered me up and made me feel better	3
Alcohol might harm my baby	4
I had personal/family problems	5
Some other reason (**please tick and write in**)	6

28

---

65. Thinking back to **when you were pregnant** please tick the box that best describes how often you usually drank each of the alcoholic drinks listed below.

(Please exclude low or non alcoholic drinks)

During pregnancy I usually drank:

	Most days	3-4 times a week	Once or twice a week	Once or twice a month	Very occasionally	Not at all
Shandy	1	2	3	4	5	6
Beer/lager/stout/cider	1	2	3	4	5	6
Wine/baby cham/champagne	1	2	3	4	5	6
Sherry/martini/vermouth/port	1	2	3	4	5	6
Spirits/liqueurs (eg. gin, whisky, rum, brandy, vodka)	1	2	3	4	5	6

Please check that there is a tick in one box on each line

66. For each type of drink you say that you had when you were pregnant, please write in the boxes the amount you usually drank each time that you had a drink

(If none write 0)

Shandy	half pints		
Beer/lager/stout/cider	half pints	large cans	small cans
Wine/babycham/champagne	glasses		
Sherry martini/vermouth/port	glasses		
Spirits/liqueurs (eg. gin, whisky, rum, brandy, vodka)	single measures (count double measures as 2)		

27

68. Compared with when you were pregnant, would you say you drink more, less or about the same nowadays?

I drink **much more** nowadays — 1 → **Go to (a)**

I drink **more** nowadays — 2 → **Go to (a)**

I drink **about the same** nowadays — 3 → **Go to Q69**

I drink **less** nowadays — 4 → **Go to (a)**

I drink **much less** nowadays — 5 → **Go to (a)**

(a) Why have you changed your drinking habits since the birth of your baby?

Please tick one or more boxes

I've had my baby now so I don't have to worry about the effect of alcohol on the baby — 1

I've got to like the taste of alcohol again — 2

Alcohol cheers me up and makes me feel better — 3

Alcohol does not make me feel sick any more — 4

Alcohol might affect my milk — 5

I do not like the taste of alcohol any more — 6

I have personal/family problems — 7

Some other reason (**please tick and write in**) — 8

....

The following question is about your family planning

69. Since your baby was born have you used either the combined pill or mini-pill (progesterone only) to prevent pregnancy?

Yes — 1 → **Go to (a)**

No — 2 → **Go to Q70**

(a) How old was your baby when you began to take the pill?

Write in how many whole weeks plus any additional days

[ ] weeks and [ ] days

If this is your first baby, please go on to Question 71

70. If this is not your first baby, we would like to know how you fed your previous children. Please fill in the details below, but **do not include your latest baby.**

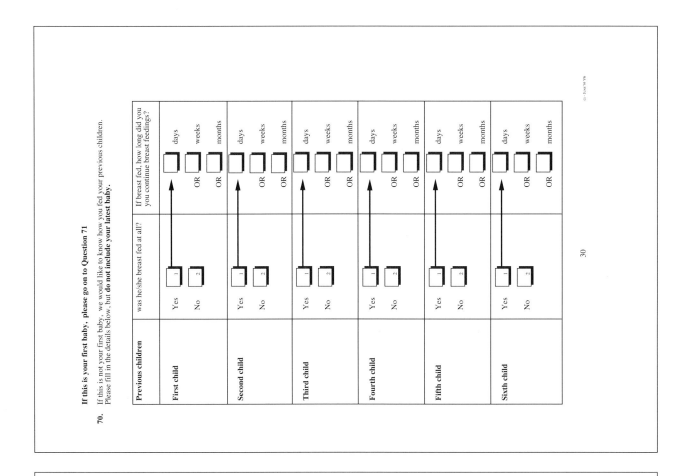

Previous children	was he/she breast fed at all?	If breast fed, how long did you continue breast feedings?
First child	Yes — 1 / No — 2	[ ] days OR [ ] weeks OR [ ] months
Second child	Yes — 1 / No — 2	[ ] days OR [ ] weeks OR [ ] months
Third child	Yes — 1 / No — 2	[ ] days OR [ ] weeks OR [ ] months
Fourth child	Yes — 1 / No — 2	[ ] days OR [ ] weeks OR [ ] months
Fifth child	Yes — 1 / No — 2	[ ] days OR [ ] weeks OR [ ] months
Sixth child	Yes — 1 / No — 2	[ ] days OR [ ] weeks OR [ ] months

71. Did you ever feel you were being pressurised into breast feeding or bottle feeding this baby?

Felt pressurised to breast feed [1]

Felt pressurised to bottle feed [2]

Did not feel pressurised to breast or bottle feed [3]

If your baby was entirely bottle fed from birth please go to Question 74
If you have ever breast fed your baby, please answer Question 72

72. If you had another baby would you breast feed again?

Yes [1]

No [2]

If you are now completely bottle feeding your baby, go to Question 74
If you are breast feeding your baby, answer Question 73

73. For how long do you think you will continue breast feeding your baby?

Until my baby is:

Please write numbers in the boxes

Either [ ] weeks old

OR [ ] months and [ ] weeks old

Don't know/have not decided **(please tick if appropriate)** [99]

31

O - June '95 V6

74. What is your present age?

Under 20 [1]

20, up to 24 [2]

25, up to 29 [3]

30, up to 34 [4]

35 or over [5]

75. How old were you when you finished full-time education? (School or college, whichever you last attended full-time)

16 or under [1]

17 [2]

18 [3]

19 or over [4]

76. Are you doing any paid work at the moment?

Yes [1]

On paid maternity leave [2]

On unpaid maternity leave [3] → **Go to Q77**

No [4] → **Go to (a)**

(a) Do you plan to start work again within the next two years?

Yes, full-time [1]

Yes, part-time [2]

No [3] → **Go to Q78**

Don't know [4]

32

O - June '95 V6

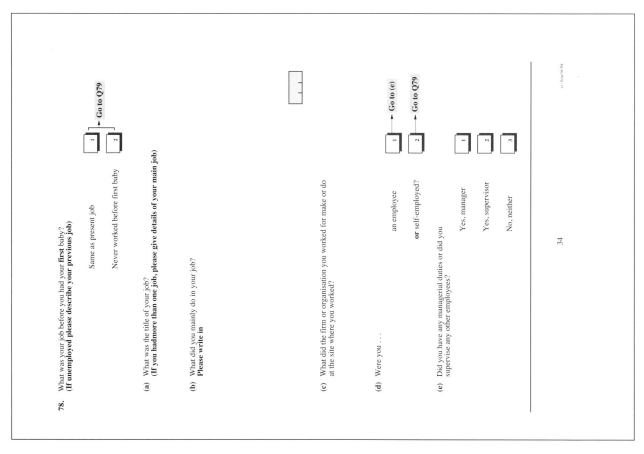

78. What was your job before you had your **first baby**?
(**If unemployed please describe your previous job**)

Same as present job ☐ 1 ⎤
                                    ⎬ **Go to Q79**
Never worked before first baby ☐ 2 ⎦

(a) What was the title of your job?
(**If you had more than one job, please give details of your main job**)

(b) What did you mainly do in your job?
Please write in

(c) What did the firm or organisation you worked for make or do
at the site where you worked?

(d) Were you . . .

an employee ☐ 1 → **Go to (e)**

or self-employed? ☐ 2 → **Go to Q79**

(e) Did you have any managerial duties or did you
supervise any other employees?

Yes, manager ☐ 1

Yes, supervisor ☐ 2

No, neither ☐ 3

34

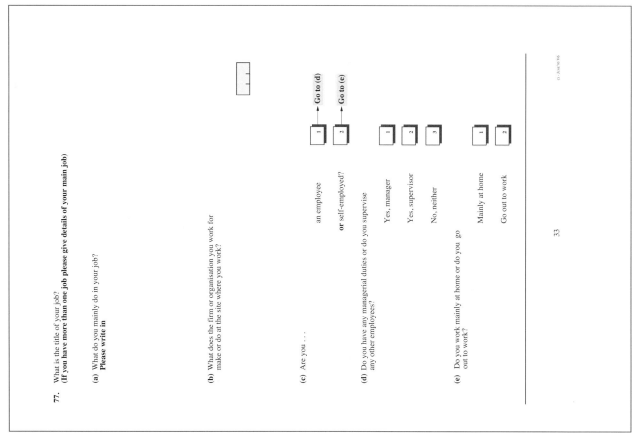

77. What is the title of your job?
(**If you have more than one job please give details of your main job**)

(a) What do you mainly do in your job?
Please write in

(b) What does the firm or organisation you work for
make or do at the site where you work?

(c) Are you . . .

an employee ☐ 1 → **Go to (d)**

or self-employed? ☐ 2 → **Go to (e)**

(d) Do you have any managerial duties or do you supervise
any other employees?

Yes, manager ☐ 1

Yes, supervisor ☐ 2

No, neither ☐ 3

(e) Do you work mainly at home or do you go
out to work?

Mainly at home ☐ 1

Go out to work ☐ 2

33

82. Is there anything else you would like to say about feeding your baby?

Yes ☐ 1 → **Please write in below**

No ☐ 2

Please give the date when you filled in this questionnaire

day ☐ month ☐ year ☐ 19

Was there anything you intended to go back and complete?
Please check.

Thank you very much for your help.

We hope to contact mothers again later to see how they are feeding their babies when they are older. If the address on the envelope was not complete or if you expect to move house in the near future and know your new address, it would help us if you could write it below:

....

....

....

36

O. June '95 V6

---

79. Are you . . .

married ☐ 1 → **Go to Q80**

living together ☐ 2

single ☐ 3 → **Go to Q82**

widowed, divorced or separated? ☐ 4

80. Is your husband/partner in a paid job at present?

Yes ☐ 1 → **Go to Q81**

No ☐ 2

81. What is the title of your husband's/partner's job?
(If unemployed, please describe his previous job)
(If he has more than one job, please give details of his main job)

Husband/partner never had a paid job ☐ 1 → **Go to Q82**

(a) What does he mainly do in his job?
Please write in

☐—

(b) What does the firm or organisation he works for make or do at the site where he works?

(c) Is he . . .

an employee ☐ 1 → **Go to (d)**

or self-employed? ☐ 2 → **Go to Q82**

(d) Does he have any managerial duties or does he supervise any other employees?

Yes, manager ☐ 1

Yes, supervisor ☐ 2

No, neither ☐ 3

35

O. June '95 V6

147

Stage 2 questionnaire

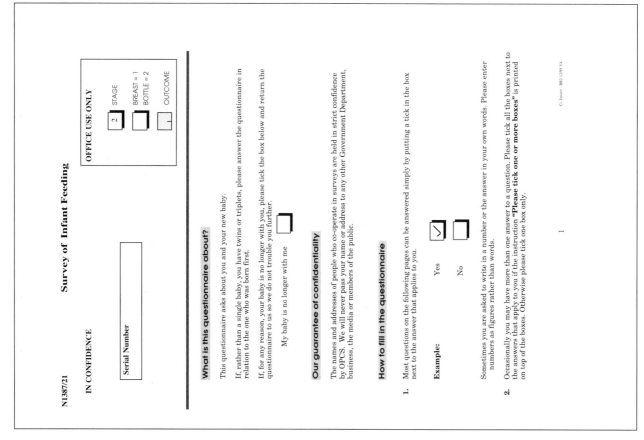

N1387/21   **Survey of Infant Feeding**

IN CONFIDENCE

OFFICE USE ONLY
[2] STAGE
[ ] BREAST = 1
    BOTTLE = 2
[ ] OUTCOME

Serial Number [   ]

What is this questionnaire about?

This questionnaire asks about you and your new baby.

If, rather than a single baby, you have twins or triplets, please answer the questionnaire in relation to the one who was born first.

If, for any reason, your baby is no longer with you, please tick the box below and return the questionnaire to us so we do not trouble you further.

My baby is no longer with me [ ]

Our guarantee of confidentiality

The names and addresses of people who co-operate in surveys are held in strict confidence by OPCS. We will never pass your name or address to any other Government Department, business, the media or members of the public.

How to fill in the questionnaire

1. Most questions on the following pages can be answered simply by putting a tick in the box next to the answer that applies to you.

Example: Yes [✓]
            No [ ]

Sometimes you are asked to write in a number or the answer in your own words. Please enter numbers as figures rather than words.

2. Occasionally you may have more than one answer to a question. Please tick all the boxes next to the answers that apply to you if the instruction **"Please tick one or more boxes"** is printed on top of the boxes. Otherwise please tick one box only.

1

C-Insert BR2 1295 V4

3. Sometimes there will be some shaded boxes to the right of a question that look like this

Example: [ ]

These are for use in the office and you should ignore them.

4. Sometimes you are asked to give an age or a length of time in weeks and days. Please follow the instructions very carefully.

For example

How old is your baby?

If your baby is 15 weeks and 2 days old enter the number of whole weeks plus any additional days

Please enter numbers in both boxes   [15] and [2]
                                       weeks   days

5. Usually after answering each question you go on to the next one unless a box you have ticked has an arrow next to it with an instruction to go to another question

Example: Yes [✓] → **Go to Q5**
            No [ ]

By following the arrows carefully you will miss out some questions which do not apply, so the amount you have to fill in will make the questionnaire shorter than it looks.

6. If you cannot remember, do not know, or are unable to answer a particular question please write that in.

7. When you have finished please post the questionnaire to us as soon as possible in the reply-paid envelope provided, even if you were not able to answer all of it.

We are very grateful for your help

2

C-Insert BR2 1295 V4

4. How old was your baby when you last breast fed him/her?

Please write numbers in both boxes

In whole weeks plus any additional days

[ ] weeks and [ ] days

(a) What were your reasons for stopping breast feeding?

Please write in the reasons

5. Would you have liked to continue breast feeding for longer or had you breast fed for as long as you intended?

Would have liked to have breast fed longer [1]

I had breast fed for as long as intended [2]

4

Section 1 - About the milk that you give your baby

1. May I just check, what is your baby's first name? Please write in below - 1 letter per box

[ ][ ][ ][ ][ ][ ][ ][ ][ ][ ]

2. How old is your baby?

Please write numbers in both boxes

Write in how many whole weeks plus any additional days

[ ] weeks and [ ] days

3. Are you still breast feeding your baby at all?

Yes [1] **Go to (a), (b) and (c)**

No [2] **Go to Q4**

(a) Do you breast feed your baby on demand or do you generally keep to set feeding times?

On demand [1]

Generally keep to set times [2]

It depends on the circumstances [3]

(b) How often do you breast feed your baby now?

Once a day [1]

Twice a day [2]

3 - 4 times a day [3]

5 - 6 times a day [4]

7 - 8 times a day [5]

More than 8 times a day [6]

(Please tick and write in number of times) [ ]

(c) Do you give your baby milk from a bottle at present (apart from expressed breast milk)?

Yes [1] **Go to Q6**

No [2] **Go to Q10**

3

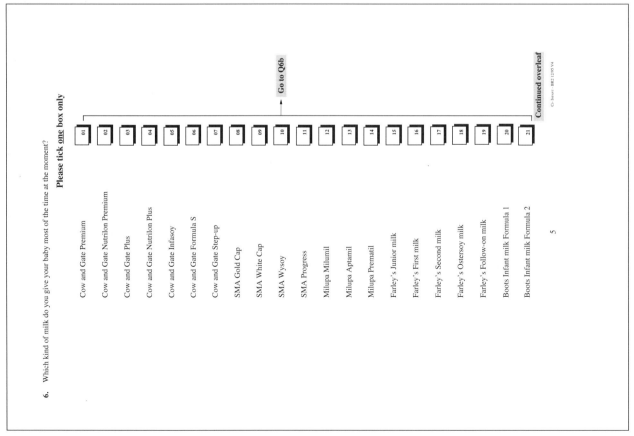

6. Which kind of milk do you give your baby most of the time at the moment?

Please tick one box only

- Cow and Gate Premium ☐ 01
- Cow and Gate Nutrilon Premium ☐ 02
- Cow and Gate Plus ☐ 03
- Cow and Gate Nutrilon Plus ☐ 04
- Cow and Gate Infasoy ☐ 05
- Cow and Gate Formula S ☐ 06
- Cow and Gate Step-up ☐ 07
- SMA Gold Cap ☐ 08
- SMA White Cap ☐ 09
- SMA Wysoy ☐ 10
- SMA Progress ☐ 11
- Milupa Milumil ☐ 12
- Milupa Aptamil ☐ 13
- Milupa Prematil ☐ 14
- Farley's Junior milk ☐ 15
- Farley's First milk ☐ 16
- Farley's Second milk ☐ 17
- Farley's Ostersoy milk ☐ 18
- Farley's Follow-on milk ☐ 19
- Boots Infant milk Formula 1 ☐ 20
- Boots Infant milk Formula 2 ☐ 21

(boxes 01–21) **Go to Q6b**

Continued overleaf

5

C: Infant · BR2 12/95 V4

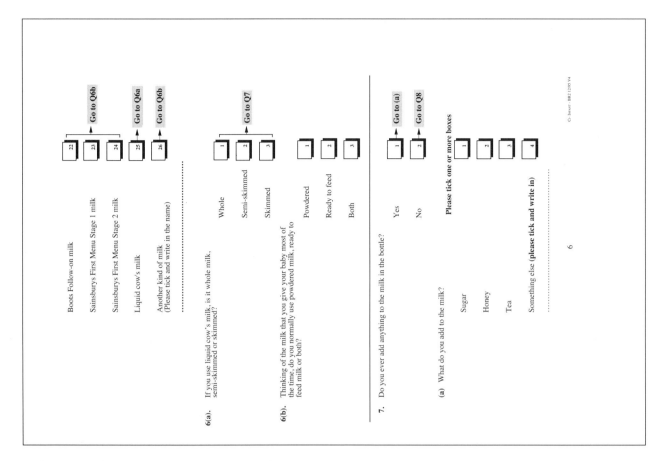

- Boots Follow-on milk ☐ 22
- Sainsburys First Menu Stage 1 milk ☐ 23
- Sainsburys First Menu Stage 2 milk ☐ 24

(boxes 22, 23, 24) **Go to Q6b**

- Liquid cow's milk ☐ 25 → **Go to Q6a**
- Another kind of milk ☐ 26 → **Go to Q6b**
  (Please tick and write in the name)

....

6(a). If you use liquid cow's milk, is it whole milk, semi-skimmed or skimmed?

- Whole ☐ 1
- Semi-skimmed ☐ 2
- Skimmed ☐ 3

(boxes 1, 2, 3) **Go to Q7**

6(b). Thinking of the milk that you give your baby most of the time, do you normally use powdered milk, ready to feed milk or both?

- Powdered ☐ 1
- Ready to feed ☐ 2
- Both ☐ 3

7. Do you ever add anything to the milk in the bottle?

- Yes ☐ 1 → **Go to (a)**
- No ☐ 2 → **Go to Q8**

(a) What do you add to the milk?

Please tick one or more boxes

- Sugar ☐ 1
- Honey ☐ 2
- Tea ☐ 3
- Something else (**please tick and write in**) ☐ 4

....

6

C: Infant · BR2 12/95 V4

Section 2 About other drinks and food that you may give to your baby

11. Do you give your baby plain tap or mineral water to drink at the moment?

Yes [1] → **Go to (a)**

No [2] → **Go to Q12**

(a) Do you add sugar or honey to the water that you give to your baby?

Please tick one or more boxes

Sugar [1]

Honey [2]

Neither [3]

12. Apart from plain tap or mineral water, are you giving your baby anything else to drink at the moment (such as fruit juice, squash or a herbal drink)?

Yes [1] → **Go to (a)**

No [2] → **Go to Q14**

(a) Please list the drinks giving the brand name (or say if homemade) and the flavour and say if it is a special baby drink or not.

Brand (or homemade)	Flavour	Please tick if it is a baby drink

8

---

8. How old was your baby when you started giving this kind of milk?

Please write a number in the box to the nearest whole week

[ ] weeks old

9. Where do you **usually** buy the milk for your baby?

Please tick one box only

From a child health clinic/hospital [1]

From a chemist shop [2]

From a supermarket [3]

From another type of shop [4]

Somewhere else (**please tick and write in**) [5]

....

10. Do you get milk tokens for free or reduced price milk?

Yes [1] → **Go to (a)**

No [2] → **Go to Q11**

(a) Where do you exchange the tokens for milk?

Please tick one or more boxes

At a child health clinic/hospital [1]

With the milkman [2]

At a supermarket [3]

At another type of shop (including chemist) [4]

Somewhere else (**please tick and write in**) [5]

....

7

15. Can you list all the cereal, rusks or solid food your baby ate yesterday.
     Please describe each fully, giving the brand name or saying if it is home made.
     For commercial baby food, please tick the column to show whether it was dried
     or tinned/jarred.

     Didn't have solids yesterday [1] → **Go to Q16**

| Type of food | Brand (or home made) | Please tick to show whether | |
		dried	tinned/ jarred

16. Do you use milk to mix up your baby's food?

     Yes [1] → **Go to (a)**

     No [2] → **Go to Q17**

     (a) Do you usually use

          Infant formula milk [1]

          or Liquid cow's milk [2]

          or something else (please and write in) [3]

17. When you give your baby solid food, do you give him/her fruit juice or
     other drinks containing vitamin C at the same time?

          Yes, usually [1]

          Yes, sometimes [2]

          No [3]

10

© Crown BR2 12/95 V4

---

13. Do you give your baby drinks mainly . . .   **Please tick one or more boxes**

          Because he/she is thirsty [1]

          To give him/her extra vitamins [2]

          To help his/her colic or wind [3]

          To help his/her constipation [4]

          To settle him/her [5]

          Some other reason [6]
          (Please tick and write in the reason)

14. Do you give your baby foods such as cereal, rusks or any other kind of solid
     food including any that you make yourself?

     Yes [1] → **Go to (a)**

     No [2] → **Go to Q20**

     (a) How old was your baby when he/she first had any food apart from milk?

                    Please write a number in the box

          Please write in the age to the nearest whole week [   ] weeks old

9

© Crown BR2 12/95 V4

20. Has a Bounty Bag of free baby products been sent to your home since you left hospital?

Yes [1] **Go to (a)**

No [2]

I had a home birth [3] **Go to Q21**

(a) How old was your baby when the Bounty Bag arrived?

Less than 4 weeks old [1]

4, less than 8 weeks old [2]

8, less than 12 weeks old [3]

12, less than 16 weeks old [4]

16 weeks old or more [5]

12

18. Does your baby usually have three meals of solid food a day?

Yes [1] **Go to (a)**

No [2] **Go to Q19**

(a) How old was your baby when he/she regularly started having three meals of solid foods a day?

Please write a number in the box

[ ] weeks old

Please write in the age to the nearest whole week

19. What do you take into account when deciding what solid foods to give your baby?

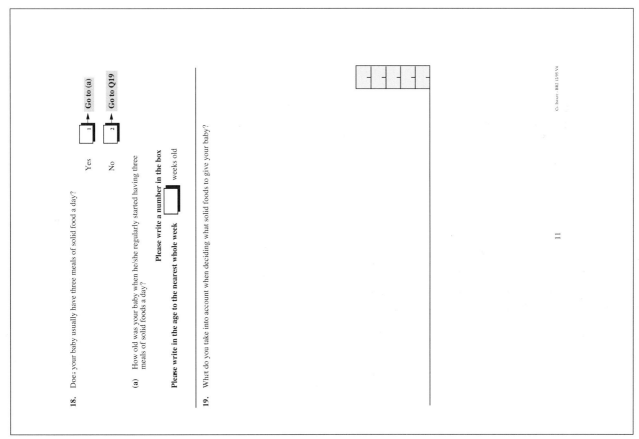

11

Section 3 About vitamins for your baby and yourself

21. Do you give your baby any extra vitamins (apart from drinks containing vitamins mentioned at question 12)?

Yes [1] → Go to (a) and (b)

No [2] → Go to Q22

(a) Do you use Children's Vitamin Drops from the child health clinic or another brand?

Children's Vitamin Drops [1]

Other brand (please tick and write in full name) [2]

....

(b) How do you **usually** get the vitamins?

Please tick one box only

Buy the vitamins myself at the child health clinic/hospital [1]

Buy the vitamins somewhere else [2]

Get the vitamins **free** at the child health clinic/hospital [3]

Get vitamins **on prescription** [4]

Other (please tick and describe) [5]

....

13

C- Issuer - BB2.1295 V4

22. Are you taking any extra vitamin or iron supplements **yourself** either in tablet or powder form?

Yes [1] → Go to (a) and (b)

No [2] → Go to Q23

(a) What type of supplements are you taking?

Please tick one box only

Iron only [1]

Vitamins only [2]

Both vitamins and iron [3]

Something else (**please tick and describe**) [4]

....

(b) How do you **usually** get the vitamins or iron supplements?

Please tick one box only

Buy the vitamins or iron supplements myself at the child health clinic/hospital [1]

Buy the vitamins or iron supplements somewhere else [2]

Get the vitamins or iron supplements **free** at the child health clinic/hospital [3]

Get the vitamins or iron supplements **on prescription** [4]

Other (**please tick and describe**) [5]

....

14

C- Issuer - BB2.1295 V4

Section 4 About check-ups for your baby

23. Do you take your baby to a child health clinic for advice or regular check-ups?

Yes, for advice or regular check-ups — 1 → **Go to (a)**

No — 2 → **Go to Q24**

(a) About how often do you take your baby to a child health clinic?

Please tick one box only

Once a week — 1

Once a fortnight — 2

Once a month — 3

Less than once a month — 4

24. Do you take your baby to your family doctor (GP) for advice or regular check-ups?

Yes, for advice or regular check-ups — 1 → **Go to (a)**

No — 2 → **Go to Q25**

(a) About how often do you take your baby to your family doctor (GP) for advice or regular check-ups?

Please tick one box only

Once a week — 1

Once a fortnight — 2

Once a month — 3

Less than once a month — 4

15

Cr. Jones\ BR2.12.95 V4

Section 5 About advice for you about feeding your baby

25. Have you had any problems with feeding your baby since the time when you filled in the previous questionnaire?

Yes — 1 → **Go to (a)**

No — 2 → **Go to Q27**

(a) What problems have you had?
Please describe

26. Did anyone give you help or advice about these problems?

Yes — 1 → **Go to (a)**

No — 2 → **Go to Q27**

Have not asked for help or advice — 3

(a) Who helped or advised you?

Please tick one or more boxes

Doctor/GP — 1

Health visitor — 2

Nurse — 3

Voluntary organisation (eg National Childbirth Trust, La Leche League or Association of Breastfeeding Mothers) — 4

Friend or relative — 5

Books/leaflets/magazines — 6

Someone else (**please tick and write in**) — 7

16

Cr. Jones\ BR2.12.95 V4

27. Has anyone given you help or advice on breast feeding since the time you filled in the previous questionnaire?

Yes [1] → **Go to (a)**

No [2]

Have not asked for help or advice [3] → **Go to Q28**

(a) Who helped or advised you on breast feeding?

Please tick one or more boxes

Doctor/GP [1]

Health visitor [2]

Nurse [3]

Voluntary organisation (eg. National Childbirth Trust, La Leche League or Association of Breastfeeding Mothers) [4]

Friend or relative [5]

Books/leaflets/magazines [6]

Someone else (**please tick and write in**) [7]

28. Have you ever wanted or tried to feed your baby when you were out in public places?

Yes [1] → **Go to (a)**

No [2] → **Go to Q29**

(a) Have you ever had problems finding somewhere to feed your baby when you were out in public places?

Yes [1]

No [2]

17

C: Issue: BR2 12/95 V4

---

29. Have you ever breast fed your baby in a public place? (**Please exclude hospitals**)

Yes [1] → **Go to (a)**

No [2]

Bottle fed from birth [3] → **Go to Q30**

(a) When you have breast fed in a public place do you:

Please tick one box only

prefer a mother and baby room? [1]

prefer to breastfeed without going to any special place? [2]

no preference [3]

30. Where do you think that it is important to have facilities for feeding babies?

Please tick one or more boxes

Shops/shopping centres [1]

Restaurants [2]

Public toilets [3]

Other places (**please tick and write in**) [4]

18

C: Issue: BR2 12/95 V4

35. What is the title of your current job (including where you are on maternity leave)?
(If you have more than one job please give details of your main job)

(a) What do you mainly do in your job?
Please write in [box]

(b) What does the firm or organisation you work for make or do at the site where you work?

(c) Are you …
an employee [1] → **Go to (d) and (e)**
or self-employed [2] → **Go to (e)**

(d) Do you have any managerial duties or do you supervise any other employees?
Yes, manager [1]
Yes, supervisor [2]
No, neither [3]

(e) Do you work mainly at home or do you go out to work?
Mainly at home [1] ⎤
Go out to work [2] ⎦ → **Go to Q37**

20

C. Jones BRI 12/95 V4

Section 6 About yourself

31. Do you smoke cigarettes at all nowadays?
Yes [1] **Go to (a)**
No [2] **Go to Q32**

(a) About how many cigarettes a **day** do you usually smoke now?
Please write a number in the box [box]

32. Does your husband/partner smoke cigarettes at all nowadays?
Yes [1] **Go to (a)**
No [2] ⎤ **Go to Q33**
No partner [3] ⎦

(a) About how many cigarettes a **day** does your husband/partner usually smoke now?
Please write a number in the box [box]

The following question is about your family planning

33. Since your baby was born have you used either the combined pill or mini-pill (progesterone only) to prevent pregnancy?
Yes [1] **Go to (a)**
No [2] **Go to Q34**

(a) How old was your baby when you began to take the pill?
Write in how many weeks to the nearest whole week [box] weeks

34. Are you doing any paid work at the moment?
Yes [1] ⎤
On paid maternity leave [2] ⎥ **Go to Q35**
On unpaid maternity leave [3] ⎦
No [4] **Go to Q36**

19

C. Jones BRI 12/95 V4

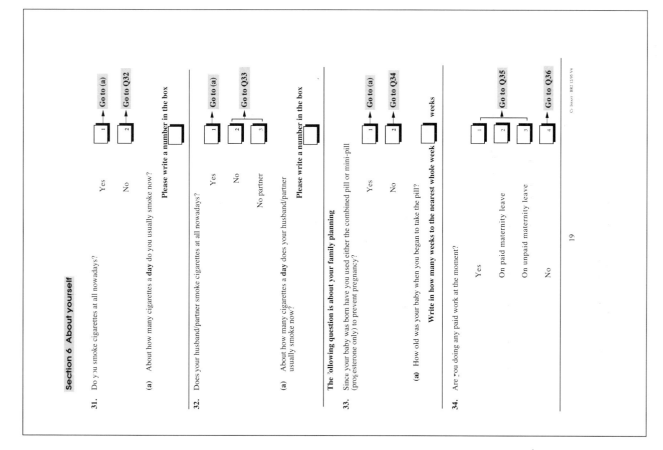

36. Do you plan to start work again within the next two years?

Yes, full-time ☐ 1

Yes, part time ☐ 2

No ☐ 3

Don't know ☐ 4

37. Is there anything else you would like to say about feeding your baby?

Yes ☐ 1 → **Please write in below**

No ☐ 2

© Isaac BR2 1295 V4

21

Please give the date when you filled in this questionnaire

day ☐ month ☐ year 1996

Was there anything you intended to go back and complete. Please check

Thank you very much for your help.

We hope to contact mothers again later to see how they are feeding their babies when they are a little older. If you expect to move house in the near future and know your new address it would help us if you could write it below.

....

....

....

© Isaac BR2 1295 V4

22

Stage 3 questionnaire

N1387/31   **Survey of Infant Feeding - Stage 3**

IN CONFIDENCE

OFFICE USE ONLY
3   STAGE
BREAST = 1   BOTTLE = 2
OUTCOME

Serial Number

What is this questionnaire about?

This questionnaire asks about you and your baby aged between 8 and 12 months.

If, rather than a single baby, you have twins or triplets, please answer the questionnaire in relation to the one who was born first.

If, for any reason, your baby is no longer with you, please tick the box below and return the questionnaire to us so we do not trouble you further.

My baby is no longer with me ☐

Our guarantee of confidentiality

The names and addresses of people who co-operate in surveys are held in strict confidence by CSU. We will never pass your name or address to any other Government Department, business, the media or members of the public.

How to fill in the questionnaire

1. Most questions on the following pages can be answered simply by putting a tick in the box next to the answer that applies to you.

Example: Yes ☑

         No ☐

Sometimes you are asked to write in a number or the answer in your own words. Please enter numbers as figures rather than words.

2. Occasionally you may have more than one answer to a question. Please tick all the boxes next to the answers that apply to you if the instruction **"Please tick one or more boxes"** is printed on top of the boxes. Otherwise please tick one box only.

1

Ci BR3 10/96 V10

---

3. Sometimes there will be some shaded boxes to the right of a question that look like this

Example: ▨

These are for use in the office and you should ignore them.

4. Sometimes you are asked to give an age or a length of time to the nearest whole week. Please follow the instructions very carefully.

For example

How old is your baby?

If your baby is 36 weeks and 2 days old enter the number to the nearest whole week.

Please write in the age to the nearest whole week   36

       weeks

5. Usually after answering each question you go on to the next one unless a box you have ticked has an arrow next to it with an instruction to go to another question

Example: Yes ☑ → **Go to Q5**

            No ☐

By following the arrows carefully you will miss out some questions which do not apply, so the amount you have to fill in will make the questionnaire shorter than it looks.

6. If you cannot remember, do not know, or are unable to answer a particular question please write that in.

7. When you have finished please post the questionnaire to us as soon as possible in the reply-paid envelope provided, even if you were not able to answer all of it.

We are very grateful for your help

2

Ci BR3 10/96 V10

Section 1 About the milk that you give your baby

1. May I just check, what is your baby's first name? **Please write in below - 1 letter per box**

2. How old is your baby?

☐☐ weeks old

Please write in the age to the nearest whole week

3. Are you still breast feeding your baby at all?

Yes ☐₁ → **Go to (a), (b) and (c)**

No ☐₂ → **Go to Q4**

(a) Do you breast feed your baby on demand or do you generally keep to set feeding times?

On demand ☐₁

Generally keep to set times ☐₂

It depends on the circumstances ☐₃

(b) How often do you breast feed your baby now?

Once a day ☐₁

Twice a day ☐₂

3 - 4 times a day ☐₃

5 - 6 times a day ☐₄

7 - 8 times a day ☐₅

More than 8 times a day ☐₆ ☐
(Please tick and write in number of times)

(c) Do you give your baby milk from a bottle or cup at present (apart from expressed breast milk)?

Yes ☐₁ → **Go to Q6**

No ☐₂ → **Go to Q14**

3

---

4. How old was your baby when you last breast fed him/her?

Please write numbers in both boxes

In whole weeks plus any additional days

☐ weeks and ☐ days

(a) What were your reasons for stopping breast feeding?

Please write in the reasons

☐☐☐☐
- - - -

5. Would you have liked to continue breast feeding for longer or had you breast fed for as long as you intended?

Would have liked to have breast fed longer ☐₁

I had breast fed for as long as intended ☐₂ → **Go to Q7**

6. Do you mainly breast feed your baby at the moment or do you mainly use formula or cow's milk?

Please tick one box only

Mainly breast feed ☐₁

Mainly use formula or cow's milk ☐₂

Use about the same amount of both types of milk ☐₃

4

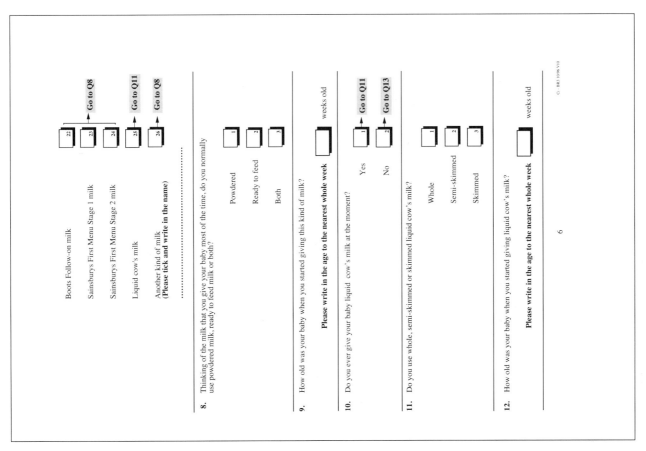

8. Thinking of the milk that you give your baby most of the time, do you normally use powdered milk, ready to feed milk or both?

Powdered	[1]
Ready to feed	[2]
Both	[3]

9. How old was your baby when you started giving this kind of milk?

Please write in the age to the nearest whole week [ ] weeks old

10. Do you ever give your baby liquid cow's milk at the moment?

Yes	[1]	**Go to Q11**
No	[2]	**Go to Q13**

11. Do you use whole, semi-skimmed or skimmed liquid cow's milk?

Whole	[1]
Semi-skimmed	[2]
Skimmed	[3]

12. How old was your baby when you started giving liquid cow's milk?

Please write in the age to the nearest whole week [ ] weeks old

O. BR3 1096 V10

6

---

7. Which kind of milk do you mainly give your baby at the moment?

Please tick one box only

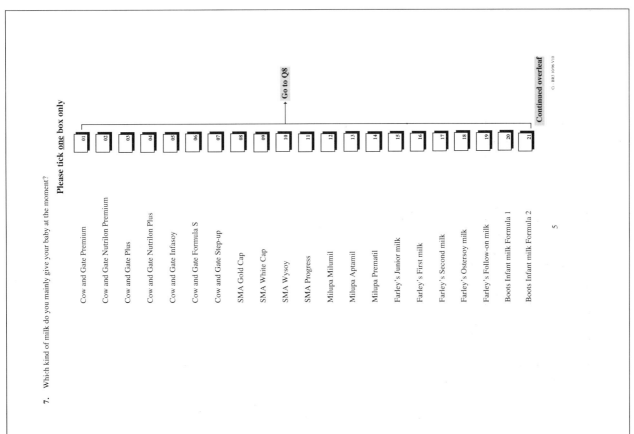

Cow and Gate Premium	01
Cow and Gate Nutrition Premium	02
Cow and Gate Plus	03
Cow and Gate Nutrilon Plus	04
Cow and Gate Infasoy	05
Cow and Gate Formula S	06
Cow and Gate Step-up	07
SMA Gold Cap	08
SMA White Cap	09
SMA Wysoy	10
SMA Progress	11
Milupa Milumil	12
Milupa Aptamil	13
Milupa Prematil	14
Farley's Junior milk	15
Farley's First milk	16
Farley's Second milk	17
Farley's Ostersoy milk	18
Farley's Follow-on milk	19
Boots Infant milk Formula 1	20
Boots Infant milk Formula 2	21

Go to Q8

Continued overleaf

O. BR3 1096 V10

5

15. Has your baby ever drunk from a cup or beaker with a spout?

Yes [1] → **Go to (a)**

No [2] → **Go to Q16**

(a) How old was your baby when he/she began to use the cup or beaker?

Please write in the age to the nearest whole week [ ] weeks old

16. Does your baby use a dummy at present?

Yes [1]

No [2]

C: BB3 10/96 V10

8

---

13. Do you ever add anything to the milk in the bottle?

Yes [1] → **Go to (a)**

No [2] → **Go to Q14**

(a) What do you add to the milk?

Please tick one or more boxes

Sugar [1]

Honey [2]

Tea [3]

Something else (**please tick and write in**) [4] ....

14. Do you get milk tokens for free or reduced price powdered baby milk or cow's milk?

Yes [1] → **Go to (a)**

No [2] → **Go to Q15**

(a) Where do you exchange the tokens?

Please tick one or more boxes

At a child health clinic/hospital [1]

With the milkman [2]

At a supermarket [3]

At another type of shop (including chemist) [4]

Somewhere else (**please tick and write in**) [5] ....

C: BB3 10/96 V10

7

The following questions are about the food that you give to your baby.

19. Do you give your baby foods such as cereal, rusks or any other kind of solid food including any that you make yourself?

Yes [1] → Go to (a)

No [2] → Go to Q34

(a) How old was your baby when he/she first had any food apart from milk?

Please write in the age to the nearest whole week [____] weeks old

20. Can you list all the cereal, rusks or solid food your baby ate yesterday.
Please describe each fully, giving the brand name or saying if it is home made.
For commerical baby food, please tick the column to show whether it was dried or tinned/jarred.

Didn't have solids yesterday [1] → Go to Q21

Type of food	Brand (or home made)	dried	tinned/ jarred

Please tick to show whether

G: BR3 10/96 V10

10

Section 2   About other drinks and food that you may give to your baby

17. Do you give your baby plain tap or bottled water to drink at the moment?

Yes [1] → Go to (a)

No [2] → Go to Q18

(a) Do you add sugar or honey to the water that you give to your baby?

Please tick one or more boxes

Sugar [1]

Honey [2]

Neither [3]

18. Apart from plain tap or bottled water, are you giving your baby anything else to drink at the moment (such as fruit juice, squash or a herbal drink)?

Yes [1] → Go to (a)

No [2] → Go to Q19

(a) Please list the drinks giving the brand name (or say if homemade) and the flavour and say if it is a special baby drink or not.

Please tick if it is a baby drink

Brand (or homemade)	Flavour	

G: BR3 10/96 V10

9

21. Do you ever use **liquid cow's milk** to mix up your baby's food?

Yes [1] → **Go to (a)**
No [2] → **Go to Q22**

(a) How old was your baby when you first used liquid cow's milk to mix up your baby's food?

Please write in the age to the nearest whole week

[ ] weeks old

22. Do you use any other type of milk to mix up your baby's food?

Yes [1] → **Go to (a)**
No [2] → **Go to Q23**

(a) What types of milk do you usually use?

Please tick one or more boxes

Infant formula milk [1]
Follow on formula milk [2]
Expressed breast milk [3]
Something else (**please tick and write in**) [4]
....

23. When you give your baby solid food, do you give him/her fruit juice or other drinks containing Vitamin C at the same time?

Yes, usually [1]
Yes, sometimes [2]
No [3]

11

---

24. How often do you usually give your baby the following types of foods nowadays?

Please tick one box in each row

Type of food	More than once a day	Once a day	3 or more times a week	Once or twice a week	Less than once a week	Never
Cereals or Rusks	1	2	3	4	5	6
Rice or Pasta	1	2	3	4	5	6
Bread	1	2	3	4	5	6
Meat	1	2	3	4	5	6
Fish (including tuna)	1	2	3	4	5	6
Eggs	1	2	3	4	5	6
Potatoes	1	2	3	4	5	6
Peas, beans, lentils or chickpeas	1	2	3	4	5	6
Raw vegetables	1	2	3	4	5	6
Cooked vegetables	1	2	3	4	5	6
Raw fruit	1	2	3	4	5	6
Cooked fruit	1	2	3	4	5	6
Cheese, yoghurt, fromage frais	1	2	3	4	5	6
Puddings or desserts	1	2	3	4	5	6
Sweets or chocolate	1	2	3	4	5	6

12

25. Do you ever give your baby home made solid foods?

Yes ☐₁ → **Go to (a)**

No ☐₂ → **Go to Q26**

(a) When you give your baby home made solid food how do you **usually** prepare it?

Please tick one box only

Sieve, blend or liquidise the food into puree ☐₁

Mash the food up ☐₂

Mince the food up ☐₃

Cut up the food finely ☐₄

Use some other way to prepare your baby's food **Please tick the box and write in** ☐₅

....

26. Does your baby usually have three meals of solid food a day?

Yes ☐₁ → **Go to (a)**

No ☐₂ → **Go to Q27**

(a) How old was your baby when he/she regularly started having three meals of solid foods a day?

Please write in the age to the nearest whole week ☐ weeks old

27. What do you take into account when deciding what types of solid foods to give your baby?

☐☐☐☐☐

O: BR3 1096 V1D

13

28. How would you describe the variety of foods that your baby generally eats? Does he/she. . . .

Please tick one box only

eat most things ☐₁

eat a reasonable variety of things ☐₂

or is he/she a fussy or faddy eater ☐₃

29. Do you avoid giving your baby foods with particular ingredients?

Yes ☐₁ → **Go to (a)**

No ☐₂ → **Go to Q30**

(a) Which ingredients do you avoid and why?

Ingredient	**Reason for avoiding**

☐☐
☐☐
☐☐
☐☐

O: BR3 1096 V1D

14

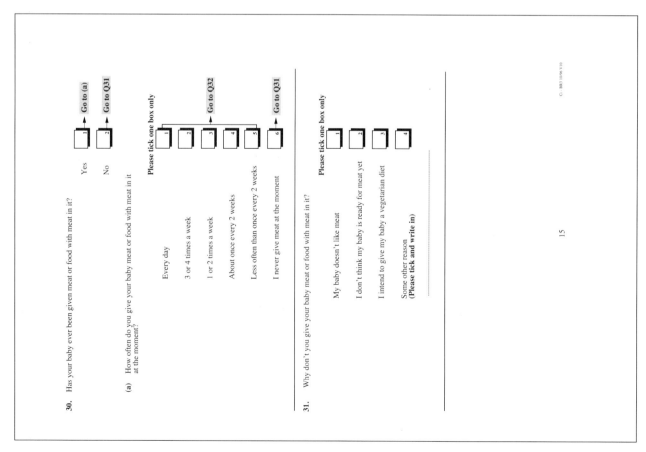

30. Has your baby ever been given meat or food with meat in it?

Yes → **Go to (a)**
No → **Go to Q31**

(a) How often do you give your baby meat or food with meat in it at the moment?

Please tick one box only

Every day
3 or 4 times a week
1 or 2 times a week → **Go to Q32**
About once every 2 weeks
Less often than once every 2 weeks
I never give meat at the moment → **Go to Q31**

31. Why don't you give your baby meat or food with meat in it?

Please tick one box only

My baby doesn't like meat
I don't think my baby is ready for meat yet
I intend to give my baby a vegetarian diet
Some other reason
(Please tick and write in)

15

O- BR3 1096 V10

32. Has it been difficult to wean your baby onto solid food?

Yes → **Go to (a)**
No → **Go to Q33**

(a) In what way has it been difficult?

Please tick one or more boxes

Baby would not take solids
Baby would only take certain solids
Baby was disinterested in food
Baby prefers drinks to food
Baby vomiting
Some other reason (please tick and write in)

33. Has your baby ever fed him/herself using a spoon?

Yes → **Go to (a)**
No → **Go to Q34**

(a) How old was your baby when he/she began to use a spoon?

Please write in the age to the nearest whole week

[ ] weeks old

16

O- BR3 1096 V10

35. Are you taking any extra vitamin or iron supplements **yourself** either in tablet or powder form?

Yes ☐1 → Go to (a)

No ☐2 → Go to Q36

(a) What type of supplements are you taking?

Please tick one box only

Iron only ☐1

Vitamins only ☐2

Both vitamins and iron ☐3

Something else (**please tick and describe**) ☐4

....

18

C: BR3 1096 V10

Section 3 About vitamins for your baby and yourself

34. Do you give your baby any extra vitamins (apart from drinks containing vitamins mentioned at question 18)?

Yes ☐1 → Go to (a) and (b)

No ☐2 → Go to Q35

(a) Do you use Children's Vitamin Drops from your clinic or do you get another brand from a shop?

Children's Vitamin Drops ☐1

Other brand from a shop (**please tick box and write full name below**) ☐2

....

(b) How do you **usually** get the vitamins?

Please tick one box only

Buy the vitamins myself at my clinic ☐1

Buy the vitamins from a shop ☐2

Get the vitamins **free** at my clinic ☐3

Get the vitamins **on prescription** ☐4

Other (**please tick and describe**) ☐5

....

17

C: BR3 1096 V10

Section 4 About advice for you about feeding your baby

36. Have you had any problems with feeding your baby' since the time when you filled in the previous questionnaire?

Yes ☐ 1 → **Go to (a)**
No ☐ 2 → **Go to Q38**

(a) What problems have you had?
Please describe

37. Did you get help or advice about these problems?

Yes ☐ 1 → **Go to (a)**
No ☐ 2
Did not ask for help or advice ☐ 3 → **Go to Q38**

(a) Who helped or advised you?

Please tick one or more boxes

Doctor/GP ☐ 1
Health visitor/Nurse ☐ 2
Voluntary organisation (eg National Childbirth Trust, La Leche League or Association of Breastfeeding Mothers) ☐ 3
Friend or relative ☐ 4
Books/leaflets/magazines ☐ 5
TV or Radio ☐ 6
Someone else (**please tick and write in**) ☐ 7
.... ☐ 8

19

C: BR3 10/96 V10

---

38. Thinking back since your baby was born, who or what has been the most helpful in giving you general advice on feeding your baby?

Please tick one or more boxes

Doctor/GP ☐ 1
Health visitor/Nurse ☐ 2
Midwife ☐ 3
Voluntary organisation (eg National Childbirth Trust, La Leche League or Association of Breastfeeding Mothers) ☐ 4
Friend or relative ☐ 5
Books/leaflets/magazines ☐ 6
TV or Radio ☐ 7
Someone else (**please tick and write in**) ☐ 8

Section 5 About yourself

The following question is about your family planning

39. Since your baby was born have you used either the combined pill or mini-pill (progesterone only) to prevent pregnancy?

Yes ☐ 1 → **Go to (a)**
No ☐ 2 → **Go to Q40**

(a) How old was your baby when you began to take the pill?

Write in age to the nearest whole week ☐ weeks

40. Are you doing any paid work at the moment?

Yes
On paid maternity leave ☐ 1 ☐ 2 ☐ 3 → **Go to Q41**
On unpaid maternity leave

No ☐ 4 → **Go to Q43**

20

C: BR3 10/96 V10

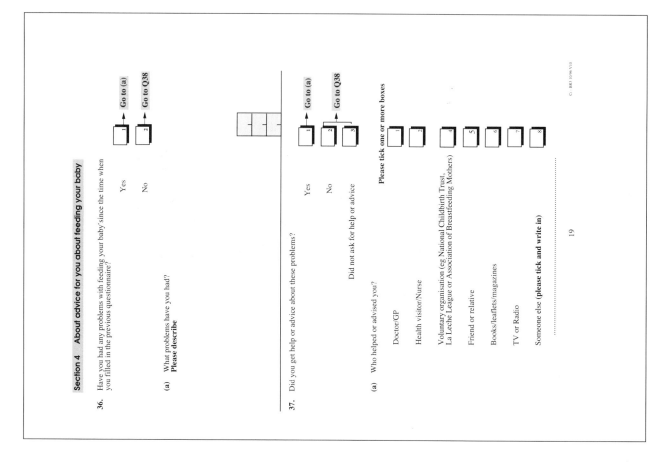

41. What is the title of your current job (including your job if you are on maternity leave)?
(If you have more than one job please give details of your main job)

(a) What do you mainly do in your job?
Please write in

(b) What does the firm or organisation you work for make or do at the site where you work?

(c) Are you . . .

an employee   □ 1   Go to (d) and (e)

or self-employed   □ 2   Go to (e)

(d) Do you have any managerial duties or do you supervise any other employees?

Yes, manager   □ 1

Yes, supervisor   □ 2

No, neither   □ 3

(e) Do you work mainly at home or do you go out to work?

Mainly at home   □ 1   Go to Q44

Go out to work   □ 2   Go to Q42

C: BB3 1096 V10

42. How do you usually feed your baby while you are at work?

Please tick one or more boxes

Baby is entirely bottle fed now (using formula or cow's milk)   □ 1

I take him/her to work to breastfeed   □ 2

I express breast milk for him/her to have while I am at work   □ 3

Baby has other milk while I am at work   □ 4

Other arrangement (please tick and describe)   □ 5

Go to Q44

43. Do you plan to start work again within the next two years?

Yes, full-time   □ 1

Yes, part time   □ 2

No   □ 3

Don't know   □ 4

44. When you look back on how you have fed your baby since birth are you happy with everything you decided to do or do you wish that you had made other decisions about feeding your baby?

Happy with my decisions   □ 1   Go to Q45

Wish that I had made other decisions   □ 2   Go to (a)

(a) What other decisions would you have made?

C: BB3 1096 V10

45. Is there anything else you would like to say about feeding your baby?

Yes ☐ 1 → Please write in below

No ☐ 2

Please give the date when you filled in this questionnaire

day ☐ month ☐ year ☐ 1996

Was there anything you intended to go back and complete. Please check

Thank you very much for your help.

We may want to contact you once more in about four to six months time to see how you are feeding your baby at that stage. If you expect to move house in the near future and know your new address it would help us if you could write it below.

....

....

....

C BR3 10/96 V10

23

C BR3 10/96 V10

24

Tables and Figures

Chapter 7

Figures

Tables

Chapter 8

Figures

Tables